CONSTRUCTION CONTRACTS
Law and management

JOHN MURDOCH
Senior Lecturer
Department of Law
University of Reading

WILL HUGHES
Lecturer
Department of Construction Management and Engineering
University of Reading

E & FN SPON
An Imprint of Chapman & Hall
London · New York · Tokyo · Melbourne · Madras

Published by E & FN Spon, an imprint of Chapman & Hall, 2–6 Boundary Row, London SE1 8HN

Chapman & Hall, 2–6 Boundary Row, London SE1 8HN, UK

Van Nostrand Reinhold Inc., 115 5th Avenue, New York NY10003, USA

Chapman & Hall Japan, Thomson Publishing Japan, Hirakawacho Nemoto Building, 7F 1–7–11 Hirakawa-cho, Chiyoda-ku, Tokyo 102, Japan

Chapman & Hall Australia, Thomas Nelson Australia, 102 Dodds Street, South Melbourne, Victoria 3205, Australia

Chapman & Hall India, R. Seshadri, 32 Second Main Road, CIT East, Madras 600 035, India

First edition 1992

© 1992 John Murdoch and Will Hughes

Typeset in 10/12pt Times by Graphicraft Typesetters Ltd, Hong Kong
Printed in Great Britain by Hartnolls Ltd, Bodmin, Cornwall

ISBN 0 419 17060 X   0 442 31489 2 (USA)

A catalogue record for this book is available from the British Library

Library of Congress Cataloging-in-Publication data available

Construction Contracts

Other titles from E & FN Spon

Avoiding Claims
A practical guide for the construction industry
M. Coombes Davies

Competitive Tendering for Engineering Contracts
M. O'C. Horgan

The Foundations of Engineering Contracts
M. O'C. Horgan and F.R. Roulston

Guide to Highway Law for Architects, Engineers, Surveyors and Contractors
Robert A. O'Hara

Management Contracting
Dearle and Henderson

The Presentation and Settlement of Contractors' Claims
G. Trickey

Project Control of Engineering Contracts
M. O'C. Horgan and F.R. Roulston

Understanding JCT Standard Building Contracts
2nd edition
David Chappell

For more information about these and other titles please contact:
The Promotion Department, E & FN Spon, 2–6 Boundary Row, London,
SE1 8HN

Contents

Introduction   ix

Table of statutes   xi

Table of cases   xii

PART ONE   Construction Contracts in Context
1   Procurement methods and contractual networks   3
     1.1   Traditional procurement systems   4
     1.2   Design and build contracts   6
     1.3   Management contracting   7
     1.4   Construction management   8

2   Contract risks and contract choice   10
     2.1   The nature of risk in construction   10
     2.2   Types of risk in construction contracts   13
     2.3   Dealing with risk   14
     2.4   Contract choice   19
     2.5   Distribution of risk through methods of payment   28

3   Roles and responsibilities in construction projects   31
     3.1   Common problems   31
     3.2   Established roles of the consultants   34

4   Tort claims in the construction context   45
     4.1   Who wants to claim in tort?   45
     4.2   Limits of tort claims   48
     4.3   Specific examples of tort claims   52
     4.4   Architect and contractor   57

5   Formation and scope of construction contracts   61
     5.1   Agreement   61

5.2 Acceptance 64
5.3 Mistake 67
5.4 Contracts made by tender 68
5.5 Terms of a contract 78
5.6 Frustration of contract 85

PART TWO   Building Design
6   The management of design 91
6.1 Decisions and stages 91
6.2 Problems in design management 94
6.3 Patterns of involvement 95
6.4 Communication patterns 104

7   Liability for defective design 106
7.1 Design duties in law 106
7.2 Legal responsibility for design 111
7.3 Tort of negligence 115
7.4 Liability under statute 115

PART THREE   Obligations of the Contractor
8   Nature and quality of the contract work 121
8.1 Nature of the contract work 121
8.2 Standard of work 132

9   Obligations as to time 135
9.1 Commencement 135
9.2 Progress 136
9.3 Completion 137
9.4 Contractor's obligations after completion 140
9.5 Extension of time 141

10   Other obligations of the contractor 153
10.1 Statutory obligations 153
10.2 Co-ordination and management 155
10.3 Transfer of materials 158
10.4 General compliance 160

PART FOUR   Obligations of the Employer
11   Payment 165
11.1 Employer's obligation to pay 165
11.2 The contract sum 167
11.3 Variations 168
11.4 Fluctuations 175
11.5 Retention money 176
11.6 Set-off 178

12   Contractor's claims for loss and expense   183
     12.1   Contract claims and damages   183
     12.2   Grounds for contractual claims   185
     12.3   Claims procedures   189
     12.4   Quantification of claims   191

13   Other obligations of the employer   197
     13.1   Implied obligations   198
     13.2   Express obligations under JCT 80   200
     13.3   Responsibility for contract administrator   202
     13.4   Responsibility for site conditions   203

PART FIVE   Contract Administration
14   Role of the contract administrator   209
     14.1   Contract administrator as the employer's agent   209
     14.2   Contract administrator as independent adjudicator   217

15   Insurance and bonds   226
     15.1   Insurance   226
     15.2   Bonds and guarantees   234

PART SIX   Sub-contracts
16   General principles of sub-contracting   241
     16.1   Novation, assignment and vicarious performance   242
     16.2   The contractual chain   244
     16.3   Types of sub-contract   245

17   Rights of sub-contractors   255
     17.1   Rights against the main contractor   255
     17.2   Rights against the employer   259

18   Defaults of sub-contractors   266
     18.1   Liability of the sub-contractor to the employer   266
     18.2   Liability of the main contractor for sub-contractor
            defaults   267
     18.3   Liability of sub-contractor to employer   280

PART SEVEN   Alternative Procurement Methods
19   Design and build contracts   285
     19.1   Background to design and build   285
     19.2   Features of design and build contracts   287
     19.3   Use of the JCT Design Build Form (CD 81)   290
     19.4   Characteristics of CD 81   295
     19.5   Risk in design and build   299
     19.6   Conclusions   301

20	Management contracts	303
	20.1 Background of management contracts	303
	20.2 The JCT Management Contract	305
	20.3 Risk in management contracting	311
21	Construction management	318
	21.1 Background of construction management	318
	21.2 Use of construction management contracts	320
	21.3 Contents of construction management contracts	323
	21.4 Allocation of risk in construction management	327

PART EIGHT   Contract Disputes

22	Damages for breach of contract	333
	22.1 Damages	333
	22.2 Liquidated damages	335
23	Suspension, repudiation and determination	342
	23.1 Suspension of work	342
	23.2 Repudiation at common law	344
	23.3 Determination under JCT 80 and related sub-contracts	349
24	Non-litigious dispute resolution	358
	24.1 Background to disputes	358
	24.2 Methods of dispute resolution	363
	24.3 Incorporating ADR	
	24.4 procedures	368
25	Arbitration and litigation	372
	25.1 The nature of arbitration	372
	25.2 Differences between arbitration and litigation	375
	25.3 Choice of procedure	380
	25.4 Procedure at arbitration and litigation	384

| Index | 397 |

Introduction

This book is aimed at those students for whom building or civil engineering contracts form part of a construction-based course. We have had in mind the syllabus requirements for first degrees in building, Civil Engineering, Architecture, Quantity Surveying and Building Surveying, as well as those of postgraduate courses in Construction Management and Project Management. We have also assumed that such students will already have been introduced to the general principles of English Law, especially those relating to contract and tort. As a result, while certain aspects of those subjects (for example, the formation of contracts by tender, and the application of negligence to cases of pure economic loss) appear here, the reader must look elsewhere for the general legal background.

Structurally, this book differs from many of the text books dealing with construction contracts, which concentrate on a particular standard form contract and seek to provide a clause-by-clause analysis of it. It is our belief that, while anyone who uses a standard form contract of course needs to understand what it contains, an over-dogmatic adherence to and application of unsuitable contractual clauses lies at the root of many construction disputes. It is far better for tomorrow's construction professionals to appreciate the principles which underlie *all* contracts, than for them to have an exhaustive knowledge of any one standard form (which may in any case fall rapidly into disuse).

This book, then, is about the *principles* of construction contract law, and the way in which those principles are applied under various contracts. As such, it does not concentrate on any one standard form of building contract, but instead draws examples as appropriate from JCT, ICE and the government forms. As the reader will rapidly discover, we have in the course of this approach frequently criticized the drafting of particular standard form provisions, and it seems only right to acknowledge that it is much easier to criticize a contract that it is to draft one. Nonetheless, we feel that it is important for students to grasp the problems in construction contracts to the fullest extent, and that the industry would not be well served if we were to disguise our criticisms of the way in which construction projects tend to be procured.

Finally, a word of warning. Those who graduate from construction-based courses, albeit courses containing a substantial legal content, do not thereby become lawyers, and should not be misled into believing that the knowledge which they have acquired along the way renders professional legal advice unnecessary. A true expert in any field is all too well aware of the limits of his or her own expertise. No self-respecting surveyor, for example, would expect to do the job of a structural engineer, and they should no more expect to do that of a specialist lawyer.

What the architect, quantity surveyor or other construction professional requires in the way of legal knowledge is the ability to resolve simple problems, and to recognize when a problem is complex enough to need specialist handling. An important skill is to understand sufficiently the problems of contracting in order to resolve disputes before they become litigious. In the absence of such amicable settlement, the construction professional must be able to discuss matters intelligently and to brief competently the specialist barrister or solicitor who is brought in to handle it. We believe that to be the level to which construction students should aspire, and this book will help them to achieve it.

Table of statutes

Ancient Monuments and Archeological Areas
Act 1979   158
Arbitration Act 1950   81, 194, 378, 379, 382,
                                                              391
Arbitration Act 1975   383
Arbitration Act 1979   388, 392–4
Building Act 1984   116
Civil Liability (Contribution) Act 1978   47, 235, 385
Defective Premises Act 1972   116
Health and Safety at Work Act 1984   153
Latent Damage Act 1986   47
Law Reform (Frustrated Contracts) Act 1943   85
Limitation Act 1990   379
Local Land Charges Act 1979   158
Occupiers Liability Act 1957   46
Sale of Goods Act 1979   133, 245, 262–3
Statute of Frauds 1677   236
Supply of Goods and Services Act 1982   82, 133, 245
Supreme Court Act 1981   194
Third Parties (Rights Against Insurers) Act 1930   227
Unfair Contract Terms Act 1977   122, 257, 338

Table of cases

ABBREVIATIONS OF LAW REPORTS USED

AC	Law Reports, Appeal Cases, House of Lords
ALJ	Australian Law Journal
All ER	All England Law Reports
BLR	Building Law Reports
CB	Common Bench Reports
Ch	Law Reports, Chancery Division
CILL	Construction Industry Law Letter
CLR	Commonwealth Law Reports
Con LR	Construction Law Reports
Const LJ	Construction Law Journal
CSW	Chartered Surveyor Weekly
DLR	Dominion Law Reports
EG	Estates Gazette
EGCS	Estates Gazette Case Summaries
Exch	Exchequer Reports
F & F	Foster and Finlason's Reports
F (Ct of Sess)	Fraser, Court of Sessions Cases
HBC	Hudson's Building and Engineering Contracts
HLC	Clark's Reports, House of Lords
IR	Irish Reports
JP	Justice of the Peace
JPL	Journal of Planning and Environmental Law
KB	Law Reports, King's Bench Division
LGR	Local Government Reports
Ll LR	Lloyd's List Reports (before 1951)
LJQB	Law Journal, Queen's Bench
Lloyd's Rep	Lloyd's List Reports (1951 onwards)
LR (no) Ch App	Law Reports, Chancery Appeals
LR (no) CP	Law Reports, Common Pleas
LT	Law Times
M & W	Meeson and Welsby's Reports, Exchequer

NSWLR	New South Wales Law Reports
NZLR	New Zealand Law Reports
QB	Queen's Bench Reports
QBD	Law Reports, Queen's Bench Division
SA	South Africa Law Reports
SC (HL)	Court of Sessions Cases (Scotland) (House of Lords)
SJ	Solicitor's Journal
SLT	Scots Law Times
TLR	Times Law Reports
WLR	Weekly Law Reports
WN	Law Reports, Weekly Notes.

Most cases are referred to using reference numbers, which are listed at the end of each chapter. In order to find each citation the page number is given (in bold), followed by the reference number in square brackets.

A.B. Contractors Ltd v. Flaherty Brothers Ltd (1978) 16 BLR 8.   **179**[14]

AMF International Ltd v. Magnet Bowling Ltd [1968] 2 All ER 789.   **46**[6], **229**[5]

Abrams (J. & J.C.) Ltd v. Ancliffe [1978] 2 NZLR 420.   **63**[4]

Acsim (Southern) Ltd v. Danish Contracting and Development Co Ltd (1989) 47 BLR 55.   **181**[24]

Anglian Building Products Ltd v. W. & C. French (Construction) Ltd 16 BLR 1.   **179**[15]

Anns v. Merton LBC [1978] AC 728.   **46**[5], **53**[5], **116**[20]

Antaois, The [1985] AC 191.   **393**[60]

Architectural Installation Services Ltd v. James Gibbons Windows Ltd (1989) 46 BLR 91.   **345**[4], **351**[31]

Archivent Sales and Developments Ltd v. Strathclyde Regional Council (1984) 27 BLR 98.   **160**[5], **263**[17]

Arenson v. Casson, Beckman Rutley & Co [1975] AC 405.   **367**[7], **374**[2]

Arthur Sanders Ltd, Re (1981) 17 BLR 125.   **264**[19]

Ashville Investments Ltd v. Elmer Contractors Ltd [1988] 2 All ER 577.   **376**[11]

Associated Bulk Carriers Ltd v. Koch Shipping Inc [1978] 2 All ER 254.   **383**[37]

BFI Group of Companies Ltd v. DCB Integration Systems Ltd [1987] CILL 348.   **339**[13], **376**[14]

B.L. Holdings Ltd v. Robert J. Wood & Partners (1979) 12 BLR 1.   **111**[10]

BWP (Architectural) Ltd v. Beaver Building Systems Ltd (1988) 42 BLR 86.   **181**[23], **181**[27]

Babanaft International Co S.A. v. Avant Petroleum Inc [1982] 3 All ER 244.   **393**[63]

Bacal Construction (Midlands) Ltd v. Northampton Development Corporation (1975) 8 BLR 88.   **204**[19]

Bagot v. Stevens Scanlon & Co Ltd [1966] 1 QB 197.   **48**[7]

Beaufort House Development Ltd v. Zimmcor (International) Inc (1990) 50 BLR 91.   **326**[3]

Beeston v. Marriott (1864) 8 LT 690. **159**[4]

Bell (A.) & Son (Paddington) Ltd v. CBF Residential Care & Housing Association (1989) 46 BLR 102. **221**[27], **340**[19]

Benstrete Construction Ltd v. Hill (1987) 38 BLR 115. **220**[26], **377**[21], **388**[21]

Birkett v. James [1978] AC 297. **390**[48]

Blue Circle Industries plc v. Holland Dredging (UK) Ltd (1987) 37 BLR 40. **169**[1]

Bolton v. Mahadeva [1972] 2 All ER 1322. **349**[25]

Bottoms v. York Corporation (1892) HBC 4th ed, ii, 208. **203**[16]

Bradley v. Eagle Star Insurance Co Ltd [1989] 1 All ER 961. **228**[2]

Bradley (D.R.) (Cable Jointing) Ltd v. Jefco Mechanical Services Ltd (1988) 6-CLD-07-19. **347**[18]

Bramall & Ogden Ltd v. Sheffield CC (1983) 29 BLR 73. **140**[9]

Brickfield Properties Ltd v. Newton [1971] 3 All ER 328. **110**[6]

Brightside, Kilpatrick Engineering Services v. Mitchell Construction Ltd (1973) 1 BLR 62. **81**[31], **181**[25]

Brightside Mechanical & Electrical Services Group Ltd v. Hyundai Engineering & Construction Co Ltd (1988) 41 BLR 110. **257**[4]

Bristol Corporation v. John Aird Ltd [1913] AC 241. **384**[42]

British and Commonwealth Holdings plc v. Quadrex Holdings Inc [1989] 3 All ER 492. **379**[28]

British Eagle International Airlines Ltd v. Compagnie Nationale Air France [1975] 2 All ER 390. **261**[14]

British Steel Corporation v. Cleveland Bridge & Engineering Co Ltd [1984] 1 All ER 504. **62**[1]

British Westinghouse Electric Co Ltd v. Underground Electric Railways [1912] AC 673. **334**[5]

Bruce (W.) Ltd v. Strong [1951] 2 KB 447. **383**[40], **384**[40]

Bruno Zornow (Builders) Ltd v. Beechcroft Developments Ltd (1989) CSW, 28 July. **84**[33]

Bryant & Sons Ltd v. Birmingham Hospital Saturday Fund [1938] 1 All ER 503. **205**[24]

C. & P. Haulage v. Middleton [1983] 3 All ER 94. **335**[8]

C.M. Pillings & Co Ltd v. Kent Investments Ltd (1985) 30 BLR 80. **180**[20], **181**[22], **378**[25]

CMA Martin Engineering Ltd v. J. Donne Holdings Ltd (1980) 15 BLR 61. **392**[55]

Cameron (A.) Ltd v. John Mowlem & Co plc (1990) 8-CLD-07-01. **367**[8], **375**[8], **383**[8]

Canterbury Pipe Lines Ltd v. Christchurch Drainage Board (1979) 16 BLR 76. **343**[1]

Caparo Industries plc v. Dickman [1990] 1 All ER 568. **48**[10]

Carr v. J.A. Berriman Pty Ltd (1953) 89 CLR 327. **198**[3], **248**[4], **347**[15]

Central Provident Fund Board v. Ho Bock Kee (1981) 17 BLR 21. **350**[29]

Chambers v. Goldthorpe [1901] 1 KB 624. **222**[31]

Chandler Bros Ltd v. Boswell [1936] 3 All ER 179. **81**[29]

Charon (Finchley) Ltd v. Singer Sewing Machine Ltd (1968) 207 EG 140. **231**[7]

Chatbrown v. Alfred McAlpine (Southern) Ltd (1986) 35 BLR 44. **378**[22]

Chichester Joinery Ltd v. John Mowlem & Co plc (1987) 42 BLR 100. **66**[9]

Clay v. A.J. Crump Ltd [1964] 1 QB 533. **46**[3], **217**[18]

Clayton v. Woodman & Son (Builders) Ltd [1962] 2 QB 533. **45**[2], **217**[17]

Clydebank District Water Trustees v. Fidelity Deposit of Maryland 1916 SC (HL) 69. **237**[9]

Commissioner for Main Roads v. Reed & Stuart Pty Ltd (1974) 12 BLR 55. **174**[5], **198**[2]

Computer & Systems Engineering plc v. John Lelliott (Ilford) Ltd [1989] CSW July 6. **144**[15]

Concorde Construction Co Ltd v. Colgan Co Ltd (1984) 29 BLR 120. **178**[9]

Cook Islands Shipping Co Ltd v. Colson Builders Ltd [1975] 1 NZLR 422. **76**[22]

Coombe v. Green (1843) 11 M & W 480. **199**[6]

Cooper v. Langdon (1841) 9 M & W 60. **210**[2]

Cort v. Ambergate, Nottingham, Boston & Eastern Junction Railway Co (1851) 17 QB 127. **348**[20]

Courtney & Fairbairn Ltd v. Tolaini Brothers (Hotels) Ltd [1975] 1 All ER 716. **64**[6]

Crestar Ltd v. Carr (1987) 37 BLR 113. **379**[33]

Crosby (J.) & Sons Ltd v. Portland UDC (1967) 5 BLR 126. **186**[1]

Croshaw v. Pritchard (1899) 16 TLR 45. **63**[3]

Croudace Construction Ltd v. Cawoods Concrete Products Ltd (1978) 8 BLR 20. **191**[7]

D. & F. Estates Ltd v. Church Commissioners for England [1988] 2 All ER 992. **49**[12], **55**[12], **115**[17], **267**[1]

Davies (A.) & Co (Shopfitters) Ltd v. William Old Ltd (1969) 67 LGR 395. **66**[10]

Davis Contractors Ltd v. Fareham UDC [1956] AC 696. **85**[34]

Dawber Williamson Roofing Ltd v. Humberside CC (1979) 14 BLR 70. **160**[5], **262**[16]

Dawnays Ltd v. F.G. Minter Ltd [1971] 2 All ER 1389. **180**[17]

Day v. Ost [1973] 2 NZLR 385. **58**[25]

Department of the Environment for Northern Ireland v. Farrans Construction Ltd (1981) 19 BLR 1. **340**[20]

Derek Crouch Construction Co Ltd v. Northern RHA (1983) 24 BLR 60. **379**[30]

Dillingham Ltd v. Downs [1972] 2 NSWLR 49. **205**[22]

District of Surrey v. Carroll-Hatch & Associates Ltd (1979) 101 DLR (3d) 218. **53**[21]

Dodd Properties (Kent) Ltd v. Canterbury CC [1980] 1 All ER 928. **334**[3]

Dodd v. Churton [1897] 1 QB 562. **142**[10]

Dunlop and Ranken Ltd v. Hendall Steel Structures Ltd [1957] 3 All ER 344. **255**[2]

Dunlop Pneumatic Tyre Co Ltd v. New Garage & Motor Co Ltd [1915] AC 79.
336[9]

Dyer (E.R.) Ltd v. Simon Build/Peter Lind Partnership (1982) 23 BLR
23. **258**[6]

ECC Quarries Ltd v. Merriman Ltd (1988) 45 BLR 90. **380**[35]

Eagle Star Insurance Co Ltd v. Yuval Insurance Co Ltd [1978] 1 Lloyd's Rep 357.
383[39]

Earth & General Contracts Ltd v. Manchester Corporation (1958) 108 LJ
665. **347**[13]

East Ham B.C. v. Bernard Sunley & Sons Ltd [1966] AC 406. **334**[2],
215[13]

Eckersley v. Binnie & Partners (1990) 18 Con LR 1. **110**[8]

Eckersley v. Mersey Docks and Harbour Board [1894] 2 QB 667. **391**[51]

Ellis Mechanical Services Ltd v. Wates Construction Ltd (1976) 2 BLR 57.
378[23]

Ellis-Don Ltd v. Parking Authority of Toronto (1978) 28 BLR 98. **193**[12]

Emson Contractors Ltd v. Protea Estates Ltd (1987) 39 BLR 126. **380**[34]

English Industrial Estates Corporation v. George Wimpey & Co. Ltd (1972) 7
BLR 122. **80**[26]

Equitable Debenture Assets Corporation v. William Moss (1984) 2 Con LR
1. **58**[28]

Eriksson v. Whalley [1971] 1 NSWLR 397. **350**[29]

Fairclough Building Ltd v. Rhuddlan BC (1985) BLR 26. **273**[9]

Fairweather (H.) & Co Ltd v. Wandsworth LBC (1987) 39 BLR 106. **143**[13]

Fakes v. Taylor Woodrow Construction Ltd [1973] QB 436. **384**[44]

Felton v. Wharrie (1906) HBC 4th ed. Vol. 2, 398. **345**[7]

Fillite (Runcorn) Ltd v. Aqua-Lift (1989) 45 BLR 27. **375**[10]

Finnegan (J.F.) Ltd v. Sheffield CC (1988) 43 BLR 124. **193**[13], **194**[16],
220[25], **377**[20]

Fisher v. PG Wellfair Ltd (1981) 19 BLR 52. **392**[53]

Florida Hotels Pty Ltd v. Mayo (1965) 113 CLR 588. **216**[14]

Frederick Mark Ltd v. Schield (1971) 1 BLR 32. **180**[18]

Freeman v. Hensler (1900) 64 JP 260. **136**[6], **199**[5]

GLC v. Ryarsh Brick Co Ltd [1985] CILL 200. **280**[14]

George E. Taylor & Co Ltd v. G. Percy Trentham Ltd (1980) 16 BLR 15. **180**[16]

Gilbert-Ash (Northern) Ltd v. Modern Engineering (Bristol) Ltd [1974] AC
689. **180**[19], **337**[12], **384**[45]

Gleeson (M.J.) (Contractors) Ltd v. Hillingdon London Borough (1970) 215 EG
165. **80**[25], **131**[7], **140**[8]

Glenlion Construction Ltd v. Guinness Trust (1987) 39 BLR 89. **200**[8]

Gloucestershire CC v. Richardson [1969] 1 AC 480. **133**[9], **268**[4]

Gold v. Patman & Fotheringham Ltd [1958] 2 All ER 497. **80**[23], **230**[6]

Goodwin v. Fawcett (1965) 175 EG 27. **350**[30]

Goodwins, Jardine & Co v. Brand (1905) 7 F (Ct of Sess) 995. **81**[28]

Greater Nottingham Co-operative Society Ltd v. Cementation Piling & Foundations Ltd [1988] 2 All ER 971. **50**[16], **52**[16]

Greaves & Co (Contractors) Ltd v. Baynham Meikle and Partners [1975] 3 All ER 99. **107**[1]

Hampton v. Glamorgan CC [1917] AC 13. **258**[7]

Hanak v. Green [1958] 2 QB 9. **179**[11], **378**[24]

Hanson (W.) (Harrow) Ltd v. Rapid Civil Engineering Ltd and Usborne Developments Ltd (1987) 38 BLR 106. **159**[3], **263**[18]

Harris v. Wyre Forest DC [1989] 2 All ER 514. **48**[10]

Hawkins v. Chrysler (UK) Ltd and Burne Associates (1986) 38 BLR 36. **108**[2]

Hedley Byrne & Co Ltd v. Heller & Partners Ltd [1964] AC 465. **48**[9], **57**[9], **115**[19]

Henry Boot Building Ltd v. Croydon Hotel & Leisure Co Ltd (1985) 36 BLR 41. **178**[8]

Henry Boot Construction Ltd v. Central Lancashire New Town Development Corporation (1980) 15 BLR 1. **156**[1], **186**[3]

Heyman v. Darwins Ltd [1942] AC 356. **375**[9]

Hickman & Co v. Roberts [1913] AC 229. **221**[29]

Higgins (W.) Ltd v. Northampton Corporation [1927] 1 Ch 128. **68**[12]

Hill (J.M.) & Sons Ltd v. Camden LBC (1980) 18 BLR 31. **343**[2], **348**[23], **350**[30]

Hobbs v. Turner (1902) 18 TLR 235. **259**[8]

Hoenig v. Isaacs [1952] 2 All ER 176. **348**[24]

Holme v. Guppy (1838) 3 M & W 387. **136**[5], **201**[11]

Holt, Re, ex parte Gray (1888) 58 LJQB 5. **261**[12]

Home and Overseas Insurance Co Ltd v. Mentor Insurance Co (UK) Ltd [1989] 3 All ER 74. **376**[12]

Hoskisson v. Moody Homes Ltd (1989) CSW, 25 May, 69. **392**[58]

Hounslow BC v. Twickenham Garden Developments Ltd [1971] Ch 253. **149**[19], **346**[9]

Hsin Chong Construction Co Ltd v. Yaton Realty Co Ltd (1986) 40 BLR 119. **264**[20]

Hunt v. Bishop (1853) 8 Exch 675. **199**[7]

Hutchinson v. Harris (1978) 10 BLR 19. **334**[4]

Imodco Ltd v. Wimpey Major Products Ltd and Taylor Woodrow International Ltd (1987) 40 BLR1. **379**[29]

Imperial College of Science & Technology v. Norman & Dawbarn (1987) 8 Con LR 107. **216**[15]

Independent Broadcasting Authority v. EMI Electronics Ltd and BICC Construction Ltd (1980) 14 BLR 1. **108**[4], **110**[9], **303**[1], **362**[2]

Investors in Industry Ltd v. South Bedfordshire DC [1986] QB 1034. **113**[15]

James Longley & Co v. South West Thames RHA (1983) 127 SJ 597. **195**[21]

Jartay Developments Ltd, Re (1982) 22 BLR 134. **178**[7]

John Jarvis v. Rockdale Housing Association Ltd (1986) 36 BLR 48. **275**[11]

John Mowlem & Co Ltd v. British Insulated Callenders Pension Trust Ltd (1977) 3 Con LR 64. **113**[16]
Jones v. Sherwood Computer Services plc [1989] EGCS 172. **374**[1]
Junior Books Ltd v. Veitchi Co Ltd [1983] 1 AC 520. **48**[11], **52**[11]

Kennedy v. Barrow-in-Furness Corp (1909) HBC 4th ed, ii, 411. **374**[5]
Kensington & Chelsea & Westminster AHA v. Wettern Composites Ltd [1985] 1 All ER 346. **213**[8]
Killby & Gayford Ltd v. Selincourt Ltd (1973) 3 BLR 104. **80**[27]
Kingdom v. Cox (1848) 5 CB 522. **348**[21]
Kirk and Kirk Ltd v. Croydon Corp [1956] JPL 585. **271**[6]

LRE Engineering Services Ltd v. Otto Simon Carves Ltd (1981) 24 BLR 127. **135**[4]
Lee v. West [1989] EGCS 160. **268**[2]
Leedsford Ltd v. Bradford Corp (1956) 24 BLR 49. **244**[2]
Leicester Board of Guardians v. Trollope (1911) 75 JP 197. **213**[7]
Leon Engineering & Construction Co Ltd v. Ka Duk Investment Co Ltd (1989) 47 BLR 139. **59**[32], **224**[36], **374**[7]
Lewis v. Brass (1877) 3 QBD 667. **65**[7]
Linden Gardens v. Lenesta Sludge Disposals Ltd. [1990] CILL 612. **56**[22], **202**[14], **242**[1]
London Borough of Merton v. Stanley Hugh Leach (1985) 32 BLR 55. **146**[16]
London, Chatham & Dover Railway Co v. South Eastern Railway Co [1893] AC 429. **194**[17]
London School Board v. Northcroft (1889) HBC 4th ed, ii, 147. **217**[19]
Lubenham Fidelities & Investments v. S. Pembrokeshire DC (1986) 33 BLR 39. **221**[28]

Marshall v. Mackintosh (1898) 78 LT 750. **348**[22]
Marston Construction Co Ltd v. Kigass Ltd (1989) 46 BLR 109. **76**[21]
Martin Grant & Co Ltd v. Sir Lindsay Parkinson & Co Ltd (1984) 29 BLR 31. **200**[9], **258**[5]
Mayfield Holdings Ltd v. Moana Reef Ltd [1973] 1 NZLR 309. **346**[11]
Mersey Steel & Iron Co v. Naylor, Benzon & Co (1884) 9 AC 434. **347**[16]
Mertens v. Home Freeholds Co Ltd [1921] 2 KB 526. **335**[6]
Merton LBC v. Stanley Hugh Leach Ltd (1985) 32 BLR 51. **186**[1], **189**[4], **198**[1], **202**[1], **203**[1]
Merton LBC v. Lowe & Another (1981) 18 BLR 130. **110**[7], **112**[13]
Metropolitan Water Board v. Dick, Kerr & Co Ltd [1918] AC 119. **85**[35]
Micklewright v. Mullock (1974) 232 EG 337. **392**[56]
Miller v. LCC (1934) 50 TLR 479. **150**[20]
Minter (F.G.) Ltd v. WHTSO (1979) 11 BLR 1. **223**[34]
Minter (F.G.) Ltd v. Welsh Health Technical Services Organization (1980) 13 BLR 1. **191**[6], **194**[19]
Modern Building (Wales) Ltd v. Limmer & Trinidad Co Ltd [1975] 1 WLR 1281. **81**[30]

Modern Engineering (Bristol) Ltd v. C Miskin & Son Ltd [1981] 1 Lloyd's Rep 135.   **392**[54]

Mondel v. Steel (1841) 8 M & W 858.   **179**[10]

Monmouthshire CC v. Costelloe & Keple Ltd (1964) 63 LGR 429.   **374**[6]

Moresk Cleaners Ltd v. Hicks [1966] 2 Lloyd's Rep 338.   **112**[12]

Morrison-Knudsen International Co Inc v. Commonwealth of Australia (1972) 13 BLR 114.   **205**[21]

Mottram Consultants Ltd v. Bernard Sunley & Sons Ltd (1974) 2 BLR 28.   **180**[21]

Murdoch v. Luckie (1897) 15 NZLR 296.   **142**[11]

Murphy v. Brentwood DC [1990] 2 All ER 908.   **49**[13], **52**[13], **54**[13], **115**[18], **281**[15]

NEI Thompson Ltd v. Wimpey Construction UK Ltd (1987) 39 BLR 65.   **181**[28]

National Westminster Bank plc v. Arthur Young McClelland Moores & Co [1985] 2 All ER 817.   **393**[62]

Nema, The [1982] AC 724.   **393**[60]

Neodox Ltd v. Swinton & Pendlebury UDC (1958) 5 BLR 34.   **186**[2]

Newham LBC v. Taylor Woodrow (Anglian) Ltd (1981) 19 BLR 99.   **111**[11]

Newport (Essex) Engineering v. Press & Shear Machinery (1981) 24 BLR 71.   **379**[32]

Nin Hing Electronic Engineering Ltd v. Aoki Corporation (1987) 40 BLR 107.   **257**[4]

Normid Housing Association Ltd v. Ralphs (1988) 43 BLR 18.   **227**[1]

Norta Wallpapers (Ireland) v. Sisk & Sons (Dublin) [1978] IR 114.   **108**[5]

North West Metropolitan Regional Hospital Board v. T.A. Bickerton & Son Ltd [1970] 1 All ER 1039.   **80**[24], **148**[18], **170**[3], **201**[10], **248**[5], **272**[7]

Northern Regional Health Authority v. Derek Crouch Construction Co Ltd [1984] QB 644.   **220**[23], **376**[15]

Northwest Holst Civil Engineering Ltd v. Proteus Tileman Ltd (1988) 5-CLD-05-16.   **376**[13]

Norwich CC v. Harvey [1989] 1 All ER 1180.   **51**[19], **52**[19]

Nye Saunders and Partners v. Bristow (1987) 37 BLR 92.   **213**[10]

O'Toole v. Ferguson (1912) 5 DLR 868.   **255**[1]

Oldschool v. Gleeson (Construction) Ltd (1976) 4 BLR 103.   **58**[27], **216**[16]

Oram Builders Ltd v. Pemberton (1985) 29 BLR 23.   **220**[24], **376**[19]

Pacific Associates Inc v. Baxter [1989] 2 All ER 159.   **52**[20], **58**[20], **223**[35], **374**[7]

Panamena Europea Navegacion v. Leyland & Co Ltd [1947] AC 428.   **221**[30]

Partington & Son (Builders) Ltd v. Tameside MBC (1985) 32 BLR 150.   **376**[18]

Peak Construction (Liverpool) Ltd v. McKinney Foundations Ltd (1970) 1 BLR 111.   **142**[12], **193**[10], **339**[17]

Pearson (S.) & Son Ltd v. Dublin Corporation [1907] AC 351.   **57**[4], **205**[20]

Percy Bilton Ltd v. GLC [1982] 2 All ER 623.   **148**[18], **201**[10], **272**[8]

Perini Corporation v. Commonwealth of Australia (1969) 12 BLR 82.   **203**[15], **348**[19]

Peter Lind & Co Ltd v. Mersey Docks & Harbour Board [1972] 2 Lloyd's Rep 234. **64**[5]

Petrofina (UK) Ltd v. Magnaload Ltd [1984] QB 127. **229**[3]

Pigott Construction v. W.J. Crowe Ltd (1961) 27 DLR (2d) 258. **345**[6]

Pillar (P.G.) Ltd v. D.J. Higgins Construction Ltd (1986) 34 BLR 43. **181**[26]

Pirelli General Cable Works Ltd v. Oscar Faber & Partners [1983] 2 AC 1. **48**[8]

Pratt v. George J. Hill Associates (1987) 38 BLR 25. **112**[14], **213**[11]

President of India v. La Pintada Cia Navegacion SA [1985] AC 104. **194**[18]

Pritchett and Gold and Electrical Power Storage Co Ltd v. Currie [1916] 2 Ch 515. **262**[15]

Public Works Commissioner v. Hills [1906] AC 368. **337**[11]

R. v. Walter Cabott Construction Ltd (1975) 21 BLR 42. **201**[13]

Ralphs v. Francis Horner & Sons (1987, unreported). **213**[9]

Ranger v. G.W. Railway (1854) 5 HLC 72. **337**[10]

Rapid Building Group Ltd v. Ealing Family Housing Association Ltd (1984) 29 BLR 5. **135**[2], **179**[12], **201**[12], **340**[18]

Rayack Construction Ltd v. Lampeter Meat Co Ltd (1979) 12 BLR 30. **177**[6]

Redpath Dorman Long Ltd v.Tubeworks Ltd (1984, unreported). **179**[13]

Reed v. Van der Vorm (1985) 35 BLR 136. **220**[25], **377**[20]

Rees & Kirby Ltd v. Swansea CC (1985) 30 BLR 1. **190**[5], **195**[20]

Richard Roberts Holdings Ltd v. Douglas Smith Stimson Partnership, 46 BLR 50. **46**[4]

Roberts (A.) & Co. Ltd v. Leicestershire CC [1961] 1 Ch 555. **68**[13]

Roberts v. Bury Commissioners (1870) LR 4 CP 755. **347**[14]

Rosehaugh Stanhope (Broadgate Phase 6) plc v. Redpath Dorman Long Ltd (1990) 50 BLR 69. **326**[3]

Royston UDC v. Royston Builders Ltd (1961) 177 EG 589. **68**[14]

Rumbelows v. AMK and Firesnow (Sprinkler) Installations Ltd (1980) 19 BLR 25. **51**[17]

Rush & Tompkins Ltd v. GLC [1988] 3 All ER 737. **386**[47], **378**[26]

Salliss & Co v. Calil (1988) 4 Const LJ 125. **223**[34]

Sauter Automation Ltd v. Goodman (Mechanical Services) Ltd (1986) 34 BLR 81. **66**[8]

Schindler Lifts (Hong Kong) Ltd v. Shui On Construction Co Ltd (1984) 29 BLR 95. **257**[4]

Scott Lithgow Ltd v. Secretary of State for Defence 1989 SLT 236. **275**[12]

Scott v. Avery (1856) 5 HLC 811. **382**[36]

Scottish Special Housing Association v. Wimpey Construction UK Ltd [1986] 2 All ER 957. **50**[15], **144**[14]

Shanklin Pier Co Ltd v. Detel Products Ltd [1951] 2 KB 854. **280**[13]

Shanning Ltd v. George Wimpey Ltd [1988] 3 All ER 475. **379**[27]

Sharpe v. San Paulo Brazilian Railway Co (1873) LR 8 Ch App 597. **204**[17], **210**[3]

Shui On Construction Ltd v. Shui Kay Co Ltd (1985) 4 Const LJ 305. **223**[34]

Sidney Kaye, Eric Firmin & Partners v. Bronesky (1973) 4 BLR 1. **35**[7]

Sika Contracts Ltd v. B.L. Gill Ltd (1978) 9 BLR 15. **210**[4]

Simaan General Contracting Co v. Pilkington Glass Ltd (No 2) [1988] 1 All ER 791. **56**[23]

Simplex Concrete Piles Ltd v. St Pancras MBC (1958) 14 BLR 80. **171**[4]

Sims v. London Necropolis Co [1885] 1 TLR 584. **158**[2]

Skopos Design Group Ltd v. Homelife Nursing Ltd (1988) 5-CLD-03-22. **383**[39]

Small & Sons Ltd v. Middlesex Real Estates Ltd [1921] WN 245. **347**[17]

Smallman Construction Ltd v. Redpath Dorman Long Ltd (1988) 47 BLR 15. **379**[31]

Smith & Montgomery v. Johnson Brothers Co Ltd [1954] 1 DLR 392. **199**[4], **212**[5], **244**[3]

Smith v. Eric S. Bush [1988] QB 743. **48**[10]

Smith v. Rudhall (1862) 3 F & F 143. **259**[9]

Southern Water Authority v. Lewis & Duvivier (No 2) (1985) 1 Const LJ 74. **58**[29]

Southern Water Authority v. Carey [1985] 2 All ER 1077. **51**[18], **52**[18]

Sunley (B.) Ltd & Co v. Cunard White Star Ltd [1940] 1 KB 740. **192**[8]

Surrey Heath Borough Council v. Lovell Construction Ltd (1988) 42 BLR 25. **144**[14], **339**[14]

Sutcliffe v. Chippendale & Edmondson (1971) 18 BLR 157. **215**[13], **222**[33], **349**[26]

Sutcliffe v. Thackrah [1974] AC 727. **58**[31], **222**[32], **367**[6], **374**[4]

Swartz & Son (Pty) Ltd v. Wolmaranstadt Town Council 1960 (2) SA 1. **349**[27]

Tara Civil Engineering Ltd v. Moorfield Developments Ltd (1989) 46 BLR 72. **346**[10]

Tate & Lyle Industries Ltd v. Davy McKee (London) Ltd [1989] 2 All ER 641. **392**[59]

Tate & Lyle Food and Distribution Co Ltd v. GLC [1981] 3 All ER 716. **193**[9], **195**[22]

Tatem Steam Navigation Co Ltd v. Anglo-Canadian Shipping Co Ltd (1935) Ll LR 161. **392**[57]

Taunton-Collins v. Crombie [1964] 2 All ER 332. **384**[41]

Temloc Ltd v. Errill Properties Ltd (1987) 39 BLR 30. **150**[21], **339**[15]

Thomas Feather & Co (Bradford) Ltd v. Keighley Corporation (1953) 53 LGR 30. **345**[5], **349**[28]

Thorn v. London Corporation (1876) 1 AC 120. **204**[18]

Token Construction Co Ltd v. Charlton Estates Ltd (1973) 1 BLR 50. **218**[22]

Tout and Finch Ltd, Re [1954] 1 All ER 127. **261**[13]

Townsends (Builders) Ltd v. Cinema News Property Management Ltd [1959] 1 All ER 7. **58**[26]

Trade Indemnity v. Workington Harbour & Docks Board [1937] AC 1. **236**[8]

Treliving (F.) & Co. Ltd v. Simplex Time Recorder Co (UK) Ltd (1981, unreported). **343**[3]

Trollope & Colls Ltd v. Atomic Power Constructions Ltd [1962] 3 All ER 1035. **67**[11]

Trollope & Colls Ltd v. North West Metropolitan Regional Hospital Board [1973] 2 All ER 260. **84**[32]

Tubeworkers Ltd v. Tilbury Construction Ltd (1985) 30 BLR 67. **378**[26]

Turner (East Asia) PTE Ltd v. Builders Federal (Hong Kong) (1988) 42 BLR 122. **391**[52]

Turner & Goudy v. McConnell (1985) 30 BLR 108. **383**[38]

Turner v. Fenton [1982] 1 All ER 8. **384**[43]

Turriff Construction Ltd v. Regalia Knitting Mills Ltd (1971) 9 BLR 20. **63**[2]

Twins Transport Ltd v. Patrick and Brocklehurst (1983) 25 BLR 65. **51**[17]

Tyrer v. District Auditor for Monmouthshire (1973) 230 EG 973. **217**[20]

University Court of Glasgow v. Whitfield (1988) 42 BLR 66. **58**[30]

Verital Shipping Corporation v. Anglo-Canadian Cement Ltd [1966] 1 Lloyd's Rep 76. **391**[50]

Victoria Laundry (Windsor) Ltd v. Newman Industries Ltd. [1949] 2 KB 528. **333**[1]

Victoria University of Manchester v. Wilson & Womersley (1984) 2 Con LR 43. **58**[28]

Victorian Railway Commissioners v. James L. Williams Pty Ltd (1969) 44 ALJR 32. **259**[10]

Vigers Sons & Co Ltd v. Swindell [1939] 3 All ER 590. **210**[1], **259**[11]

Viking Grain Storage Ltd v. T.H. White Installations Ltd (1985) 33 BLR 103. **108**[3]

Voli v. Inglewood Shire Council (1963) 110 CLR 74. **45**[1]

Waghorn v. Wimbledon Local Board (1877) 4th ed, ii, 52. **212**[6]

Walters v. Whessoe Ltd (1960) 6 LBR 23. **229**[4]

Waugh v. British Railways Board [1980] AC 521. **386**[46]

Westminster City Council v. Jarvis and Sons Ltd [1970] 1 All ER 943. **146**[17], **270**[5]

White & Carter (Councils) Ltd v. McGregor [1962] AC 413. **346**[8]

Whitley (F.G.) & Sons v. Clwyd CC (1983) 22 BLR 48. **393**[61]

Whittal Builders Co Ltd v. Chester-le-Street DC (1987) 40 BLR 82. **135**[3], **194**[15]

Wilkinson, Re, ex parte Fowler [1905] 2 KB 713. **261**[13]

William Hill Organization v. Bernard Sunley & Sons (1982) 22 BLR 1. **50**[14]

William Lacey (Hounslow) Ltd v. Davis [1957] 2 All ER 712. **75**[20]

Woodar Investment Development Ltd v. Wimpey Construction UK Ltd [1980] 1 All ER 571. **347**[12]

Wraight Ltd v. P.H. & T. (Holdings) Ltd (1968) 13 BLR 26. **191**[6], **335**[7]

Young & Marten Ltd v. McManus Childs Ltd [1969] 1 AC 454. **133**[8], **268**[3]

PART ONE

Construction Contracts in Context

1

Procurement methods and contractual networks

This book is about **construction contracts**, and this introductory chapter seeks to give a brief description of the types of arrangement within that definition. In later chapters we shall examine in more detail the rights and obligations which are created by such contracts; and also look at other areas of law, such as the tort of negligence, which affect those who participate in construction projects. For the moment, however, our attention is focused on the network of **contractual relationships** which govern a project, and especially on the way in which that network varies under different methods of building procurement.

It must be acknowledged that modern building and civil engineering projects are exceptionally complex, both in conception and implementation. No longer can one simply think in terms of 'the Builder' carrying out work for 'the Client'. In a construction project of appreciable size or importance it is probable that much of the actual construction work will be sub-contracted. Likewise, the client's role in seeing that the job is being properly carried out will probably be delegated to a professional team, including at least an architect and a quantity surveyor for a building project, or an engineer for civil engineering works. When one adds in the designers, such as architects and specialist engineers, the number of legal relationships involved dramatically multiplies.

In considering these relationships, we are for the moment concerned to identify those which are based on a *contract*. From a managerial or administrative point of view, it is of course highly desirable that a good working relationship should exist between people who are not contractually linked, most notably the contract

administrator and the main contractor. However, while such relationships may possibly give rise to claims in tort, the rights and
obligations of the parties are not identified with the same detailed
precision as they would be under a contract. Where any two parties
are linked by a contract, their mutual rights and duties are to be
found by examining and interpreting the terms of that contract,
including those which the law will imply. One of the most significant
features of the modern construction industry is that it seldom uses
simple contracts; it prefers to rely on extremely detailed standard form
contracts, drafted to deal with particular types of project. This is
also true of the terms of engagement of various 'construction professionals', although there are important exceptions; for example,
there are as yet no standard terms of engagement for 'Project
Managers'.

With these introductory points in mind, we may now turn to an
analysis of the various contractual networks which are commonly
found in construction projects.

1.1 TRADITIONAL PROCUREMENT SYSTEMS

The contractual relationships which arise under what may be described as
the 'traditional' form of building procurement are illustrated in Fig. 1.1.
These provoke a number of comments. In the first place, it is apparent
that the *design* of the building or other work is in the hands not of the
contractor, but of the '**design team**'. Exactly who is included under that
heading will vary from one project to another, but it is highly likely to be
built around an architect or a civil engineer. Specialized elements of
design which fall outside the expertise of the main designer, such as
structural engineering or services, are likely to be carried out by specialist
consultants. These may be employed either directly by the client or
alternatively by the architect (in which case they are effectively in the
position of sub-contractors).

The second point concerns the 'Contract Administrator', the person or
organization whose responsibility it is to supervise the execution of the
work on the client's behalf. This role is traditionally filled by the architect
or civil engineer in conjunction, at least on major projects, with a quantity surveyor. However, variations are often found – a client may appoint a
'Project Manager', or may choose to supervise the project personally or
through an employee. This indeed is frequently the case on public works
contracts, where the administrator concerned was formerly known as a
'supervising officer' (the title now used is 'project manager').

Of all the contracts shown in Fig. 1.1, the most important is that

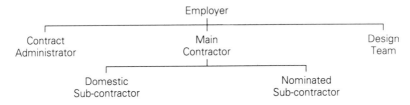

Fig. 1.1 Contractual network in traditional procurement.

between the client and the main contractor. At its simplest, this consists of an obligation on the contractor to carry out and complete the specified works in return for the employer's obligation to pay the agreed price. In the unlikely event that anyone ever entered into such a bare contract, the law would imply into it various terms, dealing for instance with such matters as the quality of work required and the time within which it must be completed. More commonly, such implication by the courts will be unnecessary, for the contract itself will have greatly refined and extended the basic obligations. It is by no means unusual where a standard form contract is adopted to find that this runs to scores, if not hundreds, of pages.

A striking feature of the procurement system represented in Fig. 1.1 lies in the fact that the client has a direct contractual link with most of the participants. The most important exception to this concerns sub-contractors and suppliers. While we shall deal with these in detail in Chapters 16–18, it is necessary to say a little more at this point about their position. Their involvement in construction stems from the fact that contractors today tend not to employ everyone whose work is needed to produce a completed building. Specialist tradesmen, such as plasterers, plumbers and electricians, have for a long time operated as 'independent contractors', and the same is often true of those who do not have such a skilled function, such as 'labour only sub-contractors'. Likewise, the design of works to include novel techniques or new materials is something for which the services of a separate organization are likely to be required.

If these aspects of building work are to be carried out not by the main contractor, but by other firms, it would be perfectly possible to arrange a scheme whereby each firm contracts directly with the employer. Indeed, this is effectively what happens under a **construction management** arrangement of the kind we discuss below. However, while such schemes are perhaps on the increase, this is not the way in which things are traditionally organized in the UK. Instead it is usual for the main contractor to take on legal responsibility for the provision of all these items as part of the main contract, and for the main contractor in turn to sub-contract with the specialists concerned for the supply of the relevant services. Then, if the sub-contracted work is defective, the sub-contractor is liable to the main contractor who, in turn, is liable to the employer. Conversely, while the sub-contractor must look to the contractor for payment for the work, the contractor will recoup this cost from the employer.

What is true of sub-contracted *work* is equally true of the supply of *materials*. While the employer might purchase all the necessary materials personally, it is far more common to find that this task is left to the contractor. Once again, the responsibility for paying the supplier, and the liability in respect of materials which are found to be defective, run up and down the chain of contracts by which the parties are linked.

A realistic picture of how sub-contracts operate in practice requires a further point to be made. One of the most striking features of English construction contracting is its widespread use of 'nominated' sub-contractors and suppliers. Under this system, the employer chooses (often after a tendering process) the sub-contractor who is to carry out a particular aspect of the work. The main contractor is then instructed, subject to certain limited rights of objection, to enter into a sub-contract with the sub-contractor concerned.

The courts in recent years have come to recognize that this is a 'shotgun marriage' between main contractor and nominated sub-contractor, under which the client may even be entitled to specify the precise *terms* of the sub-contract. As a result, the courts have substantially modified the extent to which the main contractor bears legal responsibility in respect of the sub-contracted work. This reduction of the client's legal rights has, in turn, led to a growth in the use of '**collateral warranties**' which are, in effect, direct contracts between the client and a nominated sub-contractor or supplier. Where these are used, it may indeed mean that the client has a contractual relationship with *every* other person or organization concerned with the provision of the building.

1.2 DESIGN AND BUILD CONTRACTS

As we have seen, the contractor under the 'traditional' system plays no part in designing the works, except in those grey areas where the obligation to carry out the job using satisfactory 'workmanship' shades into matters of 'design'. It is for the client, advised by a Design Team of architects and engineers, to prepare a full description of the work that is to be done; the contractor's function is merely to carry it out. However, it is increasingly common to find contracts under which the contractor undertakes full or partial responsibility for design. These are commonly known as **design and build**, **package deal** or **turnkey contracts**; they are typified by the Standard Form of Building Contract With Contractor's

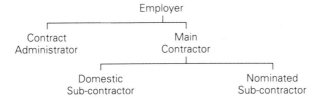

Fig. 1.2   Contractual network in design and build.

Design 1981. This, like many standard form contracts, is published by the Joint Contracts Tribunal (JCT), which is described in Chapter 2.

The contractual network which arises under a design and build system is shown in Fig. 1.2. It is immediately apparent that this follows very closely the 'traditional' structure, though with the inevitable difference that there is no separate 'design team'. However, what the figure does not reveal is the fact that, in practice, it is not uncommon for an *entire* 'design and build' job to be sub-contracted. Quite why this should be done is not immediately clear, but it is most likely to occur where the employer prefers to have direct contractual links with a large and financially stable organization; where the employer wants to make use of that organization's managerial skills; or where it is simply the fact that the contractor 'speaks the same language'.

1.3   MANAGEMENT CONTRACTING

As we have already mentioned, many aspects of a construction project are commonly carried out not by the main contractor, but by other firms acting as sub-contractors or suppliers of materials. The logical conclusion is an arrangement under which the main contractor does none of the actual building work at all, but is effectively employed simply to provide management services for the client.

When **management contracting**, in this sense, first developed, it was felt that the main or 'management' contractor should not be exposed to the same risks in respect of sub-contractor default as under a 'traditional' procurement system. This feeling is reflected in various standard form management contracts now in use, which have been quite deliberately drafted as 'low-risk' contracts from the contractor's point of view.

The JCT Management Contract 1987, the operation of which is represented in Fig. 1.3 (and which is considered in more detail in Chapter 20), provides a good example of this kind of contractual arrangement. Where this form of contract is used, it is assumed that the 'management contractor' will not carry out any of the actual construction work in a project. This will be done by 'works contractors', who are effectively sub-contractors to

Fig. 1.3   Contractual network in management contracting.

the management contractor. On a first reading of the contracts concerned, it appears that the risk of default by such works contractors lies with the management contractor. The latter is not entitled to any extension of time and is fully liable for all defects of materials, workmanship or even design (at least where the works contract in question involves a design obligation).

Closer examination of the contracts reveals that, provided the management contractor is not personally at fault, the true position is precisely the opposite. The management contractor must indeed pursue a defaulting works contractor on the employer's behalf, and the works contractor cannot defend this action by claiming that the management contractor has suffered no loss. However, clause 3.21 of the Management Contract sees to it that any shortfall in recovery is borne by the employer. Further, clause 3.21 also ensures that any other loss which is suffered directly by the management contractor – for example, in meeting claims for disruption brought by other works contractors may also be passed to the employer if the defaulting works contractor fails to pay.

Under MC 87, the management contractor is not responsible for the defaults of the works contractors, instead these are responsible directly to the client on the basis of collateral agreements. In view of this, one may ask why the contract has retained the 'traditional' structure of main contractor and sub-contractor at all. Instead of maintaining the fiction of a 'chain of contracts' along which real rights and liabilities pass, it might have been more meaningful for the client to enter into a direct contractual arrangement with each works contractor, and for the 'management contract' to restrict itself to the provision of management services. Of course, such an arrangement would in effect constitute 'construction management', an alternative procurement system to which we now turn.

1.4   CONSTRUCTION MANAGEMENT

An even more recent development than 'management contracting' is that of **construction management**, which is considered in more depth in Chapter 21. Although the lack of any established standard forms of contract

Fig. 1.4 Contractual network in construction management.

for this latter type of building procurement system renders detailed discussion somewhat difficult, the general picture is fairly clear. As can be
seen in Fig. 1.4, there is no 'main contractor' standing between the client
and the trade contractors, and thus no possibility of insulating the client
against loss caused by those trade contractors. Thus, if the defaults of one
trade contractor cause disruption to another, the latter must claim against
the client for loss and expense, assuming that the contract so permits. The
client will then, in turn, seek to recoup these losses from the defaulter.

The only qualification to this basic scenario would seem to arise where
some or all of the responsibility for the default can be attributed to the
construction manager. As to what the level of this 'responsibility' will be,
this is of course governed by the terms of the contract between the
construction manager and the client, but it is unlikely to be any higher
than a duty to use reasonable care and skill. Furthermore, in view of the
lack of previous cases dealing with this system, it may well be that the
English courts will look to cases concerning the supervisory role of an
architect in deciding what in this context amounts to 'reasonable care and
skill'.

2

Contract risks and contract choice

The purpose of this chapter is to outline the idea of risk and to introduce the major areas of risk in construction projects. We shall also examine some of the methods of dealing with these risks, including the important issue of deciding which form of contract to use.

2.1 THE NATURE OF RISK IN CONSTRUCTION

Risk may be defined as 'Hazard, chance of bad consequences, loss etc., exposure to mischance; expose oneself or be exposed to loss'.[1] Such a definition implies that there is more here than mere chance: risk involves a hazard combined with volition or will. In relation to construction projects, one usually takes risks by choosing from among a range of risks, deciding which are acceptable and 'laying off' those which are not.

Because a word such as 'risk' has both an everyday meaning and a special meaning, its analysis can present semantic problems. It is therefore important to examine fully the implications of this word.

One way of classifying risks is to look at the different approaches to **risk management** which have been taken in the past. For example, in terms of the financing of a project and its duration, risk is a term often used for describing the level of uncertainty. In this context, it implies a range of possible results, each of which has a certain likelihood of occurring. Risk management in construction is often concerned with identifying the range of likely values each potential result may have, and deciding how to manage the project most efficiently. In these terms, risk management in construction is about identifying the economic risks on a project, analysing them and responding to them to develop a rational project management approach. This is the sort of thing usually implied by those who write about 'risk management', 'life-cycle costing', and so on, but here it is not central to our concern.

2.1.1   Contractual risk

For the purposes of this book, the term **contractual risk** is used to indicate an interest different from that of the risk management approach, which concentrates on 'economic risk'. Here the emphasis is on the process of identifying the nature of risks in construction projects and deciding where they are to lie within the project team. Different types of building contract will allocate risks in different quarters. There are several mechanisms for achieving different risk distributions, chief among which are the methods available for calculating and making payments.

Perhaps the key difference between economic and contractual risk is this: economic risk is about the determination and management of costs such as the purchase of materials with which to build, the letting of a completed development or the replacement of worn-out parts of buildings. The point is that these things are undoubtedly going to happen; the risk lies in the uncertainty of the degree to which they will involve someone in expenditure. On the other hand, contractual risk is about the unexpected (floods, fire, changes in design, strikes, and so on). These are events which it is hoped will not happen at all; however, if they do, then someone will have to bear the cost.

Both types of risk are concerned with the eventual payment and responsibility for the cost. The main point about contractual risks is that the contract apportions these between the parties. If the contract is silent on a particular risk, that risk will lie with one party or the other. The contract may seek to transfer the risk by making the other party financially liable should the eventuality take place. In this way, risks are translated into financial equivalents, so that they may be transferred or otherwise dealt with.

2.1.2   Murphy's law

Clearly, contractual risk is to do with what happens when some mischance occurs. According to Murphy's law, if a thing can go wrong, it *will* go wrong; although this is usually said as a joke, it does have a serious place in any consideration of contractual risk. It is hoped that before the mischance occurs, someone has predicted that it might in some way occur one day. The point about contractual risk is that, if one is repeatedly involved in construction, anything which can go wrong eventually will. This is Murphy's law applied to construction. A client who only builds once may be fortunate enough to avoid some or even all of the risks involved. A contractor, developer, architect or surveyor, on the other hand, is statistically bound sooner or later to meet some of these terrible disasters! It is this statistical inevitability that makes the consideration of risk so important.

2.1.3   Stop/start nature of construction

One of the fundamental characteristics of construction is that it is a temporary activity taking place at a temporary location. A development site is not *always* a development site. It may begin as simply an open space, at which point it is of little concern to us; one day, if all goes well, it will have a building on it, in occupation and working satisfactorily. At some point, though, a construction project may well start, proceed and finish upon the site. The level of risk associated with the site will change as this construction process passes through it. People will come to the project, become involved in it, absorb some of the dangers and risks and perhaps be affected by them. Then their involvement will cease. However, even though they may no longer play an active role in that particular project, their involvement with the risk may stay with them for some time. Indeed, it may even continue after death, to the extent of attaching liability to their estate.

These characteristics (the impermanence of the activity and its temporary location) mean that the risks associated with construction projects are different from those in other industries. And because the risks are different, there is a whole series of contractual issues which are unique to construction projects.

2.1.4   Risk and price

Before turning to consider construction risks in more detail, a final introductory point is worth making. When a project is first under consideration, decisions will be needed about where liability for the cost of a whole range of risks is to lie. Is it to lie with the contractor, the designers, other consultants or the owner? **Mismanagement of construction risks** happens when such factors are not considered by employers and tendering contractors, for the following reason. If the cost of a possible eventuality is to be borne by the contractor, then the price submitted to do the work should include an element for this contingency occurring. This ought to be spread across a series of contracts, because the item at risk will not occur on them all. (If it is going to occur on all of them, then it ceases to be a risk and becomes a certainty.) On the other hand, the cost of the eventuality may be borne by the client. In that case, the offered price should be correspondingly lower but the final 'price' will be increased if the eventuality comes to pass. Any extra risk to be carried by the contractor should therefore be reflected in the price charged for the work.

This discussion leads to an inevitable conclusion. There is a basic principle which ought to be observed in the letting of all construction contracts. It is that wherever a transfer of risk is to occur from the contractor to the owner, there should be a counterbalancing advantage of price to balance the risk assumed by the owner.[2] This basic principle remains unappreciated by many who work in the industry. Its observance would undoubtedly remove a lot of the ambiguity which surrounds construction contracts and would probably therefore avoid many of the disputes which occur.

Recognition of the essential relationship between risk and price has another important effect. It renders unnecessary any discussion of such emotive (but misleading) issues as whether the passing of the risk to one party or the other contractor is 'unfair' or 'immoral'. As Duncan Wallace points out: 'Any discussion about whether or not a particular risk should be so included in the price is a discussion of policy, and not of "fairness", "morality" or "justice".'[2]

2.2 TYPES OF RISK IN CONSTRUCTION CONTRACTS

Any construction project, by its very nature, involves certain unavoidable risks. These have occasionally been analysed and classified by various analysts; but such analyses are all too infrequent. The following examples are drawn from the best available analyses:[3,4]

- **Physical works** – physical conditions of the ground; artificial conditions causing obstruction; defective materials or workmanship; costs of tests and samples; weather; site preparation; inadequacy of staff, labour, plant, materials, time or finance.
- **Delay and disputes** – possession of site; lateness in the supply of information; inefficient execution of work; delay outside both parties' control; layout disputes.
- **Direction and supervision** – cupidity (i.e. greed); incompetence; inefficiency; unreasonableness; partiality; lack of communication; mistakes in the documentation; defective designs; ensuring compliance with requirements; lack of clarity in specifying requirements; inappropriate choice of consultants or contractors; changes in requirements.
- **Damage and injury to persons and property** – negligence or breach of warranty; uninsurable matters outside the parties' control; accidents; uninsurable risks such as war, usurped power; consequential losses arising from the above; exclusions, gaps and time limits in insurance cover.
- **External factors** – government policy on taxes, labour, safety or other laws; delay or refusal of planning approval; financial constraints; energy and pay restraints; cost of war or civil commotion; malicious damage; intimidation; labour demands and unrest; strikes; lockouts; pickets.

- **Payment** – devaluation; delay in settling claims and certifying; delay in paying certificates; legal limits in recovery of interest; insolvency of contractor, sub-contractor or employer; funding constraints; shortcomings in the measure and value process; exchange rate fluctuations; inflation; anything not covered by a fluctuation clause; replacement cost of plant and equipment.
- **Law and arbitration** – delay in resolving disputes; injustice; uncertainty due to lack of records or ambiguity of contract; cost of obtaining decision; enforcing decisions; changes in statutes; new interpretations of common law.

In considering this list of items, it is important to think about the extent to which they can be priced for at tender stage, and indeed the extent to which they can be predicted at all. Some things may be extremely unlikely to occur; others may be likely to occur but difficult to specify accurately. These factors should have a significant effect on the way in which different risks are responded to. Extensive research has been undertaken in this area, and it has been shown that the development of an adequate contract strategy must be based upon choices about how to respond to risks.[5] Each risk can be analysed regarding its likely range of outcomes. Responses to the risks can then be chosen.

2.3   DEALING WITH RISK

There is a common misconception that people always wish to avoid risk. This is not necessarily so. Uncertainty is a problem, but the aim of engaging in construction is to take *calculated* risks! The life-blood of business is to make money by dealing with the risks which other people do not want to bear. As a result, making risk explicit does not obstruct the client's objectives but instead helps to get the project completed effectively by people who wish to take commercial decisions about engaging in commercial risk.

An understanding of this point should help construction consultants to advise their clients about risk allocation in a more meaningful way than has hitherto been the norm. The aim of contract choice should always be to distribute the risk in a clear and unambiguous manner. Unfortunately, there is a general failure within the construction industry to appreciate this; and the results of this failure are seen in excessive claims and litigious disputes.

The process of dealing with contractual risk falls naturally and logically into three stages:

1. **Identify the risks.** The list given above exemplifies the types of risk which may occur. This is useful as a preliminary checklist and for helping to provoke thoughts about the risks which may be important

on a project. The identification of risk must be linked to a clear statement of the client's priorities for a project, so that e.g. if the timing of the project is critical, the severity of time-related risks is automatically increased.

2. **Analyse the risks.** The second step in the process is to analyse each of the risks in terms of their likely frequency of their occurrence, their likely severity when they do occur and the range of possible values in terms of minima, maxima and medians for each of these aspects. This analysis may need to be fairly subjective, in order to achieve it quickly, but it is an important step in raising the level of awareness of risk exposure. Some risks may be deemed to be so critical that they need detailed quantitative analysis, but most risks will be dealt more subjectively because they are lower in priority.

3. **Respond to the risk.** The range of possible responses is discussed below. In terms of identifying a contract strategy, the result of the previous steps will be an insight into both the priorities of the client and the major risks involved. The final step is to make some decisions about who is best placed to manage a risk. The choices lie between the client, the consultants, the contractor or insurers. Any decision about laying off risks on to others must involve weighing up the frequency of occurrence against the level of premium being paid for the transfer. It is also important to consider the extent to which the risk can be controlled by certain parties. Risks connected with the design of the project are best controlled by the designers, hence it makes sense to transfer liability for defective design to them. Risks connected with the management of sub-contractors are best controlled by the contractor but, in certain circumstances, the transfer of risk of default may be prohibitive. For this reason, different procurement options allocate the risks associated with sub-contractors in different ways.

This discussion should make it clear that any arguments about whether one standard form contract, or one procurement system, is 'better' than another are specious. Each has a role to play in certain circumstances, and the consultant who habitually recommends one over another, without identifying and analysing the attendant risks, is hardly acting with that degree of skill and care which the client is entitled to expect.

We may now consider in more detail the range of possible responses to contractual risks. The choice lies between transfer, acceptance, avoidance or insurance of risk, or even, perhaps, doing nothing.

2.3.1 Transfer of risk

seeming good or sound at first sight but lacking real merit.

Risks are inevitable and cannot be eliminated. They can, however, be transferred. In accordance with the basic general principle given above, the transfer of a risk should usually involve a premium. This is best summed up by the following passage: 'It must be understood and appreciated that any attempt to burden the other party with risks which are inevitable and unpredictable is not a solution...contractors should therefore avoid participating in tenders where conditions impose too many unpredictable or excessively unbalanced risks, or undefined responsibilities.'[6]

The transfer of risk is achieved through appropriate wording in the clauses of a contract. It is absolutely fundamental to any study of building contracts to understand that contractual clauses are intended to transfer risks. To appreciate the extent to which they do this, it is necessary to understand what the legal situation would be with and without the relevant clauses. This is a basic aim of this book, and it is intended that the reader should develop an understanding of the transfer of risk by studying subsequent chapters.

A good example of the transfer of risk is provided by the way in which building contracts deal with bad weather. In JCT 80 clause 25 makes provision for the contractor to be entitled to an extension of time in the event of exceptionally adverse weather. However, clause 26 does not give the contractor any entitlement to *financial* compensation in this event. The overall result therefore is that this particular risk is shared by the employer and the contractor. By contrast, GC/Works/1 does not even allow the contractor an extension of time for bad weather. Under this form of contract therefore the effects of the weather are entirely at the risk of the contractor.

This particular apportionment of risk raises a very interesting issue. Clearly, if the contractor carries the risk of delay due to possible bad weather, a premium can be included in the tender for this. What happens, however, if the employer delays the contractor by supplying information late? The contract period can be extended for this eventuality, but the delay may mean that the work is subject to bad weather which would not otherwise have affected it. The newly revised version of GC/Works/1 takes account of this, permitting the contract period to be extended for bad weather which takes place during a period not originally envisaged to have been within the contract period. This example shows how a simple allocation of risk can become very complex when the effects of other risks are taken into account.

As a general principle, it is unwise to try to pass to the contractor a risk which is difficult to assess. Conscientious and skilled contractors will increase their prices substantially to deal with them, or they may insert qualifications in their bids to avoid them. Unscrupulous or careless contractors will disregard these risks when preparing their bids and will consequently find themselves in difficulty at a later stage. Once this happens, they will try in one way or another to pass the cost back to the owner. If this fails, they may even be forced into liquidation, which will not help the employer at all.

2.3.2 Acceptance of risk

Clients should avoid imposing undue or unbalanced risks on to contractors. It is not good business practice to try to steal an advantage over the other party in this way. It may be possible in the short term to lay off a risk on to someone else without having to pay a premium for it. In the long term, however, someone will have to pay. As Murphy's law states, anything that can go wrong *will* go wrong. Therefore, if one continues to indulge in unbalanced contracts, then eventually the worst will happen and the unwilling bearers of the risk will probably be sent out of business. When this happens, it is their creditors who pay the price, and the employer will be one of those creditors. In the long term, this process of shifting too much risk on to contractors who must accept it in order to stay in business will gradually reduce the available number of contractors tendering for work. All their competitors will have been put out of business!

There are many risks which ought to lie with the employer. If none of the contributors to a project can control or mitigate a particular risk, it makes little sense to assign that risk to them. Any explicit transfer will carry a huge premium. Similarly, a client who repeatedly engages in building procurement is wasting money by paying a premium for people to take over risks which need not be passed on. A useful analogy with this last point is provided by the government's policy towards the insurance of its buildings against fire, compared to that of a private individual. If a private householder's property is burned down, the cost of replacement is prohibitive, compared to the householder's annual income. Because of this, most individuals insure their property against fire, so that the risk is spread out among a large number of householders. If the risk is of the order of one in a thousand that a building will burn down this year, then each insured person need only pay one-thousandth of the average cost. This is obvious on an individual scale, and it sometimes comes as something of a shock to learn that the government does not insure its buildings against fire. If the chance of fire is of the order of one in a thousand, then, since the government owns thousands of buildings, there is no uncertainty associated with fire. It is certain that some buildings will burn down each year. In consequence, there is nothing left to insure!

Applying this reasoning to construction, each of the risks identified has a certain probability attached to it. If property developers or other construction clients are repeatedly engaged in the process of building, then they are wasting money by attempting to lay off all the risks. Predictable risks become certainties and should therefore be absorbed. This would apply to such things as defaults by nominated sub-contractors and inadequate design information.

Risks which are highly unpredictable and poorly defined should also be carried by the client, because the alternative will be tenders which are so inflated as to be unacceptable. Examples of such risks are those associated with war, earthquakes, invasions, and so on, which would be impossible to quantify or predict.

2.3.3   Avoidance of risk

The third option to consider in responding to risk is that of avoidance. Once the risks have been identified and considered, it may be decided that some risks are simply unacceptable. Their explicit definition may persuade the employer that the building project should be redefined or even abandoned. By examining the funding limits of a project, and the range of possible outcomes of some of the more likely risks, the feasibility of a project may be compromised. Redefining the project is a method of avoiding a risk altogether. For example, if the financial viability of the project is entirely dependent on the existence of a particular government subsidy, and there are legislative moves afoot to end such subsidies, it may be thought prudent to redefine the project such that it is not dependent on such ephemeral support.

The avoidance of risk on a whole project is one thing, but consultants who are seeking appointment will also be interested in avoiding risks. The same principles apply here. Indeed, the most important message from a RIBA report on risk avoidance for architects is to 'ensure that the commission is clear and unambiguous'.[7] The clarification of responsibilities, remuneration and expenditure, at the beginning of the consultant's appointment, will help to avoid many traps encountered by consultants in the past.

lasting only a short time

2.3.4   Insuring against risk

In dealing with 'acceptance of risk', above, we have remarked on the similarity between insurance and laying off risks. Insurance is an option in some situations. Several risks on the list can be insured against, and most of the standard forms of contract insist on certain types of insurance. Standard insurable risks are items such as indemnity against third-party claims for injury and insurance against fire. There are also opportunities to insure against loss of liquidated damages and other forms of consequential loss. The actual insurance needed for any particular project

should be considered very carefully. It is also essential for each
consultants involved to take out professional indemnity insuranꞇꞓ, ꞇꞷ
cover themselves and their clients against the risk of failure to perform
the duties with the requisite level of skill and care. These issues are fully
discussed in Chapter 15.

2.3.5 Doing nothing about risk

It frequently happens that none of the project team consider the risks that
they are about to take at the outset of a project. If a client is poorly
advised, and professional advisers fail to appreciate the level and disposition of risks, the eventual occurrence of disasters takes everyone by
surprise! On the other hand, consultants who carefully consider the
balance of risks within a project, and who decide that they already lie
with those parties who can best control them, may choose to do nothing.
Unfortunately, both these courses of action may look the same to the
casual observer. In the latter case, perhaps, the people concerned should
not keep quiet about the fact that they have considered the apportionment of risk and decided to do nothing, but should make their decisions
explicit, so that they can be questioned.

A further example of 'doing nothing' lies within the main standard
form contracts. Certain events are not envisaged by the contracts, which
therefore make no mention of them. In such a case, it would be a mistake
to believe that the contract does not apportion the risk. By the very fact
of remaining silent, the contract allocates the risk to one or other of the
parties. The problem with allocating risks in this way is that it may lead to
misinterpretation and ambiguity, which is a risk in itself. Such a situation
can rapidly lead to disputes and claims when problems arise.

2.4 CONTRACT CHOICE

2.4.1 Use of standard form contracts

Although certainly not essential, it is common practice when procuring a
building to appoint the contractor on a standard form building contract.
These forms, as will be seen, have emanated from various parts of the
construction industry and for various reasons. Each of them has a role to
play in the choice of strategy. In order for the process to work effectively,
it is essential that the standard forms are understood in terms of the way
they distribute risk. This is one of the purposes of this book. By studying
the principles behind building contracts, the apportionment of risk within
each of the standard forms should become more clear.

One of the main reasons for standardizing the contracts used in building is because the contractual complexities can be difficult to appreciate.

Many in the industry feel that the use of a standard form will help people to become more familiar with all the contractual provisions. Unfortunately, this ideal is rarely achieved, for at least two reasons. First, the standard forms are rarely used as printed. It is common in the industry for people to amend the printed form, by striking out clauses they do not like and adding in their own preferred clauses (the wisdom of this practice is questioned in Chapter 8). Second, the way in which the construction industry is structured encourages people to concentrate on particular types of work. Civil engineers and builders rarely interact. The various groups of consultants can thus fall into the trap of only knowing about one standard form. If this happens, their understanding of the contractual issues involved becomes very one-sided, and there is often a failure to appreciate the wider issues in the context of English law. This can lead to misunderstandings which are perpetuated simply because, once such consultants realize how complex the standard form is, they do not wish to add to that complexity by using a different one! The answer to this problem is to understand the principles of contract law first and then to apply these principles to the standard forms, so that the allocation of risk within each form can be appreciated.

Before detailing the main standard forms available, it is interesting to note that the Banwell Report,[8] in 1964, recommended that the building industry should develop and use a single standard form of contract for all building works. Whether or not this was a sensible suggestion, its implementation is purely hypothetical, because since 1964 there has been a proliferation of standard forms.

2.4.2 JCT contracts

Despite its name, the Joint Contracts Tribunal (JCT) does not sit in judgment on others. It is an affiliation of interest groups within the construction industry which operates as a forum for discussing and determining the content of the clauses of the standard forms of contract. It does not appear that this body was ever meant to be democratic, or even representative. Its origins lie in 1870, when the Builders' Society (now the CIOB) and the RIBA together produced the first 'standard form' of contract. This was for use only in London and seems to have been an attempt to overcome some of the problems of the day which were caused by the use of *ad hoc* building contracts.

Over the years the meetings of the various interest groups continued and, after much argument, negotiation and debate, the first national standard form became available in 1909. This was drafted by the RIBA and the NFBTE (now the BEC) with help in mediation by the Institute of Builders. It was largely based on the 1870 form, and it is said that much of the original 1870 style, if not the actual content, can still be detected in the latest JCT forms![9]

The current membership of the Joint Contracts Tribunal is as follows:

Royal Institute of British Architects (RIBA)
Building Employers' Confederation (BEC)
Royal Institution of Chartered Surveyors (RICS)
Association of County Councils
Association of District Councils
British Property Federation (BPF)
Committee of Associations of Specialist Engineering Contractors (CASEC)
Federation of Associations of Specialists and Sub-contractors (FASS)
Association of Consulting Engineers
Scottish Building Contract Committee

Examples of the forms produced by the JCT are as follows.

JCT 80: The Standard Form of Building Contract

This form of contract (called JCT 80 because it was issued by the Joint Contract Tribunal in 1980) is regarded as the 'industry standard' against which all others are measured. It is a long and complex document which consolidated all the revisions to the earlier form of contract (JCT 63), as well as making fundamental changes to such matters as the nomination of sub-contractors. JCT 80 is published in six versions:

1. Local Authority edition With Quantities;
2. Private edition With Quantities;
3. Local Authority edition With Approximate Quantities;
4. Private edition With Approximate Quantities;
5. Local Authority edition Without Quantities;
6. Private edition Without Quantities.

In addition, the following supplements are issued:

(a) Fluctuations supplement (LA);
(b) Fluctuations supplement (private);
(c) Formula Rules;
(d) Sectional completion supplement;
(e) Contractor's designed portion supplement.

Furthermore, certain sub-contract forms are designed for use with JCT 80:

NSC/1 Nominated sub-contract tender and agreement;
NSC/2 Employer/nominated sub-contractor agreement;

NSC/2a As NSC/2 but where NSC/1 is not used;
NSC/3   Nomination of a sub-contractor;
NSC/4   Nominated sub-contract;
NSC/4a As NSC/4 but where NSC/1 is not used;
TNS1   Tender for nominated suppliers;
TNS2   Warranty for nominated suppliers.

Among the major characteristics of this form are the requirement that an Architect (or a 'Contract Administrator') and a Quantity Surveyor must be appointed. The architect has wide but strictly defined powers. These include the issuing of certain instructions on behalf of the employer, and also the independent certification of payments, the quality of work, the contractor's performance, and so on. The quantity surveyor is responsible for the valuation of work done and the valuation of variations.

Another extremely important feature of JCT 80 is the provision which it makes for the nomination of specialist sub-contractors. This practice arose originally because complex electrical and mechanical services installations can take a long time to design and procure. By making provision in the contract for the employer to nominate such a specialist before the main contractor is known, it was possible to ensure that the specialist installations would be ready for inclusion in the building in good time. Without this provision, the contract could be subject to considerable delays while the main contractor procured these items. Unfortunately, the practice of nomination is now frequently adopted for ulterior motives. The employer or the contract administrator often uses this method in order to ensure that specialist work is awarded to someone with whom they have worked in the past and who can be relied on. While there is nothing wrong with this in principle, it tends to lead to the increasing incidence of nomination for the sake of nomination, rather than for the sake of expediting the works.

Further characteristics of JCT 80 are its elaborate provisions for dealing with delays to and disruptions of the work; lengthy and complex insurance provisions; and provisions for bringing the employment of the contractor to an end in the event of either party's insolvency. The way in which these detailed provisions apportion risks between the parties is the basis of analysis throughout the remainder of this book.

JCT IFC 84: Intermediate Form of Building Contract

This form is published with the following associated documents:

(a) Fluctuations clauses and formula rules;
(b) NAM/T Tender and agreement for named sub-contractors;

(c) NAM/SC Sub-contract conditions for named sub-contractors;
(d) NAM/SC/FR Sub-contract formula rules for named sub-contractors;
(e) ESA/1 RIBA/CASEC Employer/Specialist agreement.

The annual contract use survey undertaken by the RICS shows that this form is now being quite widely used.[10] Its aim is to bridge the gap between the lengthy provision of JCT 80 and the simplicity of the Minor Works Form, which was being used in place of JCT 80 for contracts for which it was totally inappropriate; IFC 84 is shorter than JCT 80 but is still fairly complex.

The main characteristic of IFC 84 is its flexibility. It can be used either for local authorities or private sector employers, with or without bills of quantities as the cost control document. Although there are no provisions for nomination of sub-contractors as such, there is a different mechanism for achieving a similar result. This is the 'naming' of a sub-contractor or supplier, which involves either including their name in the contract documents or allocating a provisional sum. There are some important legal differences between named sub-contractors under IFC 84 and nominated sub-contractors under JCT 80, which will be examined in more detail in Chapter 16.

JCT MW 80: Agreement for Minor Works

This form is published with a single associated document, the Minor Works supplement, which covers contributions, levy and tax changes and statutory tax deduction.

This contract is designed for use only on very small and simple works. The conditions give a bare outline of the parties' duties and responsibilities, and allocate risks too crudely for more complex situations. It is extremely useful for such projects as domestic extensions, but generally should not be used on contracts exceeding £50000. Its chief advantage is its simplicity, but this becomes a major disadvantage on larger projects, where its lack of detailed provisions will leave the employer dangerously exposed to many different kinds of risk.

JCT FF 76: Fixed Fee Form of Prime Cost Contract

This form is a revision of one which was issued in 1967 and which was based on JCT 63. It is intended for use in situations where it is not possible to obtain a firm price for work in advance. However, it does assume that a certain amount of design has been done because the conditions require an estimate of the probable cost to be provided. It is this probable cost which will form the basis of the contractor's calculation of the fee to be charged.

Because this form is substantially based upon JCT 63, it is issued with a warning that some of its provisions may have become obsolete. The JCT is currently endeavouring to replace it with a more up-to-date version.

JCT CD 81: Standard Form with Contractor's Design

This form is published with two associated documents:

(a) Formula rules;
(b) Contractor's Designed Portion Supplement.

These documents cater for two different situations which could exist when considering the contractor's contribution to the design of the build-ing. In both cases the contractor will be constructing the building, but the extent of the contractor's responsibility for designing the building can vary. CD 81 is intended to be used where the contractor's design respon-sibility covers the whole of the works, irrespective of the extent to which the works have already been designed by another party. However, if the contractor's design responsibility is for only part of the works, then CD 81 is not a suitable contract. In this case, the contractor's designed portion supplement is to be used. This document is a set of amendments to be made to JCT 80. The use of JCT 80 with this supplement is very different from the use of CD 81. For example, there is no provision in CD 81 for the appointment of either a contract administrator or a quanti-ty surveyor. However, there must be an 'employer's agent' who acts on behalf of the employer.

The contract is let on the basis of a document called the 'employer's requirements', which specifies precisely what it is that the contractor is being asked to do. This will often take the form of a performance specification. 'Contractor's proposals' to comply with these requirements are submitted, and the winning contractor's proposal document is then used as the major control document on the project. While there is no provision for the nomination of sub-contractors, this can be effectively achieved by careful wording of the requirements.

In other respects, apart from re-wording to eliminate the contract administrator's responsibilities and to create a situation in which the contractor is responsible for self-certification of work, the style and con-tent of much of this form is very similar to JCT 80. Particular issues of design liability under this and other forms are covered in more detail in Chapter 7, and the principles of design and build contracts are examined in Chapter 19.

JCT MC 87: Management Contract

This form of contract has the following associated documents:

WKS1/1 Section 1: Invitation to tender;
WKS1/2 Section 2: Tender by Works Contractor;
WKS1/3 Section 3: Agreement;
WKS2 Works Contract 2: Conditions of contract:
WKS3 Works Contract 3: Employer/Works contractor agreement;
Phased completion supplement;
Formula rules for the works contract.

The Management Contract was issued in 1987, having taken the JCT some 12 years to produce. There is nothing new about the idea which, in essence, simply introduces a new level of management in between the employer and the 'builders'. In some ways, it is similar to the traditional way of procuring buildings in this country, which is still sometimes used, known as **separate trades contracting**. The only difference is that the management contractor decides how the work is to be broken down into packages for letting and undertakes supervisory and agent's roles.

Before the management contract was issued, a similar pattern of involvement could be achieved under JCT 80 by using sub-contractors. The problem with this was that the employer had to sue the main contractor for any defaults or faulty workmanship or materials, leaving the main contractor to sue the sub-contractor if this was possible. Under the MC 87 arrangements, the employer and the works contractors have a more detailed set of obligations, which means that the management contractor is relieved of much of this liability. The management contract is analysed in detail in Chapter 20.

JCT Measured Term Contract

This form of contract is designed for use where an employer needs regular maintenance and minor works to be carried out, and wishes to engage only one contractor for a specified period. The single contract will then cover a number of separate jobs since the contractor carries out work from time to time on receipt of instructions from the employer.

2.4.3 Other standard form contracts

There are bodies other than the JCT which also produce building contract forms but, in most cases, this is not through a process of 'debate until consensus'. An individual interest group simply produces a contract, although this is in many cases done after extensive consultations with other interested parties. Of these other forms, the most important are as follows.

ICE Conditions of Contract

This is a negotiated form produced by the Institution of Civil Engineers, the Association of Consulting Engineers and the Federation of Civil Engineering Contractors. It was first published in 1945; the current sixth edition appeared in January 1991. There is only one version, for use with public or private clients, and it is intended for use on major civil engineering projects. These include a wide range of works such as navigable canals, irrigation schemes, roads, railways, docks, harbours, dams, bridges and tunnels. Many civil engineering contracts include building works, and vice versa.

The essential feature of the ICE 6 conditions is that they provide a contract between a promoter and a contractor. The promoter becomes the employer under the conditions, and the engineer provides the technical aspects of design and specifications and effectively translates the contract.[11] The engineer is not a party to the contract and thus has no legal rights or obligations under the contract. However, engineers have their own contract (conditions of engagement) with their employers.

The conditions create a 're-measurement' contract, also known as 'admeasurement' or 'measure and value'. This means that the contractor is paid at the contract rates (which may be subject to variation) for the actual quantities of work carried out. This is recognized by the fact that the ICE 6 conditions, unlike JCT contracts, make no reference to a 'contract sum'; they refer instead to a 'tender total'.

Work under an ICE 6 contract is to be carried out to the satisfaction of the engineer, whose powers of control and direction are both extensive and apparently arbitrary. The conditions contain wide provisions for the adjustment of the contract sum, usually in favour of the contractor.

The detailed provisions of ICE 6 are referred to throughout this book, usually in order to provide a contrast with JCT 80.

ICE Minor Works Contract

This is based on the ICE conditions, but is much more simple. Much of the wording has been redrafted into straightforward English. There is no prescribed form of tender. The method of payment can be calculated by re-measurement, lump sum, day works, cost plus fee or any combination of these. There are no provisions for nomination of sub-contractors, and the provisions for extensions of time, liquidated damages, valuation of variations, and the like, are both simplified and more limited in their application.

An interesting new provision is the step-by-step procedure in case of disputes which is outlined in clause 11. The main aim is clearly to reach an agreed settlement; this is a refreshing change from many standard forms, which seem to assume that the target is a lawsuit!

The form is intended for use on contracts of less than £100 000, with a duration of less than 6 months. However, there is no real reason why it should not be used (with care and possibly minor amendments) on larger contracts.[12] It is far more complex than the JCT minor works form MW 80.

FIDIC Conditions of Contract

This form is produced by the International Federation of Consulting Engineers (FIDIC) in association with the European International Federation of Construction (FEIC). It is substantially based on the ICE form, modified to enable it to be used anywhere in the world. It contains special provisions to enable the parties to decide under which nation's legal system the contract will be executed. This traditionally was the country of the engineer, but recently it has become more usual for it to be country of the employer.

The basic characteristics of the contract are that an engineer is employed as the client's agent and representative, as well as having certification powers. Legally this role is similar to that of a contract administrator under JCT 80. There are provisions for nomination of sub-contractors, settlement of disputes, extensions of contract period, liquidated damages and all the other complexities usually encountered in major standard forms of building contract. The provisions are not considered further in this book. Interested readers are referred to the guidance notes issued by FIDIC.[13]

ACA 2: The ACA Form of Building Agreement

The ACA form was first published in 1982. It is not a negotiated form, but rather a response to widespread criticisms of the JCT 80 range of standard forms, and is produced by the Association of Consulting Architects. A second edition, ACA 2, was published in October 1984. The conditions are remarkable in their use of standard alternative clauses, which can be used in a variety of combinations of provide a wide range of contract types. In this way, contractual arrangements can be provided which suit the parties to a particular project.

BPF System

In 1983 the British Property Federation published its controversial *Manual of the BPF System*, which proposed major changes to the way in which building projects were organized from inception to completion. These moved much of the risk back on to the building team and suggested things which, to judge by the reaction of the construction industry at the time, were considered alarming. However, many aspects of the proposals, such as fee tendering by the professionals on the project team, now seem quite acceptable.

Part of the new package was a form of building contract conditions. However, it seems to have been discovered at the last minute that the conditions in it would not be acceptable to any tendering contractors, so they were never published. Instead the BPF adopted a particular version of ACA 2 with fewer alternative clauses. Although the BPF system produced a flurry of consternation at the time, its influence has mainly been in the way the building industry perceives its clients and differentiates between them. The system itself has had very little use.

GC/Works/1: General Conditions of Government Contracts for Building and Civil Engineering Works

This contract is widely used for central government and PSA work. It is issued by the government, after consultation but without negotiation. It has been in use for many years and has recently been republished in a third edition. A significant characteristic is that many of the contract conditions give binding force to decisions of the employer, referred to as the 'Authority'.

The contract has some very unusual aspects, such as the employer's right to determine the contract without having to give any reason. Other provisions include the appointment of a project manager, unique payment provisions related to cash flow 'S-curves' instead of measured work done, acceleration provisions, extensions of time and liquidated damages. A notable feature is that many of the provisions are tailored to work for the central government and would be wholly inappropriate for other clients.

GC/Works/2: Minor Works version of GC/Works/1

This is a simplified version of GC/Works/1, intended for small and simple projects.

2.5 DISTRIBUTION OF RISK THROUGH METHODS OF PAYMENT

When examining any contract for the way in which risks are apportioned, one of the most fundamental aspects is the way in which the prices are calculated. In construction contracts, it is convenient to analyse payments as falling under one of two headings; either 'fixed price' or 'cost reimbursement'. It is useful to think of all items under a building contract as being paid for on one of these bases, with no other method of calculating payment. The difference between these two methods of payment is as follows:[14]

1. **Fixed price** items are those paid for on the basis of a predetermined estimate of the cost of the work, adding an allowance for the risk involved, as well as an allowance for the market situation in relation to the contractor's workload. The estimated price is paid by the client, irrespective of the actual cost incurred by the builder.
2. **Cost reimbursement** items are those paid for on the basis of the actual cost of the work.

These two methods are not independent of each other; it would be unusual to find a contract being discharged by one method alone. Usually a contract will employ both methods, to varying degrees, in combination. The contract will be described in terms of the method most used. Thus most of the items in a bill of quantities for a job let under JCT 80 will be of a fixed price nature. The employer will pay the rate in the bill multiplied by the quantity in the bill. Similarly, under an ICE 6 contract, which is a re-measurement contract, the rate in the bill will be multiplied by the quantity of that item fixed. In both cases, the basis of payment is the contractor's estimate and the amount of money paid has no relationship with the contractor's costs. This type of contract is known as a 'fixed price contract', even though it may have some elements which are cost reimbursable. Such elements could include fluctuations, which are often related to actual changes in market prices.

By contrast, a 'fixed fee prime cost contract' will lay down detailed provisions for paying a contractor which are based upon the contractor's actual expenditure. Even though the contract is based upon cost reimbursement, the contractor's attendance and profit margin is based on a predetermined proportion of the prime cost. As such the basis for calculation of that portion bears no relation to actual costs and is therefore of a fixed price nature. This demonstrates how each type of contract contains elements of the other.

The important point at issue in terms of the distribution of risk is that, under fixed price arrangements, the contractor undertakes to submit an estimate for the work and agrees to be bound by the judgments made in that estimate. Thus any saving over the original estimate will be to the contractor's benefit, and any over-spending will be the contractor's loss. Under cost reimbursement arrangements, the employer takes the risk of the final price being different from the estimate, keeping any savings and paying for any increases.

REFERENCES

1. Fowler, H. and Fowler, F. (eds). *The Concise Oxford Dictionary of Current English*. Oxford University Press, Oxford, 1964.
2. Wallace, I.N.D. *Construction Contracts: Principles and Policies in Tort and Contract*. Sweet and Maxwell, London, 1986.
3. Abrahamson, M. Risk management. *International Construction Law Review*, 1(3), April 1984, 241–64.
4. Bunni, N.G. *The Spectrum of Risks in Construction*. Report of the Standing Committee on Professional Liability, Fédération Internationale des Ingénieurs-Conseils, Lausanne, 1985.
5. Hayes, R.W., Perry, J.G., Thompson, P.A. and Willmer, G. *Risk Management in Engineering Construction*. Science and Engineering Research Council, Swindon, 1987.
6. Bertinelli, E. *Risk Identification and Sharing: The 'All-inclusive' Price*. Paper presented at International Bar Association and Institution of Civil Engineers Conference, 'Basic Crucial Issues in Major Construction Projects', London, June 1985.
7. Cecil, R. *RIBA Indemnity Research: Risk Avoidance*. RIBA Publications, London, 1988.
8. Banwell *The Placing and Management of Contracts for Building and Civil Engineering Works*. HMSO, London, 1964.
9. Spiers, G.S. *The Standard Form of Contract in Times of Change*. Chartered Institute of Building, Ascot, 1983.
10. Bound, C. and Morrison, N. Contracts in use. *Chartered Quantity Surveyor*, January 1991, 9–11.
11. Haswell, C.K. and de Silva, D.S. *Civil Engineering Contracts: Practice and Procedure* (2nd edn). Butterworth, London, 1989.
12. Valentine, D.G. The ICE Conditions of Contract for Minor Works. *Construction Law Journal*, 5(2), 107–16.
13. FIDIC *Guide to the Use of FIDIC Conditions of Contract for Works of Civil Engineering Construction*. Fédération Internationale des Ingénieurs-Conseils, Lausanne, 1989.
14. Aqua Group. *Tenders and Contracts for Building* (2nd edn). BSP Professional Books, Oxford, 1990.

3

Roles and responsibilities in construction projects

In this chapter we shall outline the roles and responsibilities of each of the members of the project team. The problems associated with assembling temporary teams of professionals will be highlighted.

3.1 COMMON PROBLEMS

The process of building procurement involves a series of different specialists in contributing to the work at different times. These people have widely differing skills; they often work for different organizations, in different geographic locations and at different times. The level of understanding between them is often less than would be desirable. There are several perennial problems which can stand in the way of effective team building in construction projects.

3.1.1 Professional pride

The first thing about working as a professional consultant in the construction industry is a health warning for students! Undergraduates may well be studying on a vocational course, expecting to become a professional. They may end up as any one of the following: chartered builder, chartered engineer, chartered architect, chartered quantity surveyor or chartered building surveyor, or even lawyer! It is very easy to fall into the trap of believing that any profession other than one's own is somehow inferior. The attitude which sometimes seems to prevail in the industry is that 'other' professions are peopled by greedy, self-righteous, unintelligent morons or prima donnas. One must constantly remember that they too have been educated and trained to at least the same level. The intelligence or skill of one's colleagues in construction should *never* be underestimated. Pride has its place, but when it becomes conceit it can be very destructive.

3.1.2   Brief/design/construction overlaps

There are a number of stylized representations of the process of building procurement. The simplest of these shows the building process as having three stages, discrete steps of briefing, designing and constructing. This view is commonly held in theory, but rarely found in practice. It may be convenient to teach design as a process which is separated from construction, but the world is not that simple. It is unwise to develop a brief and then freeze it before design starts, although many people would advise this. A system cannot function properly without feedback, and the construction process is a system. Thus it is important that the brief is developed and refined in parallel with the design process.

Similarly, as the fabrication activities take place on site, information is continuously passing back and forth between designers and fabricators. This consists of clarifications, revisions and 'as-built' drawings. It is essential that the designers leave some details until fabrication is under way. Furthermore, the client's organization is subject to change as time passes – and construction projects can occupy significant passages of time. During this time new processes, equipment or materials may emerge, changing the client's attitude to what was originally in the brief. Alternatively, the economic situation may change the financial viability of the project. It could be uneconomic, and sometimes disastrous to the economic success of the client's organization, if some method of accommodating such changes is not incorporated into the process.

The iteration between these processes is sometimes acknowledged in the literature on construction management, but its importance can be overlooked by specialists whose own objectives may not be quite in tune with those of the client organization.

3.1.3   Unannounced participants

Another erroneous assumption is that the project team consists of a half-dozen main consultants who come together at the start of the project and work as a team, interacting with each other to decide everything necessary to put together a building. This is a simplified picture which takes little account of a large number of other participants.

Even on a small project there may have to be a large number of consultations, as well as approvals, by building inspectors, planning

officers, environmental health officers, specialist sub-contractors, suppliers, and so on. A good illustration of this is the following list of people
attending a project meeting:[1]

Building Control Officer	Planning Officer
Health Officer	Technical Services Drainage
Drainage Inspector	Environmental Health Officer
Traffic Engineer	Fire Officers
Heating and Ventilation Engineers	Electrical Engineers
Shopfitters	Structural Engineers
Architects	Post Office Engineers
Telecommunication Engineers	Electricity Board representatives
Gas Board representatives	Water Board representatives

This is typical of the type of project meetings encountered at detail design
stages of a project, before the contractor is appointed to put it all
together! Indeed, research has shown that even on relatively small projects, as many as 200 people can be involved in the decisions on construction projects before they reach the site.[2]

3.1.4 Temporary multi-organizations

destructive to each of the parties involved.

'Fragmentation is a problem within the construction industry and the
result is often internecine strife.'[3] This quote, from an article about the
scope for quantity surveyors to become project managers, is typical of
comments about the way in which construction professionals often choose
to interact.

The reasons for this fragmentation are associated with the fact that a
variety of different people come together temporarily on a project, each
with their own set of objectives and expectations and each from a separate firm. The reason for the wide variety in the skills needed on a
construction project arises out of the sheer technical complexity of the
problems associated with procuring buildings. This creates a demand for
extremely detailed specialist knowledge. The needs of people to feel as
though they belong to a group encourages these technical specialists to
group together into professional organizations such as institutions. Each
of the specialists tends to be employed by a specialist firm, although this
is not always the case. These firms come together solely for the purposes
of completing a particular project. This situation is called a **Temporary
Multi-organization** by some writers,[4] and the full consequences are more
appropriately discussed in textbooks on project management in
construction.[5]

Here it is sufficient to note that the characteristic grouping of project teams very often results in conflict at a variety of levels. The members of the project team *expect* to enter into confrontations with one another and with the client. This expectation of adversarial conflict is at the root of the 'internecine strife', observed above. It is the purpose of 'Conditions of Engagement' and other contracts to regulate these confrontations and to provide a basis whereby one party can enforce the promise of another.

3.2 ESTABLISHED ROLES OF THE CONSULTANTS

The term 'established' is preferred to 'traditional' because some construction-based professions have not been in existence long enough to have established any traditions! None the less, 'tradition' is emphasized by those who wish to give the impression that to be a chartered surveyor, or a chartered builder, or a member of any of the other construction professions, is to be respected and admired. While this is a most laudable aim and usually quite true, it is an unfortunate trait of our professions that their high ideals of protecting the interests of clients sometimes take second place to the survival of the professional institution. The existence of a professional institution therefore should always be questioned. The impact of the professional identity may not always match up with what is required for any given project: 'As specialized institutions proliferate, institutional survival matters more than the appropriateness to changing circumstances of fiercely protected roles'.[6] The professions tend to establish a baseline of services on offer by their members, and this is usually accompanied by recommended fee scales. In this way, the professions manage to control the type of work undertaken by their members. The expected roles, then, can be discovered by looking at the relevant institutions' published 'Conditions of Engagement'. This phrase is used to describe the legal contract between the consultant and the client.

3.2.1 Conditions of Engagement

Conditions of Engagement serve various purposes. First, they form the details of a contract between two parties. In this, they are convenient to use because appointments can be made on the standard conditions simply by referring to them. There is no need to draft a specific appointment agreement. Further, so long as there is scope for amending them, they can also provide a useful starting-point for negotiations about duties for a particular project.

From the point of view of the professional institutions, standard conditions of engagement provide a framework for identifying the duties of the professional. By unifying appointments, one can be sure that similar services are offered by all members of the profession. In this sense of providing a set of rules for conduct, these documents fulfil the most laudable aims of a profession. They prevent the unscrupulous practitioner from offering second-rate services.

Another function which conditions of engagement fulfil is that of attributing fees to various aspects of the work. By listing the activities to be done sequentially, those activities can be grouped together such that parts of the fee can be paid at each of the major steps in the consultants' involvement.

This combination of a set of rules of conduct and a list of activities is a two-edged sword. While they clarify the expectations of both parties, standardized Conditions of Engagement tend to restrict consultants from carrying out particular tasks. The extent of the services on offer is limited because unusual work means that no fee structure exists. And of course since fees are the only source of income for a consultant's practice, engaging in activities which do not earn fees becomes a luxury which most practices cannot afford! This aspect of Conditions of Engagement also reduces the flexibility of interrelationships within the design team. They can stifle design teams who will slavishly do their own part of the design in isolation from everyone else. Ideally Conditions of Engagement should encourage integration, not discourage it. On some projects it has even been found that, after job completion, none of the consultants have actually known whether or not the job was finished!

Another problem is that different professions have different Conditions of Engagement, and this may lead to confusion. It can be unproductive and cause wasted work or delay because the purposes behind writing the standard terms have been to standardize the relationship between the client and the consultant. This misses the significance of teamwork in construction. It is essential that the team acts as a whole, and the fragmentation created by differing terms of appointment can compromise this.

As we have already stated, these standard Conditions of Engagement are contracts and thus subject to the rules of contract law. The terms within them relate to the obligations of the parties, and detail the services to be carried out and the payments to be made for them. These terms need to be incorporated into the contract between the parties, for they are not a contract in themselves. The general situation is that they will not be automatically incorporated unless the client is familiar with the usual relationship between client and architect and has engaged similar professionals before on similar terms.[7] Otherwise, the terms must be expressly included by reference to them from the document which forms the contract. This can be done by using a Memorandum of Agreement, signed by the parties, which refers to and expressly incorporates the Conditions of Engagement. Indeed, in the standard agreement issued by the RICS the quantity surveyor's conditions are referred to as 'the initialled copy attached to this agreement'.

3.2.2 Architect

The accepted role of the architect has long been to design the building, advise on the selection and appointment of other consultants, manage the design, select and appoint the contractor and/or sub-contractors, and generally represent the client's interests as far as possible. Coupled with these responsibilities is the duty to act in a quasi-judicial capacity under certain standard forms of contract, where the architect has to judge certain issues impartially.

Conflicts within the established roles

There are some apparent and inherent conflicts in this combination of responsibilities, which are examined in Chapter 14. These conflicts presumably explain why architecture has become a profession, so that the public could be assured that the architect would act with integrity and honour.

Recently it has been suggested that the skills necessary to be a good *designer* are not the same as the skills necessary to be a good *manager*.[8] (This, it should be said, flatly contradicts the idea that the architect can only design effectively when he or she has the highest authority in the project.[9]) Unfortunately, many people have come to interpret the first notion as meaning that the skills necessary for designing are *incompatible* with management skills, and that one person cannot possibly do both. This is clearly a very different perception from the first. The two roles are different, but not necessarily imcompatible. However, not all people can develop both sets of skills with equal facility, and it has become clear that there are some architects who are better at design than management, others who are better at management than design and still others (the most valuable type) who are equally competent at both. Similar arguments take place about engineers and their responsibilities in civil engineering projects.

An example of the conflicts which can be identified within the roles of the architect is the task of managing the design process. There is a view that design is the total process of integrating all of the constraints on a planned building project in such a way as to optimize as many of them as possible. This is a realistic interpretation of what is involved in design. It explains why design and management need to be integrated in one person. There is another view, equally compelling, which sees management as the function which integrates design information with other constraints. This view suggests that the interaction between a group of professionals, successfully managed by one who is not 'designing', will result in the optimization of as many constraints as possible. This is not the place to indicate the 'correctness' of one view or the other; here the aim is simply to raise these issues, so that the reader may recognize the arguments.

There are also arguments about the difficulty faced by an architect when making a quasi-judicial decision within a building contract. These are discussed in detail in Chapter 14.

The RIBA Conditions of Engagement

These conditions of engagement were originally produced for the mutual benefit of architects and employers to enable determination of fees, and the identification of basic services and responsibilities.[10]

The use of an agreement for architectural services is mandatory for all members of the RIBA. The actual conditions are not specified, but the use of the RIBA Memorandum of Agreement and Schedule of Services and Fees is recommended.

At one time a minimum scale of charges was laid down, but the Monopolies and Mergers Commission declared that such minima were no longer in the public interest and should be abolished. In consequence, the mandatory Conditions of Engagement were abolished in 1982 and the document 'Architect's Appointment' came into force on 1 July 1982. The main difference between this document and the previous Conditions of Engagement are that it is not mandatory and the recommended fee scales are different. The Architect's Appointment gives details about how to calculate the fees that ought to be charged on projects, but these are now only recommendations.

The RIBA Architect's Appointment document is in four parts, as follows.

Part One describes preliminaries and basic services offered by architects, based on the plan of work, but omitting the final stage (M) which is the evaluation of what has taken place.

Preliminary services are stage A (Inception) and stage B (Feasibility). This initial work is to be charged for on either a lump sum or a time basis. It does not form part of the 'basic services' which are covered by the scale of fees usually defined as a percentage. The basic services are the following stages:

C: Outline proposals;
D: Scheme design;
E: Detail design;

F: Production information;
G: Bills of quantity;
H: Tender action;
J: Project planning:
K: Operations on site;
L: Completion.

Part Two contains eight sections describing other services which may be provided in addition to the basic services. These include surveys and investigations, development services and design services such as furniture and fittings. It also defines the other consultants normally called upon to provide services; these include quantity surveying, structural, mechanical and electrical engineering, landscape and garden design, civil engineering, town planning, etc.

Part Three is the actual conditions of appointment and is in ten sections:

1. *Architect's authority* – this section sets out the limits of the architect's authority, emphasizing that the architect is acting on behalf of the client and will do nothing without first seeking the client's authority. The architect also undertakes to inform the client if the total authorized expenditure or the building contract period is likely to be 'materially varied'.

2. *Consultants* – these may be nominated by either the client or the architect, but each must seek the approval of the other. Where the client employs the consultants, whether through the agency of the architect or not, the architect is responsible for the competence, general inspection and performance of the work entrusted to that consultant. This does not affect the architects' responsibility for issuing instructions or any other supervisory duty in connection with a building contract entered into by the client with a contractor.

3. *Contractors, sub-contractors and suppliers* – these may be nominated by the client or the architect, in each case with the approval of the other. Such contracts may include elements of specialist design, in which case the client will hold the contractor, sub-contractor or supplier *and not the architect* liable for the work. This includes competence, proper execution, and performance of the work.
   The clause also states that the client will employ a contractor to execute the work. Presumably this is for the benefit of clients who may not realize that the architect is not the builder!

4. *Site inspection* – this states that the architect will visit the site at intervals appropriate to the stage of construction, and empowers the architect to appoint a clerk of works when frequent inspection is

required. It also makes provision for a resident architect where frequent or constant inspection is necessary.

5. *Client's instructions* – the client will provide the architect with such information and make such decisions as are necessary for the proper performance of the agreed service. Also, if requested by the architect, the client will appoint a responsible representative through whom all instructions will be given.

6. *Copyright* – subject to a few minor exemptions, the architect holds the copyright to all the design work and drawings executed for the project. The exceptions allow the client to exhibit parts of the drawings, provided that the work has progressed beyond stage D and that it has been paid for!

7. *Assignment* – neither party may assign the whole or any part of the contract without permission from the other.

8. *Suspension and termination* – either party must give immediate notice in writing of any situation which will prevent the completion of the work; also either party may terminate the contract anyway, by giving reasonable notice, in writing. If the architect dies, or becomes totally incapacitated and prevented from doing any more work, then the client may make use of any or all of the drawings, etc. (provided that payment of all outstanding fees and expenses has been made) for the sole purpose of appointing a replacement and completing the work.

9. *Settlement of disputes* – for a matter to be referred to the arbitration of RIBA, RIAS or RSUA, it must arise under the agreement and it must be an opinion sought on a joint statement of undisputed fact. In addition, the parties must undertake to accept the decision as final and binding. The arbitrator shall, unless otherwise agreed, be an architect.

10. *Governing laws* – this simply states that the laws of England and Wales govern the conditions. There are alternative clauses for Scotland and Northern Ireland.

Part Four describes the recommended methods of calculating fees. There are sliding scales of fees depending on the type of work and the scale of the work. The fee may be a percentage of the total construction costs, it may be based on time expended or it may be a lump sum. Fees should be paid in instalments as the work progresses; VAT is payable on fees and expenses.

3.2.3 Quantity Surveyor

The document for the appointment of the Quantity Surveyor[11] is in seven sections; they are as follows:

1. *Fees* – when to pay them and what to do if the scales of fees change mid-way through a project.
2. *Suspension and termination* – either party may terminate the agreement, provided that they give 21 days' notice in writing.
3. *VAT.*
4. *Copyright* – the quantity surveyor owns the copyright to the bills of quantity!
5. *Assignment* – basically the quantity surveyor cannot assign the appointment.
6. *Interpretation* – making the conditions prevail in the event of discrepancies between them and the fees published from time to time by the RICS.
7. *Notices* – they have to be sent by registered letter or recorded delivery.

3.2.4   Building Surveyor

Building Surveyors are increasingly called upon to design, co-ordinate and manage the process of building procurement. This is in addition to planning and implementation of maintenance work, and other work such as property surveys. The wide range of services calls for a different approach to the problem of conditions of engagement, and the RICS published new conditions of engagement for Building Surveyors in 1988.[12]

The introduction sets out the basis of the document, that it is prepared for the mutual benefit of surveyors and clients, and that the RICS is the relevant institution for building surveying services. The range of services provided by all of the divisions is indicated, and the fact that although building surveying is most likely to be offered by building surveyors, members of other divisions may be found offering these services from time to time. Presumably, this is to avoid giving the impression that building surveying encompasses all of the RICS's construction activities. It does not point out that other professions (e.g. RIBA) may also provide similar services! It also points out that there is no scale of fees, although recommended scales are published by the RICS. The importance of professional indemnity is underlined. The last paragraph of the introduction is interesting in that it points out that whilst other consultants may be appointed, their conditions of engagement should be dealt with separately by the client, to avoid any contractual responsibility for them falling on the Building Surveyor! However laudable this may seem from the point of view of the RICS, it is precisely the kind of attitude which prevents progress from being made in the development of professional services offered by *the industry* to its clients. There are 12 sections dealing with the conditions of engagement as follows:

1. *The surveyor's obligations* – These attach to the surveyor the obligation to perform with reasonable skill, care and diligence. This is the level of liability that would usually be associated with professional services. The liability is limited to that which would be covered by the professional indemnity policy of the surveyor. The frequency of visits to site for the purposes of monitoring construction operations, and the contractor's liability for workmanship and materials are also covered, relieving the surveyor of the need constantly to attend the site. Whilst the surveyor will assume responsibility for integration of the work for others, no liability can be attached to the surveyor for the design, inspection or performance of such work. Similarly, whilst assuming the right to recommend the employment of specialists as sub-contractors, the onus is on the employer to ensure the adequacy of such specialists for the task, as well as to pursue any claim against defaulters.

2. *Communications between employer and surveyor* – The employer must ensure that there is a single representative for the Building Surveyor to contact. All instructions to the surveyor must be made through this representative, and in writing. All requests by the surveyor for information must be complied with by the employer, and all formal notices, if served to the address on the agreement, by recorded delivery, will be deemed to have been served.

3. *Control of costs* – The surveyor does not have the authority to materially alter the work content of the project, without the express authority of the client. The surveyor must inform the employer of anything which will materially affect the price, time or content of the project.

4. *Payment for the surveyor's services* – All accounts must be settled within 28 days, there is no right of set-off, any amounts in dispute shall not affect any other amounts not in dispute, interest at 4% above base rate is payable on outstanding accounts, and many more items are covered in detail in this section. The surveyor is very heavily protected here, and one would imagine that the surveyor who applies all of these clauses to the letter would be viewed as a very punitive person.

5. *Insurance* – The surveyor must be able to prove that PI insurance is valid and current.

6. *Suspension or termination by the employer* – The employer can terminate or suspend the agreement at any time.

7. *Suspension or termination by the surveyor* – The surveyor's rights to terminate are more restricted, and basically can only take place in the event of the employer being in breach of contract, becoming bankrupt, or if there has been a prolonged period of suspension.

8. *Consequences of suspension or termination* – This basically just helps the parties to work out how much money the Building Surveyor is entitled to in the event of suspension or termination.
9. *Copyright* – Unless the employer is the Crown, or otherwise agreed in writing, the surveyor holds the copyright in all documentation.
10. *Assignment* – The employer can assign all (but not part) of the agreement by giving notice in writing, but the surveyor needs the employer's permission.
11. *Waiver* – This clause prevents the parties accidentally waiving their rights by indulgence.
12. *Arbitration* – This final section is an arbitration clause to enable disputes to be referred if agreement between the parties cannot be reached.

The actual schedule of services to be provided may be chosen from amongst a variety of looseleaf inserts. There are schedules for building works, building and measured surveys, project management, maintenance, insurance assessments and claims, feasibility studies as well as miscellaneous services. This range of services is a realistic reflection of the diversity of building surveying practices.

3.2.5 Engineer

The conditions of engagement published by the Association of Consulting Engineers consist of a range of documents which reflect the range of services offered. There are four basic documents:

Agreement 1, for report and advisory work;
Agreement 2, for civil, mechanical and electrical work, and for structural engineering work where an architect is not appointed;
Agreement 3, for structural engineering work where an architect is appointed (with another version harmonized with the RIBA Architect's Appointment);
Agreement 4, in different versions, for different types of engineering services related to sub-contract or direct works.

The documents all follow a similar pattern. They introduce the scope of the engineer's appointment and give general explanations about the nature of advising, designing, supervising, and so on. This is followed in each case by the detailed conditions, which are in three sections, as follows.

Section 1 covers general conditions such as duration of the engagement, copyright and an arbitration clause.

Section 2 covers the obligations of the engineer in relation to the work to be provided – the engineer undertakes to use care and diligence; the normal duties are listed; and relationships with professional advisers are explained.

Section 3 deals with the obligations of the employer, which are mainly to do with payment.

There are appendices specifying the details of the duties to be undertaken, and these are followed by a model Memorandum of Agreement which incorporates all terms of engagement into the contract.

The ACE Conditions of Engagement are notable in being the only conditions which even begin to take account of the terms of appointment of other consultants, that is in the sense of attempting to harmonize them. There are moves afoot to rationalize the ACE conditions such that there is just one document, which can be used for structural engineering and services engineering by using schedules of duties as appendices to deal with the actual tasks to be undertaken. The publication of the new Conditions of Engagement is to be eagerly anticipated, as it seems that they may address some of the criticisms outlined above.

3.2.6 Builder

The status of Chartered Builder is a relatively new concept and does not yet have a formal set of conditions of engagement. The contract between the client and the builder is likely to be one of the standard forms of building contract discussed in this book. The emergence of procurement procedures which require the advice of a construction fabrication expert, possibly in a supervisory role, introduces the possibility of a contract for services, rather than a contract for construction duties. This would be more in line with the arrangements used by consultants, leaving the trade and specialist contractors with the only contracts for actually producing work on site. What the industry and its clients will make of this possibility remains to be seen.

REFERENCES

1. Carpenter, J.B.G. The UK System of Construction Procurement and What is Wrong: How to Improve it. RICS Quantity Surveyors' 12th Triennial Conference, 7–9 April 1981.
2. Hughes, W.P. Organizational analysis of building projects. PhD thesis, Liverpool Polytechnic, 1989.
3. Relph-Knight, Lynda. Project management. *Chartered Surveyor Weekly*, **11**, 11 April 1985, QS supplement, 9.

4. Cherns, A.B. and Bryant, D.T. Studying the client's role in construction management. *Construction Management and Economics*, **2**, 1984, 177–84.
5. Walker, A. *Project Management in Construction* (2nd edn). BSP Professional Books, Oxford, 1989.
6. Andrews, J. The age of the client. *Architect's Journal*, 13 July 1983, 32–3.
7. *Sidney Kaye, Eric Firmin & Partners* v. *Bronesky* (1973) 4 B.L.R. 1.
8. Honeyman, S. (chairman). *Construction Management Forum: Report and Guidance*. Centre for Strategic Studies in Construction, University of Reading, 1991.
9. Gutman, R. *Architectural Practice: A Critical View*. Princeton Architectural Press, New York, 1988.
10. Males, A.R. Architect's appointment. In Speaight, A. and Stone, G. (eds) *AJ Legal Handbook* (4th edn). Architectural Press, London, 1985.
11. Royal Institution of Chartered Surveyors. *Appointment of a Quantity Surveyor*. Surveyor's Publications, London, October 1983.
12. Royal Institution of Chartered Surveyors. *Conditions of Engagement for Building Surveying Services*. RICS, London, 1988.

4

Tort claims in the construction context

A **tort** is a breach of a legal duty owed by one person to another. This is independent of any contractual liability, and the remedy for it is the recovery of damages. This chapter examines, first, the general principles which govern such claims, and second, the aspects of construction in which they are of most significance.

4.1 WHO WANTS TO CLAIM IN TORT?

4.1.1 Claims by outsiders

In order to understand the full significance of tort claims for negligence in the construction context, it is first necessary to identify the persons who will wish to make such claims. First and foremost among these are **outsiders**, in the sense of persons who have no contractual involvement whatsoever in the construction process, even as clients. This category would include, for example, a subsequent owner or tenant of a building or a visitor to that building, or even a passer-by. If such persons suffer injury, damage or loss because of defective or dangerous building work, it follows that any claim which they make must lie in tort which, in practice, usually means the **tort of negligence**.

A straightforward example of this kind of liability may be seen in the Australian case of *Voli* v. *Inglewood Shire Council*,[1] concerning an architect who had designed a public hall. When the stage collapsed during a meeting due to a design fault, the architect was held liable in negligence to a person who was injured.

The *Voli* case seems clear enough. However, care must be taken not to ignore the relative responsibilities of architect and contractor when deciding whether someone is guilty of negligence. An architect does not normally have any control over a contractor's working methods, and consequently responsibility for the safety of site operations would fall upon the contractor.[2] However, the architect may be held to have assumed responsibility if he or she inspects part of the site and declares it to be safe.[3] Furthermore, it is common for the working methods of a contractor on a civil engineering project to be under the control of the engineer, which can again lead to a different allocation of responsibility. These matters are considered in more detail in Chapter 14.

An unusual type of 'outsider' claim arose in *Richard Roberts* v. *Douglas Smith Stimson*,[4] where the employer under a contract to rebuild a dye works was a holding company, while the dyeing business was actually carried on by a subsidiary, which occupied the premises under licence. When breaches of contract by the main contractor caused substantial loss of profits to this subsidiary company, it was held that any claim which it might make would have to rely on tort since the subsidiary was not party to the building contract itself.

Until very recently, the most important tort claims in respect of defective buildings were those brought by subsequent owners or tenants against architects, contractors, sub-contractors and local authorities – indeed, against anyone connected with the construction of the property in question. The foundation of such claims was the famous decision of the House of Lords in *Anns* v. *Merton LBC*,[5] which although it concerned a local authority, was regarded also as governing the position of builders and others. However, the House of Lords has now completely rewritten this area of law, and in so doing has dramatically reduced the significance of construction-related tort claims. This recent development will be dealt with in detail later in the chapter.

Although negligence is the most important basis for a claim in tort, it is not the only one. In *AMF International* v. *Magnet Bowling*,[6] where a bowling-alley was being built, it was held that both the employer and the main contractor were 'occupiers' of the site within the meaning of the *Occupiers' Liability Act 1957*. They negligently failed to protect the premises against the risk of flooding. This caused damage to valuable timber belonging to a firm of specialist sub-contractors, who were to install the timber bowling-lanes. The plaintiffs were held to be 'visitors' within the meaning of the *Occupiers' Liability Act 1957* and, as a result, they were successful in recovering damages from both the employer and the main contractor.

4.1.2   Participants without contractual links

While most of the persons or firms who contribute to a construction project are linked to the employer by direct contract, there are some (e.g. sub-contractors) who may not be. The employer may therefore wish to seek legal redress for defective work or services from someone with whom there is no contract (even of the 'collateral warranty' kind). Such actions must be brought in the tort of negligence and, as we shall see, recent legal developments mean that they will seldom be successful.

Leaving aside the employer, a contractual link between two participants in the construction process, such as the contract administrator and the contractor, is the exception rather than the rule. As we shall see, the law of tort has proved somewhat reluctant to supply the missing link. However, what must not be overlooked is the part played by the *Civil Liability (Contribution) Act 1978* in construction disputes. This statute is relevant where one person is held liable to pay damages to another, either in tort or for breach of contract. Such a person may claim a contribution from any other person who is liable for the same damage *or who would have been so liable if the victim had chosen to sue him or her.* Thus, even if the *employer* chooses to sue a single defendant, say, the main contractor, that defendant may bring into court all the others (e.g. sub-contractor, architect, structural engineer), who might also have been sued. Where this is done, the court can make such order as to contribution as it thinks just and equitable, up to and including a complete indemnity.

4.1.3 Enhancement of contractual remedies

There is a third group of potential tort claimants, which consists of those who *do* have a right to sue for breach of contract, but who none the less wish to make a claim in tort. This will happen when they regard such a claim as offering some practical advantage.

The most important advantage concerns the rules which govern limitation of actions. By this is meant the time within which a plaintiff must issue a writ in order for the claim not to be statute-barred. The relevant period of limitation in actions for breach of contract is usually 6 years, but it is 12 years if the contract is made in the form of a deed. The time starts to run from the moment that the contract is breached. In a tort action, by contrast, the plaintiff obtains the benefit of the *Latent Damage Act 1986.* This means that the right to sue will not finally expire until 15 years after the defendant's relevant 'breach of duty'. Within that period, the plaintiff will have 6 years from the date on which *damage* occurs. Alternatively, if it expires later, the period is 3 years from the date on which the damage ought reasonably to have been discovered. It thus happens, in many cases, that the right to sue in tort remains long after the 'contract' limitation period has expired.

The crucial question is whether a victim is free to choose the cause of action in such circumstances. It has on occasion been suggested by the courts that this course is not open, most notably where it was actually held that an architect's liability to the client was a matter of contract *only*.[7] However, later cases have appeared to proceed on the basis that a plaintiff may choose the cause of action. Indeed, one of the leading cases on limitation in tort was one in which the plaintiffs, for whom a factory chimney was being built, sued a firm of consulting engineers. Here of course the parties were linked by a contract, but the House of Lords did not regard this as in any way precluding a claim in tort.[8]

4.2   LIMITS OF TORT CLAIMS

In view of the advantages which may be obtained by framing a claim in tort rather than in contract, it is vital to appreciate the limited circumstances in which it is now possible to make such a claim. This requires an understanding of recent developments in tort law.

4.2.1   Negligent advice and reliance

For a very long time the law did not permit a person to claim damages in tort for the financial loss which was suffered by relying on negligent advice. Even when this was finally allowed, following the decision of the House of Lords in *Hedley Byrne & Co. Ltd* v. *Heller & Partners Ltd*,[9] it was made clear that negligent words could not simply be treated in the same way as negligent acts. This is because it might expose defendants to an unacceptably wide area of liability. As a result, the courts would not hold people liable for what they said merely because they ought reasonably to have foreseen that someone might rely on it. Instead they looked for what they described as a 'special relationship' which indicated a 'voluntary assumption of responsibility' on the defendant's part.

More recently, the House of Lords has abandoned the 'special relationship' requirement as such;[10] however, it has continued to approach cases of negligent advice in a restrictive way. The form of words currently adopted is the requirement of a considerable degree of 'proximity' between the parties. Only where this exists will it be regarded as 'just and reasonable' to impose responsibility in tort for the advice given.

4.2.2   Negligent acts and economic loss

An action for breach of contract may enable a plaintiff to recover compensation for losses which are purely financial or 'economic'. This means losses which do not result from personal injury or physical damage to property. English law has long held to the view that an action in tort for negligence will not extend to purely financial loss. Thus the House of Lords' decision in *Junior Books* v. *Veitchi*[11] came as a considerable shock to the entire construction industry. It was held that a nominated sub-contractor was liable in tort to the employer for the financial losses caused by negligent performance of the sub-contract. The court in that case claimed to have found sufficient 'proximity' in the relationship between the parties to justify cutting across the normal network of contractual relationships in construction cases. No collateral warranty agreement had been entered into; however, it was said that the employer's 'reliance' on the sub-contractors had produced a relationship which was almost as close as a contract.

Notwithstanding this reasoning, there appears in truth to be nothing in the facts of the *Junior Books* case which would not be present in any case involving a nominated sub-contractor. It is thus hardly surprising that the decision provoked such alarm. In the event, however, *Junior Books* has been consistently 'distinguished' by subsequent courts, often on fairly strained grounds. Indeed, it has even been said by a judge in the Court of Appeal that *Junior Books* is not worth citing. In fact, but for some remarks by members of the House of Lords in *Murphy* v. *Brentwood DC* (dealt with below) which appear to regard the case as justifiable, it could probably have been treated as simply an unfortunate aberration.

The basic legal position is that tort claims for physical damage are actionable, while those for purely economic losses are not. Given this, it is easy to imagine the problems which have been caused in the construction context. The English courts were for many years unable to decide whether damage to a building itself due to some inherent defect should properly be classified as 'physical' or 'economic'. Until very recently, there was considerable authority for treating this as physical damage, at least where either one part of the structure could be said to have 'damaged' another, or where the whole building was 'dangerous'. However, in a remarkable shift of judicial opinion, the House of Lords has now closed both of these loopholes. This follows the decisions in *D. & F. Estates*[12] and *Murphy* v. *Brentwood*.[13] It is now clear that liability in tort for negligent construction work will enable compensation to be obtained only in cases of personal injury or damage to other property.

4.2.3 The effect of contract on tort

It is clear from the above discussion that the part played by the tort of negligence in the construction context is rather less important than it might have been. This is due to the inherent limitations which are placed upon claims for negligence, both in word and deed. Even where a claim *could* lie, however, the courts have recently begun to acknowledge that negligence claims in this and similar contexts must be approached against the background of 'the parties' contractual rights and obligations. Thus, in deciding whether it would be 'fair and reasonable' to impose a duty of care on a particular party, it may be relevant to consider both his or her contractual position and the contractual position of other persons involved.

Contracts between plaintiff and defendant

Where plaintiff and defendant are joined by a contract, the general principle is that any duty of care in tort should cover no wider ground than is covered by that contract. For example, under a contract which provided that the architect's final certificate should be conclusive, the Court of Appeal held that the employer could not avoid the contractor's defence by claiming in tort.[14] Indeed, there have even been suggestions that an employer in such a case should *only* be allowed to claim in contract. This would mean, for instance, that the employer would not be able to gain the benefit of a longer limitation period. Such suggestions, however, seem contrary to a great deal of authority and can probably be ignored.

The practical importance of looking to the contract when considering the tort can be shown by reference to two recent cases decided by the House of Lords and the Court of Appeal. In the first of these cases, *Scottish Special Housing Association* v. *Wimpey Construction*,[15] work was being done under a JCT Standard Form contract (equivalent, in this respect, to the 1980 version). This made the contractor liable for all damage caused to the property by his negligence, except for those risks against which the employer was obliged by the contract to insure. When a fire caused by the contractor's negligence damaged the property and the employer sued him in tort, the contractor argued that he should not be liable, pointing out that damage by fire to existing structures and their contents fell within these 'excepted risks'. This argument convinced the House of Lords, which held that the contract clearly intended that the employer should bear all risk of fire, even where this arose from contractors' negligence. Accordingly the contractor was not liable.

In *Greater Nottingham Co-operative Society* v. *Cementation*[16] the defendants, who were piling sub-contractors, entered into a collateral agreement with the plaintiff employer. In this, they specifically undertook to use reasonable skill and care in design of the work and selection of materials. Due to negligent *execution* of the work by the defendants (about which the collateral agreement said nothing), the plaintiffs suffered substantial economic losses. It was held by the Court of Appeal that they could not recover these by an action in tort. The court ruled that the parties must be assumed to have defined their relationship exhaustively in their agreement, so that it would not be just and reasonable to impose a wider duty of care. Thus the existence of the collateral agreement, far from making this a stronger case than *Junior Books*, was the decisive element in defeating the plaintiffs' claim!

Contracts with a third party

How far can the rights of A against B *in tort* be affected by a contract which either A or B has with a third party? Take, for example, a situation where an employer wishes to sue a sub-contractor directly. Will the employer be bound by an exemption clause in the sub-contract, or can the sub-contractor take the benefit of an exemption clause in the main contract?

The legal problem is obvious, for English law insists that neither the benefit nor the burden of a contract can affect anyone who is not a party to it. Thus, in *contract law* terms, the answer to these questions is clearly that the clauses must be ignored. Yet there is a strong argument for saying that, in deciding whether it would be 'just and reasonable' to impose a duty of care *in tort*, the contractual situation of the parties should not be ignored. The overall legal position is not yet fully clarified, although there is a good chance that the tort view will ultimately prevail.

In *Junior Books*, where a sub-contractor was held directly liable to the employer for negligence, the House of Lords noted the potential relevance of contractual terms in this area; indeed, it was suggested that 'negligence' could only be given a sensible meaning in the light of whatever obligations had been undertaken by contract. Despite this lead, however, judges have twice refused to take into account exemption clauses *in a sub-contract* when dealing with similar claims by an employer against a sub-contractor.[17]

As for exemption clauses *in the main contract*, a very different picture emerged in *Southern Water Authority* v. *Carey*.[18] It was there held that sub-contractors could not *directly* take the benefit of such clauses, for intance, by arguing that the main contractor had acted as their agent in negotiating them. However, they could none the less rely on the clauses to show that the employer had accepted a particular risk and should not therefore be allowed to sue in tort.

That this was the correct approach to the problem was confirmed by the Court of Appeal in *Norwich CC* v. *Harvey*.[19] Here, in the course of constructing an extension to a swimming-pool complex, a sub-contractor negligently caused a fire which damaged both the contract works and the existing structure. The main contract was in a similar JCT form to that in the *Scottish Special Housing Association* case (above), which clearly placed the risk of fire damage (and the duty of insuring against it) on the employer. Against this contractual background, the Court of Appeal held that it would not be just and reasonable to impose a duty of care in tort upon the sub-contractor, who thus escaped liability for the effects of his negligence. (It should be noted that under JCT 80, as currently amended, *domestic* sub-contractors will only escape liability for damage to the works. They will be liable for negligently causing damage to existing structures.)

Although it is in relation to actions between employer and sub-contractor that the courts have most commonly felt it necessary to consider the contractual background, this is not the only area in which this approach has been adopted. In rejecting a contractor's action against an engineer in respect of alleged undercertification,[20] the Court of Appeal paid close attention to the way in which the civil engineering contract allocated certain risks to the contractor, and to its clear assumption that the engineer should be immune from liability.

4.3 SPECIFIC EXAMPLES OF TORT CLAIMS

We may now consider some of the relationships, within the general area of the construction industry in which tort claims for negligence have been made over recent years. We have already described some of the cases in our discussion of general principles. These and others which are now to be mentioned for the first time have met with varying degrees of success.

4.3.1 Employer and sub-contractor/supplier

As we have already mentioned, the House of Lords in the *Junior Books* case[11] threw the entire construction industry into a state of confusion bordering on panic. This was the result of their ruling that, if a relationship of sufficient 'proximity' existed, a sub-contractor would owe a duty of care to the employer to carry out the sub-contract works in such a way that the employer would not suffer financial loss. Subsequent courts have repeatedly refused to find such a relationship, either because of the terms of the main contract[18,19] or because of the drafting of a direct collateral agreement between the parties themselves.[16]

Until very recently, it would have been regarded as almost unthinkable that *Junior Books* would be followed except in very unusual circumstances. It would certainly have been assumed that the normal degree of 'reliance' which is placed on a nominated sub-contractor by the employer making the selection would not be enough to create a duty of care. However, considerable doubt has now been cast on such assumptions by dicta from the House of Lords in *Murphy* v. *Brentwood*.[13] Although that case was in itself specifically concerned with the position of local authorities, wider issues of construction liability were discussed. Two members of the House of Lords appeared to regard *Junior Books* as a perfectly legitimate example of liability for economic loss caused by negligent *advice*! If this is correct, it undeniably raises the possibility that the case might indeed be followed in future.

The House of Lords in *Murphy* set another substantial cat among sub-contractors' pigeons. It suggested that if a sub-contractor's defective work caused physical damage to other parts of the structure (as, for instance, where a defective electrical installation caused a fire), the sub-contractor would be liable in negligence for this. If *this* is correct, it is an even more wide-ranging development than the revival of *Junior Books*. It would operate in favour of both employers and subsequent owners and, further, would apply equally to domestic and nominated sub-contractors.

Whether or not it is accurate to describe *Junior Books* as a case of negligent advice, it certainly does seem that negligent advice is a potential source of liability for a sub-contractor. In the Canadian case of *District of Surrey* v. *Carroll-Hatch*[21] the defendant structural engineers were employed by an architect (i.e. as sub-contractors to him) to advise on foundations. The defendants, who were not soil specialists, reported that a deeper site investigation was needed. They did not, however, ensure that this information reached the employer. They prepared a foundation design based on a visual examination of shallow test-pits. When the subsoil proved insufficient for the loading, and differential settlement took place, it was held that the defendants as well as the architect were liable to the employer for failing to give him an adequate warning.

4.3.2 Actions by subsequent owners

It is in the nature of construction defects that they may well take a long time in coming to light – long enough certainly for the property to have changed hands at least once. Where this occurs, the current owner is likely to find no legal redress against the vendor (because of the notorious doctrine of '*caveat emptor*'). Thus, if he or she is to obtain compensation for the defects or damage, it must be by means of a claim in tort against any person who can be proved to have been responsible. A number of possibilities suggest themselves, although as we shall see they are now of doubtful value.

Claims against local authorities

As we noted earlier in this chapter, the House of Lords in *Anns* v. *Merton*[5] laid down the rule that a local authority owed a duty of care in carrying out its building inspection functions. This duty is to future owner-occupiers to ensure that their property would not constitute a danger to health or safety. If it failed in this duty, then the owner-occupier would be entitled to recover damages based on the cost of restoring the property to a state in which it was no longer dangerous. The practical importance of this ruling was of course enormous. In many subsequent cases, where the original negligence was that of a builder, sub-contractor, architect or consulting engineer, by the time the case reached court the the local authority would represent the only solvent defendant.

We have also previously mentioned that the *Anns* v. *Merton* principle was recently reconsidered by the House of Lords in *Murphy* v. *Brentwood*.[13] That case concerned a house in Brentwood, purchased by the plaintiff in 1970, which had been built the previous year over filled ground on a concrete raft foundation. The design of the foundation had been submitted to the defendant local authority for approval. The defendants, having taken advice from a firm of consulting engineers, had duly approved it. In the early 1980s after serious cracks had begun to appear in internal walls an investigation revealed that the concrete raft had been subject to differential settlement. This later led to the cracking of both gas and soil pipes, a matter which the courts were subsequently to regard as constituting a danger to health and safety. The plaintiff in 1986 sold the house (which should have been worth £65 000) for £30 000 and his insurance company, which had paid him £35 000 for subsidence damage, began an action in his name against the local authority.

The trial judge concluded that the consulting engineers had been negligent and that the defendants were responsible for this. The cost of making the house safe would have been approx. £45 000, and it was held that the plaintiff was entitled to recover his loss on the sale from the defendants. This decision was upheld by the Court of Appeal which, however, gave the defendants leave to take the case to the House of Lords.

As already intimated, the House of Lords had clearly decided that the time had come for a thorough reform of this area of law. It was acknowledged that the House of Lords' power to reverse its own previous rulings should be used sparingly (to avoid creating too much uncertainty in the law). The unanimous view was that this was an appropriate occasion for its use. The ruling in *Anns* as to the liability in tort of local authorities was declared wrong (following detailed criticism of its inherent illogicalities) and the defendants' appeal was accordingly successful.

As far as actions against local authorities are concerned, the reversal of *Anns* leaves only one point of uncertainty. Clearly, there can be no claim to recover the cost of making the building safe; but what is the situation if someone is actually injured by its defective condition? Several members of the House of Lords in *Murphy* recognized that this question might one day have to be answered – however, none was prepared to answer it on this occasion.

Claims against builders

The decision of the House of Lords in *Anns* v. *Merton* was directly concerned with the liability of a local authority for the negligent carrying out of a building inspection. In addition, it was also of great importance indirectly in defining the legal position of a builder. This was because their lordships all agreed that it would be wholly unjust to impose liability on the local authority for failing to prevent the builder from breaching the building regulations, unless the builder himself could be liable for that breach. Thus it appeared that a builder would be held liable to a subsequent owner in the tort of negligence for the cost of rendering safe a building which was dangerous. However, the builder would not be liable for the cost of repairing *non-dangerous* defects since this would be regarded as pure economic loss.

Although this statement of the builder's position was never authoritatively clarified, it was generally accepted as accurate. However, it was heavily criticized by the House of Lords in *D. & F. Estates*.[12] The plaintiff company in that case was the tenant of a flat in a block which had been built some 15 years previously by Wates (in a joint development venture with the Church Commissioners). Due to the negligence of sub-contractors (who were described as 'not worth suing'), the walls and ceilings of the flat needed to be completely replastered. The plaintiffs thereupon sued Wates in tort, claiming the cost of remedial work already carried out, the estimated cost of future work (approx. £50 000) and prospective loss of rent.

In rejecting the plaintiffs' claims, the House of Lords gave two separate rulings of profound importance to the construction industry. First, it was held that main contractors owe no duty of care in tort to supervise the work of sub-contractors, and that consequently they cannot be held liable for defects in that work. Second (and more significantly), it was laid down that a builder's liability in tort is, in any event, limited to defects which cause either injury to persons or physical damage to *other property* (as, for instance, where a defective garage roof falls on the occupier's car). Damage to *the defective item itself* will be regarded as pure economic loss and therefore irrecoverable.

In limiting the builder's liability in this way, the House of Lords left open two possible loopholes. First, it was suggested that in the case of a 'complex structure' it might be possible to treat separate parts as 'other property' for the purpose of liability. Second, while ridiculing the logic of the *Anns* distinction between 'defective' and 'dangerous', the House of Lords did not specifically declare that distinction to be wrong.

In *Murphy* v. *Brentwood* the House of Lords returned to this topic, and in so doing decisively closed both these possible loopholes. The 'complex structure' approach was declared to be wrong. Since *Anns* itself was overruled, that aspect of a builder's liability which was based upon it also fell. In consequence, it seems (subject to one possible exception) that injury to persons and damage to other property now represent the limits of the builder's responsibility in the tort of negligence. The one exception mentioned is that, where the *original* owner has a claim in the tort of negligence against the builder, it may be possible for this to be *assigned* to a subsequent owner or tenant when the building is sold or leased.[22]

Claims against sub-contractors

In view of the treatment given to tort claims against both local authorities and builders by the House of Lords in *D. & F. Estates* and *Murphy*, one might expect to find an equally decisive rejection of the idea that an employer or subsequent owner might claim in tort against a sub-contractor. Surprisingly, however, a number of remarks which were passed in *Murphy* suggest quite the opposite.

The problem arises out of the 'complex structure' idea (under which a builder might be held liable if one defective part of the building caused damage to another part). As we have seen, the House of Lords emphatically rejected this idea as a means of imposing liability upon a builder responsible for the entire work of construction. However, no fewer than three judges expressed the view that liability might arise where different parts of the work had been carried out by different contractors. It was suggested, for example, that an electrical sub-contractor, whose negligent installation work later caused a fire in which the building itself was damaged, could be held liable in tort to the owner of the building at that time.

4.3.3 Main contractor and sub-sub-contractor

A supplier, whether or not nominated by the employer, naturally owes **contractual obligations** to the main contractor or sub-contractor to whom the supply is made. However, the question which arises in the present context is whether a main contractor can if necessary miss out a link in the chain of contracts by suing sub-contractor's supplier *in tort*.

This question was addressed by the Court of Appeal in *Simaan* v. *Pilkington Glass (No. 2)*.[23] Here the plaintiffs were the main contractors for the erection of a building in Abu Dhabi. They sub-contracted the curtain walling to an Italian company, which obtained specified glass units from the defendants as nominated suppliers. These units, once installed, were rejected by the architect on the ground that they were not of the uniform colour demanded. The employer accordingly withheld payment from the plaintiffs, who sued the defendants in tort to recover their loss.

On these facts it was emphatically held by the Court of Appeal that there was no justification for departing from the usual practice of liability flowing along the chain of contracts. The court recognized that it might, in some circumstances, be possible to construct a relationship of sufficient 'proximity' between an *employer* and a supplier (along the lines of *Junior Books*). However, no such relationship existed between the *main contractor* and the nominated supplier of a sub-contractor.

4.4   ARCHITECT AND CONTRACTOR

Perhaps the most intriguing aspect of the use of tort within the construction field concerns the possible liabilities which might arise between an architect and a contractor or sub-contractor. The architect, in acting as contract administrator, is the employer's representative and must look after his or her client's interests. In so doing, the contract administrator undoubtedly owes the client a duty of care. The question which now arises is whether the contract administrator, if *too* protective of the client, might incur personal liability to the contractor for any loss which the latter suffers. This question has been asked in respect of several functions which the contract administrator is expected to fulfil on the client's behalf.

4.4.1   Information

It has long been settled that in drawing up plans an architect or engineer does not guarantee they are practicable, nor that bills of quantities are accurate. Therefore, in principle, contractors who wish to tender on the basis of such information must satisfy themselves as to its soundness. However, there are limits to this principle. For example, if the architect *fraudulently* gives inaccurate information at the pre-tender stage, he or she will be liable to the contractor. This is so even if the contract provides that the contractor must not rely on any representation contained in the plans.[24]

Whether the principle in *Hedley Byrne*[9] might be used in similar circumstances to render the architect liable for a mis-statement which is *negligent* rather than fraudulent does not yet appear to have been tested in court. However, there seems no logical reason why this should not be done. This is especially so since the principle was used in a New Zealand case[25] against an architect who negligently assured a contractor that he would receive full payment from the employer for certain work. The contractor relied on this assurance in completing the job, and when the employer failed to pay, the architect was held liable.

The most striking English case in this area is *Townsends* v. *Cinema News*,[26] in which a contractor had been liable to the employer for certain breaches of statute (installation of toilets in contravention of a by-law, and failure to serve notices). The Court of Appeal held that since the architect had led the contractor to rely on him to serve the relevant notices and ensure compliance with the by-laws, the contractor was entitled to recover from the architect the damages which he had to pay the employer.

4.4.2 Warning

The need for careful demarcation between the duties of a contract administrator and those of a contractor has already been noted. The courts are careful to avoid any suggestion that the contract administrator has any duty (or indeed any right) to control the way in which the contractor chooses to carry out the work. The most that can possibly be argued in this respect is that where the design is not faulty, but the contract administrator can see that failure to take proper precautions is exposing property to risk of damage, there *may* be owed a duty of care to warn the contractor.[27]

In two recent cases[28] it has been argued that a contractor owes a duty to an architect in tort to warn of any defects which are found in the architect's design. However, this seems wrong and it has certainly been held that a *sub-contractor* owes no duty to a supervising engineer to warn of defects in the work.[29] All that can be said is that the contractor has a *contractual* duty to warn the *employer*.[30]

4.4.3 Certification

The final area in which it has been sought to hold an architect or engineer liable to a contractor concerns the function of certification under a building contract. Given the decision of the House of Lords in *Sutcliffe* v. *Thackrah*[31] that an architect owed a duty of care to the employer, it was inevitable that sooner or later an architect would be used by a contractor alleging negligent failure to certify. This duly occurred in the case of *Pacific Associates* v. *Baxter*,[20] which reached the Court of Appeal. Unfortunately for contractor, the court's decision (discussed in more detail in Chapter 14) was that no duty of care was owed in these circumstances. The case might possibly have been regarded as turning on some special provisions the contract concerned, but it has since been treated as laying down a general principle of non-liability.[32]

REFERENCES

1. *Voli* v. *Inglewood Shire Council* (1963) 110 C.L.R. 74.
2. *Clayton* v. *Woodman & Son (Builders) Ltd* [1962] 2 Q.B. 533.
3. *Clay* v. *AJ Crump Ltd* [1964] 1 Q.B. 533.
4. *Richard Roberts Holdings Ltd* v. *Douglas Smith Stimson Partnership* (1988), 46 B.L.R. 50.
5. *Anns* v. *Merton LBC* [1978] A.C. 728.
6. *AMF International Ltd* v. *Magnet Bowling Ltd* [1968] 2 All E.R. 789.
7. *Bagot* v. *Stevens Scanlon & Co. Ltd* [1966] 1 Q.B. 197.
8. *Pirelli General Cable Works Ltd* v. *Oscar Faber & Partners* [1983] 2 A.C. 1.
9. *Hedley Byrne & Co. Ltd* v. *Heller & Partners Ltd* [1964] A.C. 465.
10. *Smith* v. *Eric S. Bush; Harris* v. *Wyre Forest DC* [1989] 2 All E.R. 514; *Caparo Industries plc* v. *Dickman* [1990] 1 All E.R. 568.
11. *Junior Books Ltd* v. *Veitchi Co. Ltd* [1983] 1 A.C. 520.
12. *D. & F. Estates Ltd* v. *Church Commissioners for England* [1988] 2 All E.R. 992.
13. *Murphy* v. *Brentwood DC* [1990] 2 All E.R. 908.
14. *William Hill Organisation* v. *Bernard Sunley & Sons* (1982) 22 B.L.R. 1.
15. *Scottish Special Housing Association* v. *Wimpey Construction UK Ltd* [1986] 2 All E.R. 957.
16. *Greater Nottingham Co-operative Society Ltd* v. *Cementation Piling & Foundations Ltd* [1988] 2 All E.R. 971.
17. *Rumbelows* v. *AMK and Firesnow (Sprinkler) Installations Ltd* (1980) 19 B.L.R. 25; *Twins Transport Ltd* v. *Patrick and Brocklehurst* (1983) 25 B.L.R. 65.
18. *Southern Water Authority* v. *Carey* [1985] 2 All E.R. 1077.
19. *Norwich CC* v. *Harvey* [1989] 1 All E.R. 1180.
20. *Pacific Associates Inc.* v. *Baxter* [1989] 2 All E.R. 159.
21. *District of Surrey* v. *Carroll-Hatch & Associates Ltd* (1979) 101 D.L.R. (3d) 218.
22. *Linden Gardens* v. *Lenesta Sludge Disposals* Ltd (1991) C.S.W, 24 January.
23. *Simaan General Contracting Co.* v. *Pilkington Glass Ltd (No. 2)* [1988] 1 All E.R. 791.
24. *Pearson* v. *Dublin Corporation* [1907] A.C. 351.
25. *Day* v. *Ost* [1973] 2 N.Z.L.R. 385.
26. *Townsends (Builders) Ltd* v. *Cinema News Property Management* Ltd [1959] 1 All E.R. 7.
27. *Oldschool* v. *Gleeson (Construction) Ltd* (1976) 4 B.L.R. 103.
28. *Equitable Debenture Assets Corporation* v. *William Moss* (1984) 2 Con. L.R. 1; *Victoria University of Manchester* v. *Wilson & Womersley* (1984) 2 Con. L.R. 43.

29. *Southern Water Authority* v. *Lewis & Duvivier* (*No. 2*) (1985) 1 Const. L.J. 74.
30. *University Court of Glasgow* v. *Whitfield* (1988) 42 B.L.R. 66.
31. *Sutcliffe* v. *Thackrah* [1974] A.C. 727.
32. *Leon Engineering & Construction Co. Ltd* v. *Ka Duk Investment Co. Ltd* (1989) 47 B.L.R. 139.

5

Formation and scope of construction contracts

Most students who take a specialist course in construction law or building contracts will, at an earlier stage of their studies, have examined the general principles of contract law. These principles are undoubtedly applicable in this field. The object of this chapter is to take a fresh look at some of these basic rules, to see what they mean in practical terms in the construction context.

5.1 AGREEMENT

A contract is a legally enforceable agreement. An agreement is usually defined in terms of an **offer** made by one party and an **acceptance** of that offer by the other. This need to find an offer and acceptance will cause few, if any, problems where it is clear that the parties' contractual relationship is to begin when, and only when, a formal document is signed. However, life is not always this simple, and even in those cases where such a document *is* signed by both parties, it is quite likely that this document will be seen merely as the formal record of a contract which already exists. Indeed, it is by no means uncommon to find a project running for months or even years before 'the contract' is finally executed.

Where no single **contract document** can be identified, identifying the offer and acceptance may prove rather more difficult, partly because these may take the form of written communications, the spoken word or even mere conduct.

5.1.1 Offer

The traditional distinction drawn by the law of contract is between an 'offer' and an 'invitation to treat'. The significance of this distinction is whereas an offer is turned into a contract immediately on its 'acceptance' by the person to whom it is addressed, an 'invitation to treat' has no such power – it is merely a stage in negotiations, inviting the other party to make an offer.

The acid test is whether the other party can bring about a contract by merely replying 'Yes'. In the construction context, two particular aspects of the problem call for comment.

5.1.2 Letters of intent

As we have mentioned, it is by no means unusual to find work on a construction project started before (even long before) a formal contract is drawn up and signed. Indeed, it is not unknown for this to take place after the job is finished! In such circumstances, the employer may be asked to write a **letter of intent**, which indicates a firm intention to award the contract in question to that contractor. As a general rule, such letters are naturally not of binding force. This will seldom matter because a contractor who does start work will, in any event, be entitled to claim on a *quantum meruit* (reasonable sum) basis for whatever is done.

Occasionally, however, the status of a 'letter of intent' *does* matter, as is shown by the case of *British Steel Corporation* v. *Cleveland Bridge*.[1] The defendants there, who had successfully tendered for the steelwork in a bank in Saudi Arabia, approached the plaintiffs for the manufacture of a variety of steel nodes, and sent them a 'letter of intent' which proposed that the defendants' own standard form of sub-contract should be used. The plaintiffs did not agree to this, and there were further disagreements over price and delivery dates (plus a telex from the defendants stating that the nodes must be manufactured in a particular order). None the less, the plaintiffs manufactured and delivered the nodes. When the plaintiffs sued for payment, the defendants counterclaimed for damages for delivery of the nodes late and out of sequence, arguing that a contract had come into existence when the plaintiffs started work.

It was held that since vital terms of the parties' arrangement remained unresolved, it was impossible to say that the commencement of work created a contract between the parties. As a result, the plaintiffs were entitled to be paid on a *quantum meruit* basis for the nodes, and the defendants' counterclaim failed. It is also worth noting that, had the point arisen, the absence of a contract would have meant that the plaintiffs were under no legal obligation to complete the job.

Although the judge in the *British Steel* case refused to hold that a contract had been brought into existence by the commencement of work, he recognized that this *could* happen in appropriate circumstances. Indeed, he cited with approval the earlier case of *Turriff Construction* v.

Regalia Knitting Mills.[2] In that case the plaintiffs having tendered for the design and construction of a factory for the defendants, were told that they were successful, whereupon they asked for 'an early letter of intent-...to cover us for the work we will now be undertaking'. Such a letter was sent, stating: 'the whole to be subject to agreement on an acceptable contract.' The plaintiffs then carried out the detailed design work necessary to seek planning permission and obtain estimates. When, 6 months later, the defendants abandoned the project, it was held that the plaintiffs had made it sufficiently clear that they wanted an assurance of payment for their preparatory work in any event, and that the letter of intent constituted that assurance. There was therefore a contract under which the plaintiffs were entitled to be paid.

5.1.3 Estimates and quotations

It is sometimes said that, in the context of construction, the law draws a sharp distinction between an **estimate**, which is a mere invitation to treat, and a **quotation**, which is an offer in the legal sense. While there may be at least a grain of truth in this, in that a court will tend to assume that this is what the parties intend, the labels cannot be regarded as conclusive. This point is clearly illustrated by the old case of *Croshaw* v. *Pritchard*.[3] The defendants there, in response to an architect's invitation to tender, wrote a letter headed 'Estimate' which stated: 'Our estimate to carry out the...alterations to the above premises according to the drawings and specifications amounts to £1230.' The plaintiff employer replied 'accepting' this figure, but the defendants thereupon purported to withdraw their 'estimate'. When the plaintiff sued for the extra cost involved in having the work done by another contractor, it was held that the defendants were liable. Notwithstanding its heading, their letter was an offer.

Where an estimate is *not* treated as an offer, it is obvious that the employer cannot, by purporting to 'accept' it, compel the contractor to do the work at the price stated, or indeed to do any work at all. Further, even if the contractor does begin work after giving an estimate, neither party can insist that payment be measured by the amount of that estimate. If there is no further agreement, the employer will be liable to pay what the court regards as a 'reasonable sum'. This may be higher or lower than the quoted figure. Nevertheless, the fact that the contractor may incur no *contractual* liability in such circumstances is not the end of the matter.

This last point is graphically illustrated by the New Zealand case of *Abrams* v. *Ancliffe*[4] in which the defendant, who wished to develop a building plot behind his house, was given an estimate by the plaintiffs, who then began work. Despite frequent requests, the plaintiffs repeatedly refused to give a firm price (on the ground that not all the sub-contracts had been finalized), although they rapidly realized that the work would cost far more than originally envisaged. Eventually the plaintiffs submitted a price of almost double the estimate, which meant that the defendant made a very substantial loss on the project.

When the plaintiffs brought an action for the price of the work, the defendant made a counterclaim for his losses. It was held that the plaintiffs were guilty of negligence in not informing the defendant of changed circumstances and escalating prices until it was too late for him to back out of the project and cut his losses (which he would have done). They were accordingly liable in tort for all the extra losses which he had incurred.

5.2 ACCEPTANCE

Assuming that an offer in the full legal sense has been made, a binding contract will come into existence when this is accepted by the other party. However, it is important to note the requirements for a valid 'acceptance' in this context.

5.2.1 Certain and unambiguous acceptance

In order to create a contract, a party's acceptance must unequivocally relate to the other party's offer. Further, the resulting agreement must be certain in all its essential terms. If these requirements are not met, there will be no contract.

In one case[5] the plaintiff contractors submitted two alternative tenders for the construction of a freight terminal. One of these was at a fixed price, the other was on a 'cost plus' basis. When the defendants purported to accept 'your tender', but did not specify which one, it was held that there was no contract, since it was impossible to say to which offer the 'acceptance' related.

A second case,[6] although rather less straightforward, again demonstrates the need for certainty in contractual dealings. The plaintiff builders agreed that they would introduce a source of finance for the defendants' proposed motel development, provided that they were then employed on the project and that the defendants instructed their quantity surveyor 'to negotiate fair and reasonable sums in respect of...the projects...based upon agreed estimates of net cost and general overheads with a margin for profit of 5%'. The defendants agreed to these terms, whereupon the plaintiffs arranged the finance, but they were not then given the work. On these facts it was held by the Court of Appeal that in the absence of agreement on price, or the provision of a method of ascertaining it, there was no contract between the parties.

5.2.2 Unconditional acceptance

Where what looks like an acceptance (or, for that matter, an offer) is made conditional upon the happening of some event, no contract is created at that point. For example, the use of the phrase 'subject to contract' in negotiations will in normal circumstances prevent the document in which it is contained from being treated as a binding offer or acceptance. However, it is perfectly possible for parties to make an informal agreement at the outset and for this to be legally binding, even though they expressly contemplate that their agreement will be put into formal shape at a later stage. (The subsequent making of the formal contract is of great practical significance since it will mean that claims for breach of contract are subject to a 12-year limitation period instead of the normal 6-year one.)

In one case[7] a defendant's tender was accepted by the plaintiff's architect (with the plaintiff's authority) in a letter which stated: 'The contract...will be ready for signature in the course of a few days.' The defendant discovered a mistake in his tender and sought to withdraw it, but it was held that he was too late; there was already a binding contract.

Apart from communications which are explicitly made conditional, difficulties may arise in the case of negotiations which take place over a long period of time. A purported acceptance which does not exactly reflect the offer will take effect as a counter-offer, destroying the original offer and leading to a contract only if it is itself accepted by the other party. When faced with a long series of letters, each of which accepts some of the other party's terms and proposes alterations to others, a court must try to see whether, at any given point, the parties are in complete agreement on everything which is at that time regarded as an essential term. If this is so, then a contract may be held to have come into existence, and the effect of later negotiations can be ignored.

One aspect of this matter which has caused particular problems is what is known as the **battle of forms**. This refers to the situation where the parties communicate entirely by letters which attempt to incorporate their own standard terms into the contract. In such cases, where work has actually been carried out, a court may well be able to rule that the last letter prevails, on the ground that its terms have been accepted by conduct. However, every case depends upon a careful examination of the entire correspondence, seen in context, and this may show an earlier contract or even no contract at all.

In practice, battles of forms appear to be fought most frequently between a main contractor on one side and a sub-contractor or supplier on the other. In *Sauter Automation* v. *Goodman*,[8] for example, a quotation submitted by sub-contractors for the supply and installation of boiler equipment was expressed to be subject to their standard conditions, which included a retention of title clause. The main contractors, having decided to accept this quotation, sent an order stating: 'Terms and conditions in accordance with the main contract' (which of course did not contain a retention of title clause). When the sub-contractors, without further communication, delivered the equipment to the site, it was held that this amounted to an acceptance by them of the main contractors' counter-offer.

The *Sauter* case may be contrasted with *Chichester Joinery* v. *John Mowlem*,[9] in which a quotation for joinery submitted by sub-contractors was accompanied by their standard conditions. The main contractors sent a purchase order containing their own standard terms, which cunningly stated: 'Any delivery made will constitute an acceptance of this order.' The sub-contractors duly delivered their joinery to the site, but not until after they had sent the main contractors a printed form headed 'Acknowledgment of order', which stated that the order was accepted 'subject to the conditions overleaf'! On this occasion, it was the sub-contractors' conditions which prevailed, as it was held that, by accepting the joinery, the main contractors had accepted the terms on which it was delivered.

5.2.3   Acceptance by conduct

The 'battle of forms' cases, cited above, demonstrate an important principle. The contractual problems arising out of a lengthy exchange of correspondence may sometimes be resolved by examining the *conduct* of the parties. It sometimes happens that the conduct of one party can show an acceptance of the terms as they exist at that time. This principle is of great importance in construction cases. Work is frequently started (and may indeed reach a fairly advanced stage) before a formal contract is drawn up and signed. If a dispute arises before this happens, a court may well be able to find sufficient 'acceptance' of terms contained in earlier documents, either by the contractor in starting work or by the employer in giving possession of the site.

The case of *Davies* v. *William Old*[10] is a good illustration of acceptance by conduct. The employer's architect there 'accepted' a tender from the plaintiffs as nominated sub-contractors under a RIBA 1963 Form of Contract. The architect's letter stated that the defendant main contractors would 'place an order' with them. When placed, this 'order' in fact introduced a new term, a 'pay when paid' clause (which as we shall see in Chapter 18 is frequently a bone of contention between contractors and sub-contractors). On this occasion, the plaintiffs did not protest, but started work. Because of this, it was held that they had accepted the offer which was contained in the main contractors' 'order'.

5.2.4 Retrospective acceptance

There are cases where a formal contract is not signed until long after work has commenced. An important question which may arise is whether the contract governs work which is done in the interim period (assuming that the contract itself does not make this point clear). If the contract does *not* apply, then that work will be paid for on a *quantum meruit* basis. The other rights and duties of the parties will have to be governed by whatever terms the court is able to imply in the circumstances. These are unlikely to reflect with any degree of accuracy what the parties would have agreed had they dealt expressly with the matter. Therefore a court may be fairly ready to imply a term for retroactive effect of the contract when finally formed.

The leading case is *Trollope & Colls* v. *Atomic Power Constructions*,[11] which concerned a sub-contract for which the plaintiffs tendered in February 1959. In June of that year, while negotiations were still continuing, the defendants asked the plaintiffs to commence work and gave them a letter of intent. A contract was not finally agreed until April 1960, and the question which then arose was whether a term of that contract (a variation clause) applied to work done before April 1960. It was held that, in these circumstances, a 'retroactivity' term was to be implied. The judge was quite satisfied that, if the parties had been asked in April 1960 whether the contract was to be retrospective, they would immediately have replied that this was what they intended.

5.3 MISTAKE

For present purposes, the term **mistake** is used to describe the situation in which an 'offer' made by one party and its 'acceptance' by the other do not truly correspond. When this occurs, it might be expected that the law would treat the resulting 'contract' as invalid, but this is not necessarily the case. The law looks not at the secret thoughts of the parties, but at what they have said and written, and if on this objective basis there appears to be agreement, then their contract will be held binding and enforceable.

A good example of this 'objective' view of contractual agreement is provided by the case of *Higgins* v. *Northampton Corporation*,[12] where the plaintiffs in tendering for a contract for the construction of 58 semi-detached houses made errors in completing their tender. As a result of these errors, the plaintiffs' tender price totalled £1613 per pair of houses, instead of £1670 per pair. On discovering this, the plaintiffs sought to be released from the contract, but it was held that they were bound by the terms on which they had tendered. Their mistake in formulating those terms was legally quite irrelevant.

There are exceptions to this general principle. For example, it has been accepted by the courts that, if one party is actually aware of the other's mistake, that party may not be allowed to snap up an 'offer' which clearly was not really intended. The extent of the protection thus given is somewhat uncertain, but some guidance is given by a comparison of two cases. In the first of these,[13] the plaintiffs submitted a tender specifying a completion period of 18 months. The defendants altered this to 30 months in the formal contract, and the plaintiffs signed this without noticing the alteration. Before the defendants signed the contract, they became aware as a result of preliminary meetings between the parties that the plaintiffs believed the contract period to be 18 months. When despite this the defendants simply signed the contract without comment, it was held that the plaintiffs were entitled to have the contract period altered to 18 months.

This may be contrasted with a second example,[14] in which bills of quantities listed certain materials and prices as subject to a fluctuations clause in the contract. A director of the defendants told the plaintiffs' surveyor that they would require the clause to cover all materials. The surveyor neither agreed nor disagreed, and the contract was signed without alteration. In these circumstances, it was held that there was no ground on which to alter the written contract, even though the plaintiffs had inadvertently paid on certain interim certificates which had been based on the assumption that the clause applied.

5.4 CONTRACTS MADE BY TENDER

As far as the need for an agreement based on offer and acceptance is concerned, building contracts are no different from any other kind of contract. In principle, the same is true when one examines the *way* in which offer and acceptance come about; but here the point should be made that most contracts for building projects of any appreciable size are created by the process of tender. The first question to be answered is why this is so, and just what it is that the tendering process seeks to achieve.

5.4.1 Purpose of tendering

The purposes of any tendering procedure are twofold. The first purpose is to select a suitable contractor, at a time which is suited to the circumstances of the project. The second purpose is to obtain from the relevant contractor at the appropriate time an acceptable tender or offer upon which a contract can be let.

The wise contractor will take account of the conditions of contract when calculating the contract price. The way in which risks are distributed in a building contract will have a significant effect upon the contractor's pricing strategy. Along with the conditions, the contract drawings and the bills of quantity (if used) make up the contractual arrangements. The contractual arrangements are dictated by the procurement strategy of the employer. This is often not an explicit decision on the part of the employer, especially if the employer is unfamiliar with the construction industry. The contractual conditions give a legal basis to the rights, liabilities and duties of the parties to the contract. They theoretically form the basis of the organizational strategy adopted for the project. But there are very definite differences between contractual arrangements, procurement strategies and tendering procedures. It is important to remember that there is no direct relationship between the type of tendering procedure and the form of contractual arrangement. There is often little relationship between the form of contract and the procurement strategy.

The tendering procedure, then, consists of two strands. In the first instance, the contractor has to be chosen; and in the second, the price for the contract works has to be estimated, so that it can form a basis for the letting of the contract. This process marks the beginning of a contractual relationship. Therefore, the tender stage of a construction project is as much a beginning as an end. Too often, there is a tendency in construction for some professional consultants to view the tendering procedure as the end of their involvement with the project. As in many spheres of human activity, there must be a 'follow-through'.

5.4.2 Types of tender

Legal analysis of tendering procedures recognizes that there are two different kinds of tender. The first, which is comparatively rare, is a 'standing offer', under which a contractor tenders for, say, such maintenance work as may be required by the employer over a specified period. The 'acceptance' of such a tender by the employer does not in itself create a binding contract. The employer is not bound to order any work, nor is the contractor prevented from withdrawing before the period is over. However, any orders placed during the period must, if the contractor's offer has not *already* been revoked, be carried out.

The second, and more usual, type of tender is simply an offer by the contractor to carry out the work specified in the invitation to tender. Once this is accepted by the employer, then (assuming that the acceptance is not conditional), it forms a legally binding contract.

From a practical point of view, tendering procedures ought to vary according to the kind of contract which they are intended to bring about. However, it is often the case that tendering procedures and forms of contract are not related to each other.

5.4.3 Tendering procedures

In the construction industry a variety of tendering procedures have evolved. The predominant feature which distinguishes them is the extent of competition. There is a very strong tradition in the construction industry that the best price can be gained by making tendering contractors bid for work, so that the lowest price gets the job. However, there is also an increasing level of dissatisfaction with competition because all it really guarantees is the lowest tender price. It is very important to bear in mind the actual price that will be paid for the works once they are finished. For example, a contractor who bids too low, in order to be sure of getting the job, may find that the job actually loses money. Contractors who bid as low as this tend to be those who are desperate for work because they are on the brink of insolvency. While a low tender may seem appealing at tender stage, it becomes very sour when the contractor ceases trading and the employer has to appoint others to complete the works. This can cost the employer a great deal more than a higher initial bid would have done.

As tendering procedures have evolved to confront this kind of problem, they have been codified by the National Joint Consultative Committee (NJCC), which consists of the major professional institutions involved with construction. We briefly describe their Codes of Procedure below, before looking at more novel forms of selecting a contractor.

Open tendering

This method was probably the 'traditional' method until more sophisticated techniques were accepted. The process begins by the placing of an advertisement in the technical press. The advertisement will carry brief details of the location, type, scale and scope of the proposed works. Contractors who are interested in bidding for the work can apply for the documentation. There will usually be a refundable charge for this documentation to prevent people from applying out of idle curiosity. Either the advertisement or the documentation will explicitly state that the employer is not bound to accept the lowest tender, or indeed any tender. This means that the issuing of documentation or the placing of an advertisement is not an offer on the part of the employer, but an invitation to treat.

Open tendering is an indiscriminate request for tenders. This approach can be unprofitable because there is no reliable method of ensuring high-quality building. Research has shown that with open tendering only about one in twenty contractors' bids are successful. The preparation of such tenders places upon the industry an unnecessary burden of time, effort and expense. This expense ultimately is passed back to the clients of the industry. Because of the indiscriminate nature of open tendering, contractors can be awarded work for which they are not properly equipped, in terms of either resources or experience. Although an employer is not bound to accept the lowest bid, a committee in charge of public expenditure is under a lot of pressure to accept the lowest. When the lowest bid is accepted, this can easily result in the employer awarding the contract to the builder who has the least appreciation of the complexities of the projects or the greatest willingness to take risks or the lowest current workload of all the bidders. It would be unusual, or even lucky, if these factors resulted in the best value for money for the employer.

Because of the problems associated with open tendering, its use has been declining in recent years. However, it is still often used by local authorities to obtain tenders for building work. Indeed, the indications are that its use will increase for public sector work because of a European Community Directive.[15] This Directive covers any public procurement programmes in excess of certain (rather low) thresholds. The intention is that open tendering should become the main form of procurement, even though the Directive will allow the use of restricted or negotiated procedures. Public procurement means procurement by any association governed by public law (central or local government) and includes health authorities, education authorities and the police. Therefore, the effect of this Directive is extremely wide.

It is unfortunate that having recognized the large number of problems associated with open tendering, and having successfully moved away from it as the main form of tendering in the UK, the European scene means that we will be reverting back to a far from satisfactory situation. Similar pressures apply in the international market, especially where organizations such as the World Bank are involved.

Single-stage selective tendering

The first step away from the problems of open tendering is to restrict the number of tenderers being invited to submit bids. This is the purpose of

single-stage selective tendering, which is also known simply as 'selective tendering'. Basically it consists of pre-selecting a limited number of contractors to tender for the work. An employer who builds regularly will usually have an approved list of contractors, from which a shortlist can be drawn up. In local authority work, for example, it is usual for there to be a definite process for a contractor to be entered on the approved list. This is quite distinct from the process of being selected for a particular project.

If the employer does not build regularly, then an *ad hoc* list of approved contractors may be drawn up. According to the NJCC, this will consist of contractors of established skill, integrity, responsibility and proven competence for work of the character and size contemplated.[16] It is recommended that the number of tenderers should be limited to a maximum of six. The Code of Procedure gives the points which should be considered when considering a contractor for inclusion on the list. Clearly, once the pre-selection process has been done properly, any of the contractors is satisfactory to the employer. Therefore, tenders may be considered on price alone, and the lowest one may be selected. Provided that tenders are checked carefully for mistakes by the bidders, and that the list of approved tenderers is regularly revised, some of the worst problems associated with inappropriate selection can be avoided.

However, other problems *may* still occur. Some of the major problems on construction projects happen because the design team do not have the benefit of the contractor's experience at a stage in the design when it would be most useful. Issues such as continuity of work, production cost savings, 'buildability' and sub-letting specialist items can have a significant impact on the final price of a project. The successful management of some types of construction project can be totally dependent on getting this kind of knowledge into the design team at an early stage in the process. A variety of techniques have emerged to deal with this, and their purpose is to separate the processes involved with selection of the contractor from the processes for determining the pricing mechanisms to be employed when paying the contractor.

Two-stage selective tendering

One of the processes used to involve a contractor at an early stage is known as **two-stage selective tendering,** sometimes called 'negotiated tendering'. It must be emphasized that the purpose is not to involve the contractor with *responsibility* for design. It is to get the main contractor involved, in an advisory capacity, before the scheme has been fully designed.

In this system the process is split into two stages. The first stage is a process for the selection of a contractor, and for the establishment of a level of pricing for subsequent negotiation. It is at this stage that the competitive selection takes place, based upon a minimum amount of information which indicates simply the basis of the layout and design of the works. The detail needs only to be sufficient to provide a basis for competition, and a basis for the negotiation of the price during the second stage. In the second stage the pre-contract process is completed. The employer's professional team collaborates with the selected contractor in the design and development of production drawings for the whole project. Also bills of quantities for the works are prepared and priced upon the basis of the first-stage tender. The result of the second stage is an acceptable sum for inclusion in a form of contract, and complete contract documentation is prepared with the contractor.

This form of tendering is used where the building works are of a highly complicated nature; where the magnitude of the work may be unknown at the time for selection of the contractor; or where an early completion date is paramount. The process is fully described in a Code of Procedure published by the National Joint Consultative Committee for Building.[17]

There are other methods of negotiated contracts not covered by the Code of Procedure, such as 'serial contracting', where contractors are asked to bid for a project on the basis that, if they build this one satisfactorily, others of a similar type will follow and the same bill rates will be used.

Selective tendering for design and build

A further process for which there is a code of procedure is for use where a **design and build contract** is being undertaken. This method is used where the contractor will design as well as build the project. It is envisaged that the form of contract associated with this tender process will be the JCT Form of Contract with Contractor's Design.

As we will see in Chapter 19, under this form of contract there is no architect, consulting engineer or quantity surveyor named in the contract. The purpose of the form is to obviate the need for the employer to appoint any consultants. The contractor provides all professional services in connection with the building. The employer's interests are looked after by the person named in the contract as the Employer's Agent: this person may be drawn from any of the recognized professions. The requirements of the employer are set down in a document called the Employer's Requirements; and the tendering contractors put forward their solutions and prices in a document called the Contractor's Proposals.

In this system of tendering the tender is the price for which the contractor offers to carry out and complete, in accordance with the conditions of contract, the works referred to in the Employer's Requirements. The word 'tender', in this context, is taken to cover the whole of the Contractor's Proposals, including both price and design. It is envisaged by the NJCC that any tendering contractor will have been pre-selected to a certain extent, as in two-stage tendering.[18]

Negotiation

A more radical approach to the selection of the contractor is offered via negotiation. This approach is more suited to procurement strategies which are markedly different from traditional methods. **Construction management**, for example, as described in Chapter 21, involves the use of a series of direct contracts with different types of specialist. **Management contracting** (Chapter 20) involves the early appointment of the main contractor whose responsibilities are not the same as they would be under JCT 80 or other more traditional forms of contract. These newer forms of procurement demand a less adversarial approach at all levels and all stages in the building process. The inherent flexibility demanded by such approaches means that there is no standard method for negotiating a contract.

Experience has shown that one of the most effective ways of selecting a contractor under 'non-traditional' approaches is to negotiate the deal as the relationship develops. It seems that the single most important factor of such a relationship between the employer and the contractor is familiarity. They have worked together before, and they expect to work together again in the future. The preservation of an on-going commercial relationship becomes more important than simply securing the lowest price for the employer, or the highest profit for the contractor. Because of this, it is essential that the employer is familiar with some or all of the building process, the professional team, the contractor and the specialists. These themes are developed more fully in Chapters 20 and 21.

Joint ventures

Certain construction projects are so complex that the distribution of liability between the consultants becomes a problem. One solution is to approach the design and implementation of the project as a joint venture between all the consultants and some or all of the specialist contractors. This is an even more radical departure from the so-called 'traditional' methods than the 'management-based' methods. It involves all of the parties to the **joint venture** agreement taking on joint and several liability for the design and/or execution of the project. It is not necessary to set up a special joint venture company to do this, but it is possible. The agreements between the parties to the joint venture will have to be carefully examined, and probably backed up by performance bonds and/or parent company guarantees. The NJCC has issued guidance on tendering under this approach, and further details can be found there.[19]

5.4.4 Tendering problems

While the adoption of a suitable tendering procedure, and adherence to the appropriate NJCC Code of Practice, will help to reduce if not to eliminate the potential waste of time, effort and money, there remain certain difficulties which are inherent in the way in which the law analyses tenders. Since a contractor's tender is seen as an offer which it is up to the client to accept, it follows that no legal rights or obligations can come into existence unless and until this happens, and this can raise problems in two respects, namely costs and withdrawal of tenders. A third problem area relates to the processes which are used by contractors in actually formulating their bids.

Costs of tendering

Given the law's insistence that the 'invitation to tender' is merely an invitation to treat, and the tender itself an offer, it follows that the employer is normally under no legal obligation to accept the lowest (or, indeed, any) tender submitted. In practice, this protection of the employer's position is frequently made explicit when tenders are invited. The only limitation appears to be that by analogy with cases concerning the advertisement of auctions a person who invites another to tender with no intention whatsoever of accepting that tender will be liable for any expenses which the latter incurs.

This unlikely possibility aside, the basic legal position is that the costs of tendering (which may be considerable, especially where substantial design work is required) are to be borne by the contractor. Of course, these costs can be reflected in the tender price and thus recouped by the successful bidder, but the unsuccessful competitors must in normal circumstances bear their own costs, unless a promise to pay on the part of the employer can be implied. Such a promise might be implied where the preliminary work goes beyond what would normally be expected, or where the employer can make some profitable use of it.

An example of what will suffice to justify departing from the basic rule is provided by *William Lacey* v. *Davis*,[20] in which the plaintiffs, who had tendered for the reconstruction of war-damaged premises, were led by the defendant to believe that they would receive the contract. At the defendant's request, the plaintiffs then prepared various calculations, schedules and estimates which the defendant used in negotiating a claim with the War Damage Commission. When the defendant sold the property with the benefit of an agreed War Damage claim, without ever having concluded a formal contract with the plaintiffs, it was held that a promise by the defendant to pay a reasonable sum for these services could be implied.

The claim of the contractors in the *Lacey* case was a strong one, since the client had specifically asked for the work in question to be done and, moreover, had actually made a substantial profit from it. However, in a more recent case[21] the court reached a similar conclusion in respect of work which the client had only requested by implication, and where the profit to him from that work was still only a potential one.

Withdrawal of tender

Conventional contract law lays down that since a contractor's tender is merely an offer, it may be validly revoked at any time before it has been accepted. If this happens in respect of a main contract, the client may well be disappointed (especially if the tender in question was the lowest!). However, the client is unlikely to suffer any great financial loss as a result. By contrast, the withdrawal of a *sub-contractor's* tender may have a disastrous effect on the main contractor, as is demonstrated by a New Zealand case.[22] There the defendant main contractors, having obtained a written estimate of transport charges from the plaintiffs, relied on this in pricing their tender for certain work. The defendants' tender was accepted by the client, but the plaintiffs then announced that they were increasing their prices (which, in effect, meant that they were withdrawing their original offer). It was held that in the absence of a binding contractual obligation the plaintiffs were quite entitled to withdraw which, of course, left the defendants with an uneconomic contract to fulfil.

As the law currently stands, an English court would probably come to exactly the same conclusion on this matter as its New Zealand counterpart. However, in an extremely interesting recent development the Canadian courts have prevented both sub-contractors and main contractors from withdrawing tenders in similar circumstances, at least once the other party has relied on the tender by making some sort of commitment. Whether English law will develop along similar lines must, for the moment, be a matter of speculation, but there is much to be said for the idea, at least from the point of view of business convenience. Failing this, the practical solution would appear to lie in requiring contractors to supply a **bid bond**, that is a promise by deed not to withdraw the bid, backed by a financial guarantee.

Formulation of bids

Conventional textbook wisdom describes contractor's tendering procedures in a very logical and objective manner. For example, it is always said that in pricing a bill of quantities a contractor will ascertain such things as the price of materials, the cost of labour and plant, and the availability of resources. This information is used to 'build up' rates which can be entered in the bills. So, for example, if a certain quantity of brickwork is described in the bills, the contractor will determine the cost of the raw materials (based upon the relevant quantity discounts), the rates of pay for the skilled and unskilled elements of the labour, the number of hours needed to actually put together a square metre of brickwork, the number of hours needed to mix the mortar, an amount of money for supervision, plant, and so on. These amounts are added together in such a way as to identify a rate for a square metre of brickwork. This rate can then be inserted into the bill and multiplied by the actual quantity required.

This process, known as **estimating**, takes place for every item in the bill. The first problem with it is that it takes little account of the way in which contractors' costs are incurred; it is based solely on historical information which does not relate the location of the work to its cost. An easy example is that brickwork on the second floor is cheaper than brickwork on the seventeenth floor, because of the distance that the materials have to be moved, but this difference is rarely reflected in the built-up rates.

The second, and more important problem, is the 'myth of tendering'. What is not often reported is that although contractors have very detailed information related to costs, and can work out very accurate rates for the bills, these are frequently *not* the rates which actually appear in the bills!

Contractors know about costs (what they pay for their resources); they know about prices (what they charge for their product); and they know about value (what the client is willing to pay for a building). The difference between 'cost', 'price' and 'value' is rarely appreciated outside quantity surveyors' offices. It is this distinction which accounts for the difference between the textbook method of tendering and the additional process which is not usually reported.

Upon being invited to tender, a contractor will first make a decision about whether or not the job is wanted. A contractor will almost never submit a null return, for fear of not being asked to tender again in the future. There is a certain amount of stigma attached to a contractor who declines to tender. If the job is not wanted, the contractor will submit an inflated tender, called a **cover bid**. While the contractor will know what the rates in the tender ought to be, these will all be altered to make the final figure clearly too high to be acceptable.

If the contractor wants the job, then a further decision is about the state of the market, and an assessment of what this type of building is selling for at the moment. This assessment is then modified by the level of risk associated with the project, particularly in terms of the contractual conditions put forward by the employer. A high level of contractual risk needs to be allowed for in the contractor's bid, so that the risks are covered. This works in the same way that insurers examine and price risk.

Finally, the contractor's own cash flow has a significant effect on the tendering process. Having a detailed knowledge of costs and finance, the contractor can predict the monthly net flow of cash in or out of the project. If the project takes place near the end of a tax year, the contractor may want to reduce the level of profit appearing on the balance sheets for the purpose of reducing tax liabilities. This can be done by artificially reducing the rates for work at the beginning of the project, and adding a corresponding proportion on to the rates for work later on in the project. Alternatively, the contractor may need to get cash in quickly to meet liabilities, or to show a good return for shareholders' dividends. In this case, the rates at the beginning of the project can be increased, with a corresponding decrease in the rates at the end. The former process is known as 'back-loading the bill'; the latter is known as 'front-loading the bill'. Neither process makes any difference to the contract sum, but both can have a significant impact on the continued survival of the contractor's business.

This brief analysis shows that, notwithstanding the contractor's detailed knowledge of costs and prices, the skill of a good contractor is in pitching the contract sum at a level which will maximize the chances of winning jobs that are wanted, while ensuring that profits are adequate. The bill rates are then manipulated to add up to the desired contract sum, and internally adjusted to regulate the cash flow according to the financial position of the contractor.

This shows how dangerous it can be to attach too much credence to individual bill rates when analysing tendering procedures. It also illustrates one of the major pitfalls in using bill rates for valuing variations, as examined in Chapter 11.

5.5 TERMS OF A CONTRACT

Assuming that a contract has been properly made, it becomes necessary to identify precisely what obligations it imposes on the parties – that is, what **terms** it includes. In considering this question, what emerges is that there are three types of contractual term: those 'express terms' which are contained in the main contractual document itself; those (also express terms) contained in other documents to which the main contract document refers; and those terms which are 'implied' by law.

5.5.1 Express terms

Terms and representations

English law does not as a general rule require a contract to be made in any particular form. Thus it is, in principle, quite possible for the parties' agreement to be spread over a number of documents, and even to include oral statements. Even where the parties have eventually signed a document described as 'the Contract', it is open to a court to decide that this document does not paint a complete picture, and that the true contract consists of that document plus other terms.

The result of this view of contracts is to create a degree of uncertainty in respect of the status of a statement or promise which is made by one party to the other during the course of negotiations leading to the signing of a formal contract. Such a statement (which might be oral, or might equally be contained in, say, a letter) can be treated in law as a term of the contract. In this case, if it is untrue, the innocent party may bring an action for breach of contract. Alternatively, if it has operated as an inducement to the other party to enter into the contract, the statement may be treated as a misrepresentation. In this case, the legal remedies available will depend on whether it was made fraudulently, negligently or innocently. This is not the place to discuss the remedies for misrepresentation, which will be found in any textbook on the law of contract. Suffice it to say that they are generally less beneficial to the innocent party than a right to sue for breach of contract.

In seeking to decide whether a particular statement is a term or a mere representation, the courts make use of a number of guidelines. Some of these may point in opposite directions. It is, for example, presumed that a statement made at a very early stage of negotiations is probably a representation, while a statement made by an 'expert' is more likely to be treated as a term. However, what is very often decisive in the context of construction contracts is the strong presumption that where the parties have signed what purports to be a complete contract document, this does indeed represent the whole of their contract. As a result, any collateral statement or promise is likely to take effect, if at all, as a mere representation.

The task of deciding just what is included in a contract may also arise in relation to bills of quantities, drawings, specifications, etc. However, modern standard form contracts normally avoid problems in this area by carefully defining those documents which are to have contractual force. This matter is dealt with in detail in Chapter 8.

Conflicting terms

It is a general principle of the interpretation of contracts that, in cases of inconsistency, written words prevail over printed words. However, as we discuss in Chapter 8, this principle is overridden by many standard form construction contracts. In particular, JCT 80 specifically provides (in clause 2.2.1) that nothing in the contract bills shall override or modify the articles, conditions or appendix. This clause does not prevent the bills from imposing *extra* obligations. However, a similar provision in JCT 63 has been interpreted to mean that, where a particular matter is dealt with in the conditions, any special provisions on that subject in the bills are to be ignored.

Applying a clause of this nature, the courts have felt bound to ignore clear provisions in the contract bills which purported to deal with the contractor's duty to insure;[23] the nomination of sub-contractors;[24] sectional completion;[25] and the taking of possession by the employer.[26]

5.5.2   Incorporation by reference

Many, if not most, building contracts – and certainly those which concern projects of any great size – are drawn up and executed by the parties in a formal manner. The terms of those contracts are therefore easily identifiable and, if the parties intend to incorporate other documents by reference, this will by made clear in the main contract document. However, it sometimes happens (perhaps out of meanness, laziness or simply an over-casual approach to business procedures) that no such formal contract is executed at all, despite the fact that the parties intend to contract under one of the standard forms with which they are familiar. The question which then arises is whether the terms found in the appropriate standard form contract are applicable.

It may be stated at the outset that there is in general nothing to prevent the incorporation of an entire standard form contract by simply referring to it, and indeed this is what happened in *Killby & Gayford Ltd* v. *Selincourt*.[27] In that case an architect wrote asking a contractor to price certain work and and stated: 'Assuming that we can agree a satisfactory contract price between us, the general conditions and terms will be subject to the normal standard form of RIBA contract.' When the contractors submitted an estimate which the architect accepted, and the work was done, it was held that the current RIBA form of contract was incorporated, although no formal contract was ever signed.

The principle of incorporation by reference applies equally to contracts which are themselves made orally or by conduct. If it is clear that that is what the parties intend, then their contract will be subject to the appropriate standard form. However, it should be noted that the contract remains an oral one, which may have certain important legal implications. For example, although an arbitration clause in the standard form contract would be duly incorporated, there would be no 'written agreement to submit...to arbitration', and thus the provisions of the *Arbitration Act 1950* would not apply.

One danger in the practice of incorporation is that not all references to well-known forms of contract are as clear and unequivocal as in the *Killby* case, and if the parties fail to express properly what they mean, it cannot be assumed that a court will always rescue them. In particular, it has consistently been held that a sub-contractor's undertaking to carry out work in accordance with the main contract does not necessarily incorporate *all* the terms of that main contract, so that in *Goodwins, Jardine & Co.* v. *Brand*,[28] for example, an arbitration clause was not included.

An even more worrying illustration is *Chandler Bros Ltd* v. *Boswell*,[29] where a main contract empowered the employer to order the main contractor to remove a sub-contractor who was guilty of delay. The sub-contract dealt specifically with many of the matters in the main contract, but did not in terms give a power of removal for delay. When, in accordance with an order from the employer under the main contract, the main contractor purported to remove a defaulting sub-contractor, it was held by the Court of Appeal that he was guilty of a breach of contract. The sub-contractor's undertaking to carry out the work in accordance with the terms of the main contract was not enough to incorporate the power of removal for delay.

Notwithstanding these two decisions and others to similar effect, there are numerous cases in which the courts have tried very hard to make sense of what the parties have said or written, and to give effect to what they really intended. For instance, where sub-contractors were appointed 'in full accordance with the appropriate form for nominated sub-contractors RIBA 1965 edition', it transpired that not only was there no RIBA 1965 edition (the current form was the 1963 version), there were no RIBA forms of sub-contract at all! Despite this appalling drafting, the Court of Appeal was convinced on the evidence that what the parties had in mind was the FASS 'green form' of sub-contract; it was accordingly held that that form should be incorporated.[30]

The decision in *Brightside Kilpatrick Engineering Services* v. *Mitchell Construction*[31] is perhaps even more generous in the face of sloppy drafting. A sub-contract was there placed on an order form which identified the main contract and concluded: 'The conditions applicable to the sub-contract shall be those embodied in RIBA as above agreement.' Printed references on the order form to the 'green form' of sub-contract had been deleted, although the Standard Form of Tender, to which reference *was* made, stipulated that a 'green form' sub-contract should be used. The main contractors argued that the *whole* of the RIBA 1963 form of contract was to be incorporated into the sub-contract but the Court of Appeal, after some hesitation (based on the extreme difficulty of making any sense at all of the words used!), agreed with the sub-contractors that what were to be incorporated were those terms of the main contract which dealt with nominated sub-contractors. And since these contemplated a 'green form' or equivalent sub-contract, this is what would be implied.

5.5.3 Implied terms

Building contracts are, like other contracts for work and materials, subject to the implied terms contained in the *Supply of Goods and Services Act 1982*. In addition, it may be possible for terms to be implied *by the courts* into such contracts, although this is less likely to happen where the contract document itself is detailed and apparently exhaustive.

In considering this question, it is important to appreciate that two different kinds of implication may be involved. First, certain terms will be automatically implied *as a matter of law* into certain *classes* of contract, provided only that they are not inconsistent with any express terms. Second, and far less common, a term may be implied *as a matter of fact* into an *individual* contract where that contract would be commercially unworkable without it. These two kinds of implication may be separately considered.

Implication in law

The law regards certain terms as 'usual' in building contracts, so much so that, if the contract is silent on these matters (as may well be the case with small informal agreements), these terms will be implied. However, it must be stressed once again that the court will not re-write a contract freely entered into, and so there will be no implication of terms which would be inconsistent with the express agreement. This will have a direct practical effect: where, as under the main standard forms of building contract, all the 'usual' matters are covered in some detail, implied terms are rendered largely (though not entirely) irrelevant.

The terms which are regarded as 'usual' in this respect, and which will therefore be implied into construction contracts, will be dealt with in more detail elsewhere (notably in Chapters 8–13). None the less, a brief summary of the most important terms may be useful at this stage.

- *Employer's obligations*
  The implied obligations of the employer, though capable of appearing as a list, can effectively be reduced to two: a general duty not to hinder the contractor's efforts to complete the work and, more positively, a duty actively to co-operate with the contractor. The former branch has been held to be breached, for example, by an employer causing delay via servants or agents (who include, for this purpose, the contract administrator, but not independent third parties or even nominated sub-contractors); interfering with the supply of necessary materials to the contractor; and interfering with a contract administrator's function as independent certifier under the contract.

  As to the duty of positive co-operation, this involves such matters as giving possession of the site; appointing an architect and nominating sub-contractors and suppliers; supplying the necessary instructions, information, plans and drawings; and if the contract administrator persists in applying the contract in a wrongful manner, dismissing him or her and appointing a replacement. All these things must be done and, what is more, they must all be done without undue delay.

- *Contractor's obligations*
  Where a building contract does not specify a date for completion or, more commonly, where a contractual completion date has passed, the contractor's implied duty is to complete within such a time as is reasonable in all the circumstances. In addition, there will normally, though not always, be an implied obligation to carry out the work with due diligence so as to maintain a reasonable rate of progress.

  As to the *standard* of the work, it is implied that the contractor will use proper workmanship and, in most cases, that the materials used will be of good quality and fit for their purpose. However, the 'fitness for the purpose' warranty will be excluded where it is clear that the employer has placed no reliance on the contractor's 'skill and judgement' in selecting the materials, such as where the employer specifies the material and nominates the supplier. Further, there may be circumstances in which even the warranty as to quality will not be implied, for example, where the employer knows that the contractor will have no right of recovery against the actual supplier of the materials.

  Apart from the fitness for the purpose of the *materials* used, there may in certain cases be an implied warranty that the completed *works* will be fit for their purpose. Such a term depends upon the employer's *reliance* on the expertise of the contractor. Accordingly, it cannot apply where the contractor is merely to build in accordance with detailed plans and specifications. Similarly, it cannot apply where the contractor is under the supervision of an architect. A warranty of fitness will be fairly readily implied, for example, into a contract to buy a house which is in the course of being built. However, the sale of an already-completed building is subject to the doctrine of *caveat emptor*; consequently, it attracts no such implication.

Implication in fact

We have seen earlier that a court will strain to make sense of the parties' agreement, for example, in identifying the form of contract to which they have inaccurately referred. However, what the courts have repeatedly stated that they will *not* do is to make or improve contracts for the parties. The principle of freedom of contract means that, if parties have entered into a contract which is unreasonable, inconvenient or commercially unwise, it is not for the courts to change their arrangement. They must simply be left to bear the consequences. A term will not be implied into a particular contract just to make it more convenient, reasonable or sensible; it will only be implied if its absence is so glaringly obvious that both parties *must* have intended to include it.

A good example of the courts' extreme reluctance to imply a term just to 'improve' a contract is the decision of the House of Lords in *Trollope & Colls* v. *NWMRHB*.[32] A contract for the construction of a hospital extension in phases provided that Phase III should commence 6 months after the issue of the certificate of practical completion of Phase I, but that Phase III should itself be completed by a fixed date. There were express provisions for extensions of time to be granted in respect of Phase I, but no express provision for this to have a 'knock on' effect on Phase III. Delay in completing Phase I (for virtually all of which extensions of time were granted) effectively reduced the period for Phase III from 30 months to 16 months, whereupon the contractors argued that a term should be implied permitting the Phase III time to be extended in accordance with any extensions to Phase I. However, the House of Lords refused to make any such implication, ruling that since the contract was clear and unambiguous in fixing a time for completion for Phase III, the parties must live with the agreement which they had made.

A recent example of the same judicial reluctance to intervene is *Bruno Zornow* v. *Beechcroft Developments*,[33] a case in which sloppy drafting made it very difficult even to discover what were the *express* terms of the contract. In the end, the judge was prepared to imply a completion date (on the basis that no commercial party would contemplate a contract without one); however, he absolutely refused to imply a term for sectional completion, even though it appeared that this was what the parties had intended.

5.6   FRUSTRATION OF CONTRACT

The scope of a contract may be insufficient to deal with some external event which renders it impossible, illegal or radically different. If this happens through the fault of neither party, and the contract itself makes no sufficient provision for what has occurred, it is possible that the law may treat the contract as terminated under the doctrine of **frustration**. In such a case, both parties are freed from any further obligations under the contract. As for any losses which have already been incurred, these will be allocated between the parties in accordance with the *Law Reform (Frustrated Contracts) Act 1943*.

It is important to realize that this doctrine is very limited in its application. If the general law terminates a contract in this way, it interferes with the balance of risks between the parties. In the building and civil engineering fields, in particular, the courts recognize that the kind of risks involved in such cases often fall naturally on one party or the other, and that to give the risk-bearing party an escape route would unfairly distort this balance. What is more, most standard form contracts make express provision for many of the eventualities which might lead a party to claim that a contract has been frustrated, and the doctrine cannot be used to override clear contract terms.

Two decisions of the House of Lords may be used to illustrate the doctrine of frustration and give an idea of its limits. In the first of these, *Davis Contractors* v. *Fareham*,[34] the parties in 1946 entered into a fixed-price contract for the construction of 78 houses in 8 months. The work in fact took 22 months to complete and cost the contractors far more than the contract price. This was due partly to bad weather, and partly to labour shortages caused by the slow demobilization of the Second World War troops, both of which were unforeseeable. The contractors sought to argue that the contract was frustrated, and thus to claim a reasonable sum for the value of the work. However, it was held that what had happened was squarely within the risk assumed by the contractors, so that no relief could be granted to them.

The earlier case of *Metropolitan Water Board* v. *Dick, Kerr & Co.*[35] arose out of a fixed-price contract for the construction of a reservoir. The contract, which was entered into on the eve of the First World War, provided that the work was to be completed within 6 years, but gave the engineer very wide powers to order extensions of time. After some 18 months, the government ordered the contractors to stop the work and to sell all their plant. This development, it was held, was sufficient to bring the contract to an end. It went far beyond the extension of time provisions in the contract and rendered the project fundamentally different from what had been envisaged.

REFERENCES

1. *British Steel Corporation* v. *Cleveland Bridge & Engineering Co. Ltd* [1984] 1 All E.R. 504.
2. *Turriff Construction Ltd* v. *Regalia Knitting Mills Ltd* (1971) 9 B.L.R. 20.
3. *Croshaw* v. *Pritchard* (1899) 16 T.L.R. 45.
4. *J. & J.C. Abrams Ltd* v. *Ancliffe* [1978] 2 N.Z.L.R. 420.
5. *Peter Lind & Co. Ltd* v. *Mersey Docks & Harbour Board* [1972] 2 Lloyd's Rep. 234.
6. *Courtney & Fairbairn Ltd* v. *Tolaini Brothers (Hotels) Ltd* [1975] 1 All E.R. 716.
7. *Lewis* v. *Brass* (1877) 3 Q.B.D. 667.
8. *Sauter Automation Ltd* v. *Goodman (Mechanical Services) Ltd* (1986) 34 B.L.R. 81.
9. *Chichester Joinery Ltd* v. *John Mowlem & Co. plc* (1987) 42 B.L.R.100.
10. *A Davies & Co. (Shopfitters) Ltd* v. *William Old Ltd* (1969) 67 L.G.R. 395.
11. *Trollope & Colls Ltd* v. *Atomic Power Constructions Ltd* [1962] 3 All E.R. 1035.
12. *W. Higgins Ltd* v. *Northampton Corporation* [1927] 1 Ch. 128.
13. *A. Roberts & Co. Ltd* v. *Leicestershire CC* [1961] 1 Ch. 555.
14. *Royston UDC* v. *Royston Builders Ltd* (1961) 177 E.G. 589.
15. Directive 88/295/EEC.
16. National Joint Consultative Committee for Building. *Code of Procedure for Single Stage Selective Tendering.* RIBA Publications, London, 1989.
17. National Joint Consultative Committee for Building. *Code of Procedure for Two Stage Selective Tendering.* RIBA Publications, London, 1983.
18. National Joint Consultative Committee for Building. *Code of Procedure for Selective Tendering for Design & Build.* RIBA Publications, London, 1985.
19. National Joint Consultative Committee for Building. *Joint Venture Tendering for Contracts in the United Kingdom.* RIBA Publications, London, 1985.
20. *William Lacey (Hounslow) Ltd* v. *Davis* [1957] 2 All E.R. 712.
21. *Marston Construction Co. Ltd* v. *Kigass Ltd* (1989) 46 B.L.R. 109.
22. *Cook Islands Shipping Co. Ltd* v. *Colson Builders Ltd* [1975] 1 N.Z.L.R. 422.
23. *Gold* v. *Patman & Fotheringham Ltd* [1958] 2 All E.R. 497.
24. *North-West Metropolitan Hospital Board* v. *T.A. Bickerton & Son Ltd* [1970] 1 All E.R. 1039.
25. *M.J. Gleeson (Contractors) Ltd* v. *Hillingdon London Borough* (1970) 215 E.G. 165.
26. *English Industrial Estates Corporation* v. *George Wimpey & Co. Ltd* (1972) 7 B.L.R. 122.
27. *Killby & Gayford Ltd* v. *Selincourt Ltd* (1973) 3 B.L.R. 104.

28. *Goodwins, Jardine & Co.* v. *Brand* (1905) 7 F. (Ct of Sess.) 995.
29. *Chandler Bros Ltd* v. *Boswell* [1936] 3 All E.R. 179.
30. *Modern Building (Wales) Ltd* v. *Limmer & Trinidad Co. Ltd* [1975] 1 W.L.R. 1281.
31. *Brightside Kilpatrick Engineering Services* v. *Mitchell Construction Ltd* (1973) 1 B.L.R. 62.
32. *Trollope & Colls Ltd* v. *North West Metropolitan Regional Hospital Board* [1973] 2 All E.R. 260.
33. *Bruno Zornow (Builders) Ltd* v. *Beechcroft Developments Ltd* (1989) C.S.W., 28 July.
34. *Davis Contractors Ltd* v. *Fareham UDC* [1956] A.C. 696.
35. *Metropolitan Water Board* v. *Dick, Kerr & Co. Ltd* [1918] A.C. 119.

PART TWO

Building Design

6

The management of design

The problems associated with the management of design stem from its nature as an information processing system. The processing of technically diverse information, much of which is innovative and is being worked upon by a variety of different technical consultants, produces a series of problems for management very different from those found in other industries.

In order to put the problem into perspective, this chapter presents an analysis of the way in which construction projects are managed from the point of view of generating information. The range of construction projects is large, so this analysis uses as an example commercial construction projects for private sector clients in developed countries. The process of construction is split into a series of stages which are common to all projects. Variability between projects arises from changes in intensity between these stages. The people who are involved also change from one stage to another. Leadership of the process, too, is variable in the way that it has an impact on the processes of design.

6.1 DECISIONS AND STAGES

An important step in examining the problems of managing the construction process is to identify the extent of commonality between projects. Clearly, all projects go through a similar series of steps between their inception and their completion. These have been classified in different ways by various interest groups, but there are common stages. The output of the design process is information to be used in the fabrication of the building. What is often not appreciated is that the information produced

by designers will not be sufficiently accurate or detailed for use as fabrication drawings, so that specialists will add much more detail to the documentation in order to satisfy their own information requirements.

In terms of modelling information generation activities, there is little to
be gained in studying the pre-briefing or post-handover situations. This
analysis is therefore restricted to the events between the appointment of
the project management team and the handover of the project. The
stages between inception and handover can be classified as briefing,
concept development, engineering, production information and construction. Each of these is briefly described below.

6.1.1   Briefing

The processes leading up to the appointment of the project team are
internal to the client's organization. There may be involvement of construction professionals before this point, but for the generation of design
information the important starting-point is the commencement of
briefing. In this first stage, the process which is being managed is the
extraction from the client of a thorough description of what will be
required. This needs to be presented in terms that are readily transform-
able into a design concept. To enable the design team to develop the
concept, the brief should be documented such that the scope of the
project is adequately defined. This document, a succinct statement of the
brief, establishes the basic policy for the project. Eliciting a good brief is
one of the most difficult and least understood processes in a construction
project.

6.1.2   Concept development

The completed description of the scope of the job triggers the concept
stage. This second stage in the process is where the designer develops the
concept for the job. The description of the scope sets the parameters
within which the designer can create the conceptual ideas. This is done in
conjunction with cost planning, which assigns a budget to that concept.
These two sets of documentation can together be signed off by the client
as the concept for the whole scheme. This concept is the designer's
translation of the brief. It consists of proposals for the building and
detailed objectives for each of the sub-systems, and it is developed by
the design team in conjunction with cost advice. Up to this point, cost
planning is a reaction to what is being produced by the designer. Whatever the designer produces has a cost attached to it, so in these early
stages cost planning can be said to be reactive.

6.1.3 Engineering

There is a problem of semantics attached to the use of the term 'engineering' in the UK. However, these problems do not seem to exist in the rest of the world, where it is considered quite normal and respectable to use the word 'engineer' to describe people who undertake the translation of concepts into schemes which can be fabricated. It is the most appropriate term, so it is used here without apology!

After the production of the cost plan, the project can enter the engineering stage. Normally there will be a certain amount of negotiation about costs, and this may obscure the transition between these two stages. Ultimately, the client signs the project into the engineering stage, where designers at a different level start to engineer the project and work out the technical details. As the various systems are engineered and detailed, they can be manipulated into packages which can be let as individual contracts to specialist trade contractors. For example, the structural engineer's work may be let as a steel-erection package, and the mechanical services engineer's work may be let as a series of packages.

During this stage, the design team leader will be co-ordinating the efforts of the different specialist engineers and ensuring that the design philosophy laid down during the concept development stage is not compromised.

6.1.4 Production information

Once the packages have been put out to tender, the specialists can start to produce their detailed information. This must be co-ordinated and tied in with all the other documentation that has been produced up to this stage. The people who are going to fabricate the work will be producing their own documentation. In order that the design is not compromised, the design team leader and the engineers will continue to be involved in monitoring and checking this information. It is at this point that problems arise in identifying responsibility for detailed design decisions. This is because the precise role of the various people who are adding to or checking the growing pile of documents can become very difficult to determine.

6.1.5 Construction

From this point on, documentation is provided solely for construction purposes. For management, its purpose is co-ordination. Much of the documentation will be in the form of 'as-built' drawings for future reference. Ultimately, the process heads towards completion, at which point the project can be signed off and handed over. The client can then accept it and begin to operate it.

6.2   PROBLEMS IN DESIGN MANAGEMENT

6.2.1   Managing the designer's continuity of creativity

There must be a stage where the designer is permitted to develop the concept with some degree of freedom. There needs to be an atmosphere conducive to creative and innovative thinking. However, this must be arrested at an early stage, so that the concept design can be evaluated and developed. Even so, it would be wrong to interrupt the design process before this change from reactive cost planning to proactive cost planning. This is one of the fundamental tensions which always exists in the process of the management of design. It cannot be eliminated without destroying the value of the process, but it needs to be acknowledged and controlled if misunderstandings and disputes are to be avoided at a later stage.

It is unwise to allow design to be a continuous process. Given a free rein, designers will tend endlessly to develop their ideas, with a view to reconciling every aspect of the building. There have to be break-off points during the process at which progress can be reviewed. A commercial client is not usually seeking a comprehensive statement of perfection; what is required is a functional solution which will be adequate, rather than perfect.

There would of course be a natural break if the design process were to be worked right the way through, but in order to make the process a commercial viability, the client needs to take stock of the situation at earlier points. Opportunities for control by the client are provided by 'milestones' which act as distinct breaks. These impose a discipline on the project team which interrupts the creative chain.

This underlines the nature of the major decision points. In principle, these are opportunities for the client to gain control of the project and to review what is being produced. The client needs to decide about the extent to which the design meets his or her requirements. The characteristics of these decision points are that there is a documentation package which goes to the client, and a decision which comes back. On well-managed projects, the stages will be clearly defined.

6.2.2   Sub-systems as miniature projects

The strength of modelling the system of producing design information lies in its applicability at a variety of levels. It is important to acknowledge that each sub-system within the building process is a procurement process in its own right. For example, the purchase and installation of lifts is a process which can be subjected to the same analysis as the analysis of the processes in the procurement of a building. It is therefore clear (on well-managed projects) that what is true at the detailed level of the procurement of a lift should also be true at the more general level of the procurement of a building. The important thing is that people who are procuring things use a similar process at all the different levels in the hierarchy. For example, when a bid package is let, what should happen within that part should be a model that is based on the foregoing analysis. A significant feature of this view is a point that seems obscured in many 'fast-track' projects. There is a clearly perceived level of overlap in such a project. An assumption often goes with this that the overlapping of design with production is an opportunity to delay the detailed design decisions. This should never be the case. Each package is a miniature project in its own right and needs to be bought with as full documentation as possible. This means in a similar way to the view embodied in a fixed price 'JCT-type' of contract – i.e. a full and complete set of working documentation. This is an important and often misunderstood fact in the UK construction industry.

6.2.3 Decisions

Not all decisions will be taken by the client of the building process; many are taken by the client for a particular package. In consequence, the level of sub-system needs to be clear in order to determine who has the responsibility for particular decisions.

In addition, there are various influences outside this decision-making process which might detract from the idealized model. When the concept design is completed, there are decisions to be taken by outside bodies such as the planning authorities, the Royal Fine Arts Commission, and so on (Chapter 3). Such decisions introduce more variations around the basic definitions of decision points. These external processes can have a significant impact on the final cost plan. They can also significantly affect the durations of the various stages, and compromise efforts to make the management of the process more effective.

6.3 PATTERNS OF INVOLVEMENT

The important thing about the stages described above is that different people have differing levels of involvement with the project at each stage. This is contrary to the popularly held view that contributors to a project (including the client) have a certain level of involvement which ought to remain static throughout the life of the project. This section deals with the changing levels of involvement of the central contributors to the project.

6.3.1   The client's involvement

Many people believe that the client should have a steady and high level of involvement throughout the project. Of course, the client needs to remain involved during the life of the project. However, as professional consultants are appointed and responsibility is delegated to them, so the client should expect a reduced frequency of contact with the project. The client's involvement is therefore at its highest during the **brief stage**, and it should then reduce during the **concept**, **design** and **engineering stages**. During the construction stage, as the client heads towards takeover, so involvement with the *building itself* should again increase. But during this stage, the client's involvement with the *construction process* (and therefore with the construction industry) should demonstrate a steady decline to zero.

The changing level of the client's involvement is shown in Fig. 6.1. Clearly, this is an idealized picture which assumes that nothing is wrong with what is being produced! In practice, when things go wrong, the level of client's involvement obviously increases in direct proportion to the scale of the problems.

An important feature of this curve is that it describes the client's involvement with the process of construction. It does not attempt to describe the client's involvement with the building, which of course would be a very different curve. It is also important to point out that perhaps if different types of building were considered for different types of clients, then different curves would result. This particular curve refers to commercial office buildings.

The value of this diagram is that it provides a device with which to explain certain observations. There can be much debate about where the line falls exactly, but this debate is precisely the kind of thing that tends *not* to happen on poorly managed projects. It would be most useful for a construction manager to ask the client at the very beginning of the project: 'What type of curve would you like to see for your particular project?' By making this sort of thing explicit, many problems that seem inherent in the construction process, and therefore many construction disputes, may be predicted and possibly overcome before they create too much havoc.

6.3.2   The architect's involvement

The next curve in this series (Fig. 6.2) demonstrates typically a JCT type of contract where the architect leads the concept development stage after helping the client to develop a brief. This shows how the architect's role relieves the client of a certain amount of involvement.

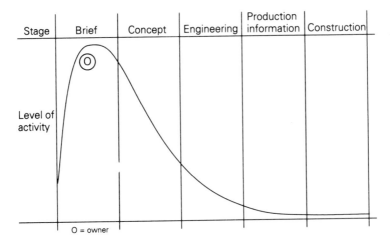

Fig. 6.1   Owner's involvement with construction process.

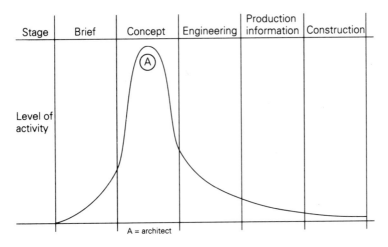

Fig. 6.2   Architect's involvement with construction process.

6.3.3   The engineers' involvement

By 'engineering' is meant structural engineering, services engineering, and so forth. As we have mentioned in the previous section, the work that these professionals do to the project is not usually termed engineering in the UK. These people become introduced to the project during the concept development stage, and as the project moves into the engineering stage, so their involvement increases. The differing levels of involvement are not absolute, but rather relative levels, intended simply to show where the focus of activity (i.e. the deployment of resources) lies.

6.3.4   Specialists' involvement

The next stage in the process requires the specialists or the trade contractors to produce the documentation required for the fabrication of the building. Their involvement increases during the engineering stage and reaches a peak when they are producing working drawings. This is shown in Fig. 6.4.

This combination of curves up to this point represents an idealized and greatly simplified model of what happens in the building process. For this to happen, a fairly rigid sequential approach needs to be adopted on the project. For example, no engineer should start to do much detailed work on the job until the designer has finished the concept development. To achieve this demands a very strong client who can take plans away from an architect and stop him or her from designing any further at a particular time. The problem of architects and other designers wishing to continue to design to the greatest level of detail that they can achieve seems almost universal. There is always a need to take the plans away from a designer at a specific time, so that the engineering detail can be done by engineers. Similarly, towards the end of the engineering stage the specialists and trade contractors need to be given the information at a particular time. This enables them to produce their parts of the documentation packages, so the process can continue in a regular manner.

6.3.5   The contractor's involvement

The curve that describes the contractor's involvement under general contracting arrangements seems like a very sharp burst of involvement during the construction stage. This indicates the type of involvement in the UK traditional general contracting model. Here the contractor does not become involved with the process of construction procurement until after the contract is won. This is shown in Fig. 6.5, which demonstrates the extent of the contractor's exclusion from all but the most detailed

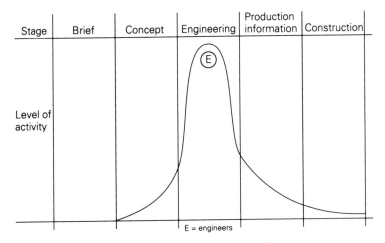

Fig. 6.3 Engineer's involvement with construction process.

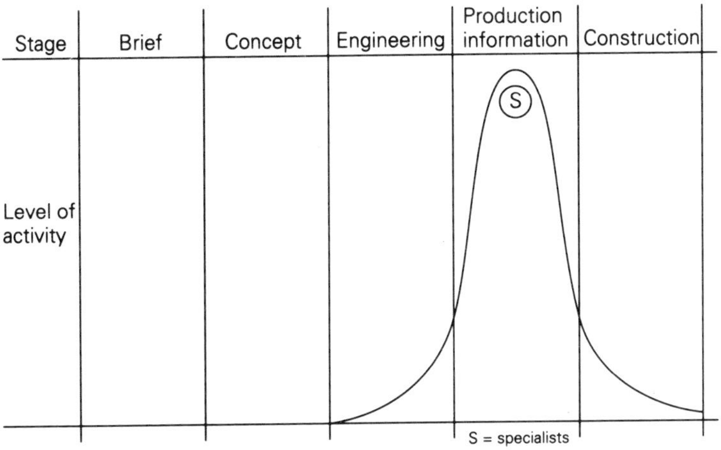

Fig. 6.4 Specialist's involvement with construction process.

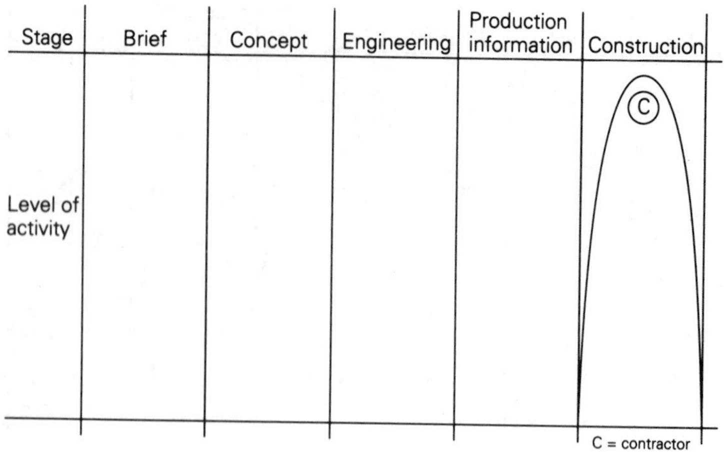

Stage	Brief	Concept	Engineering	Production information	Construction
Level of activity					

C = contractor

Fig. 6.5 General contractor's involvement with construction process.

decisions. If the contractor is to play a professional role in this process, then an earlier involvement is needed. Combining all the preceding five curves on to one chart results in Fig. 6.6.

One of the most important features of this diagram is the overlap between the curves. This coincidence of responsibility is one of the major causes of disputes in construction projects. The fact that at any one point in the process there are several professions interacting is one of the greatest causes of concern in the area of construction contracts. One of the fundamental principles of the English law of contract is 'privity of contract'. This means that each contract is between only two of the individuals in the process. Usually each of the consultants and specialists will have a separate contract with the client. The harmonization of these contracts has already been discussed in Chapter 3. Figure 6.6 shows why this problem is so difficult to solve in contractual, as well as organizational, terms.

Before examining the patterns of involvement under alternative procurement systems, a further refinement should be added to Fig. 6.6.

6.3.6 Wheel of dominance

The idea that there is one natural project leader throughout the life of the project has much to commend it and is common throughout the literature on construction project management; however, in practice, the situation is different. It has become clear that different people dominate the process at different stages in the life of the project. There is a triple

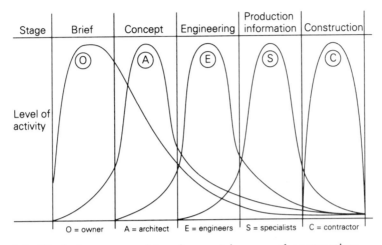

Fig. 6.6 Typical patterns of involvement in general contracting.

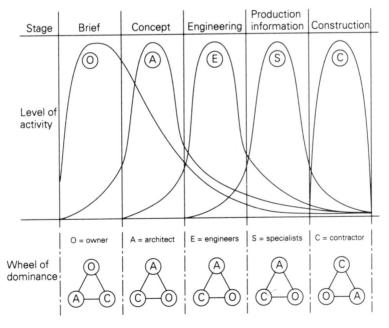

Fig. 6.7 General contracting.

relationship consisting of the client, the archited and the contractor or manager. The device used to indicate this is the 'wheel of dominance' shown at the bottom of Fig. 6.7, which indicates who is leading the project at each stage.

Considering general contracting as an example, then clearly the client is the person who dominates and leads the briefing process. Once this is concluded and the scheme moves into concept development, the architect, who has teased out the brief from the client, becomes the dominating influence. In theory, it is the architect who is the arbiter of all decisions at this point. Therefore, if there is any conflict between consultants or conflict between consultant and the client, it should be the architect who decides the issue. It is the architect who is providing the conceptual scheme, and aesthetic considerations should dominate at this point in the project. This shows that the tripartite wheel of dominance has turned.

In the subsequent stages the situation remains the same until the construction stage. At this point, the wheel turns again and it is the contractor who becomes the dominant partner of the tripartite relationship.

If the **construction management** procurement method is compared with this situation, as in Fig. 6.8, it can be seen that the first turn of the wheel happens at a much earlier stage in the project. It is debatable whether the manager begins to dominate immediately or whether the architect dominates during the concept stage. This is a matter to be decided from project to project, depending upon the circumstances. Whatever, this procurement system involves the manager in running the project completely from the time of first appointment, and it allows a complete separation of architectural and management roles.

Clearly, the involvement of the contractor in construction management procurement is very different. Not only is the contractor appointed at a much earlier stage, but his or her involvement does not consist of being contracted to undertake the construction work. The substitution of the word *manager* for *contractor* reflects the fact that, in the construction management model, the construction manager is acting as a professional manager. This also implies the executive nature of the role on the project; it therefore means that the person or organization concerned does not undertake any of the contract work. The actual work for the project is done by the specialists and trade contractors under the guidance and supervision of the manager.

By contrast with the preceding two scenarios, the English **management contracting** system (Fig. 6.9) demonstrates the wheel turning at a point mid-way between the previous two examples.

The wheel of dominance is a very useful device that describes more or less the type of leadership patterns that can be observed in practice. It is

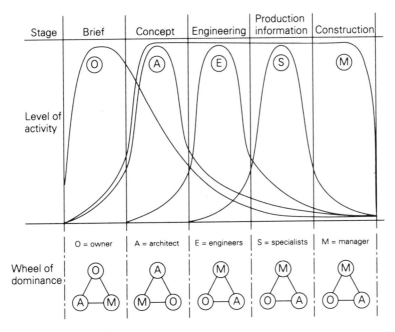

Fig. 6.8 Construction management.

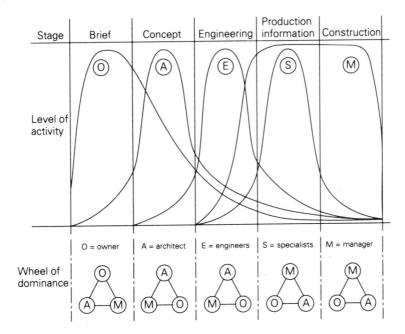

Fig. 6.9 Management contracting.

a device that reveals as pointless the constant arguments about which profession should be the project leader. Claims are often put forward that chartered architects, chartered engineers, chartered quantity surveyors or chartered builders are uniquely qualified to be project managers. Indeed, there is even a project management institute which argues for a new emerging profession of project management.

While these suggestions are sometimes useful, there is clearly far more to it than this. It is essential that the procurement system can take account of the conflicting requirements of each of these power groupings. It must be sufficiently flexible to allow the different demands of dominance at different stages in the process. It is interesting that the practice in the USA is for this wheel to turn at a much earlier stage than we would expect in the UK. Indeed, in the ideal construction management model, at a theoretical level, we would expect this wheel to turn at the very beginning and for the construction manager to remain dominant throughout the project. Clearly, however, this would not always be the case in practice.

6.4   COMMUNICATION PATTERNS

The foregoing analysis begs the question of communication. It introduces a problem about the responsibilities of the specialists and trade contractors. There is clearly a problem between *their* design responsibility and the design responsibilities of the engineers and the architects. Although the specialist is under the authority of the managing contractor, information must move between specialists and designers. The management of this communication is critical, and frequently the cause of disputes regarding liability for design.

What tends to happen in the UK is that, because the organizational structure has evolved over a long period, it is predominantly dictated by institutional roles that have developed over the years. Because it is familiar, and because there are a lot of expectations about what each team member is going to be doing, the informal organization falls into place very easily, and the formal organization has evolved to fit it. Institutional conditions of engagement reinforce this familiarity. On straightforward projects it is like a well-oiled machine. Each member of the team knows who to ask for a particular piece of information or a decision. Everyone knows his or her role, and the team can function according to tried and tested management patterns.

However, when a different procurement system is superimposed on to this pattern, there will be a mismatch between the *expected* communication channels and the *required* communication channels. This is reflected in a mismatch between the *formal* and the *informal* organizational structures.

Communication patterns do not acknowledge the differences between formal organization structures and informal organization structures. The specialists are under the authority of the managing contractor. People anywhere in the process begin to create communication routes wherever they feel they are necessary. These are informal and identify very strongly with an informal organizational structure. The informal communications take place at all levels and are very difficult to co-ordinate. To exercise the formal structure, and achieve effective co-ordination, whenever agreement is reached, letters or requests for confirmation should be sent via the formal organization. In other words, every design decision taken by a specialist contractor should be channelled through the person who is managing the process, in order to achieve co-ordination. This should happen even where the specialist has entered into direct discussions with his or her counterpart in the architect's organization. In this way, a clear distinction can be drawn between formal organization structure and informal organizational structure. It is rare to find such a distinction in the UK, confusion therefore follows. The inevitable result of this confusion is that responsibility for design decisions becomes lost. Liability is then a very difficult thing to establish.

7

Liability for defective design

Traditional building procurement systems draw a strict dividing line between the functions of design and construction. **Design**, which includes not only the broad concept of the building, but also matters of considerable detail, is the responsibility of the employer's design team. This normally consists of an architect, backed up where necessary by specialists such as structural engineers. **Construction** is the responsibility of the contractor, whose obligation is simply to construct in strict accordance with the contract documents provided. Under such a procurement system, it is naturally important to decide whether any defect in the finished building is the result of a design fault, or whether it arises out of bad construction, since this will determine who is to be legally responsible for the defect.

Of course, not all procurement methods are of this traditional kind. **Design and build** and **package deal** contracts (dealt with in Chapter 19) are well-established arrangements under which legal responsibility for both design and construction lies with the same party. In this situation, the *nature* of a defect in the finished building may be less important. Even here, however, it cannot be completely ignored for reasons which will appear below.

In dealing with liability arising out of defective design, we must consider, first, how the law actually defines design obligations; and second, which participants in the construction process may be liable in respect of design faults.

7.1 DESIGN DUTIES IN LAW

Under this heading, we look at some of the factors which a court will take into account in deciding whether or not a designer is in breach of legal obligations. We are not concerned at this stage with detailed questions of how those obligations arise or to whom they are owed.

7.1.1 Standard of liability

From a legal point of view, perhaps the most interesting question concerning a designer's duty is whether it is limited to an obligation to use reasonable care and skill, or whether it goes beyond this to a *guarantee* that the design will be fit for its purpose. If the former is correct, it means in effect that a designer will only be liable if 'professional negligence' can be proved. The latter interpretation, on the other hand, would impose a type of liability equivalent to that of a seller or other supplier of goods.

Apart from its legal interest, this question also has practical implications which are of critical importance. As we shall see, the courts have made it clear that a guarantee of 'fitness for intended purpose' will fairly readily be implied into a design and build or package deal contract. Under such a contract, then, the main contractor will be strictly liable to the client for any defect resulting from an error of design. Now if as is frequently the case the actual design has not been carried out 'in house' by the main contractor, but has been sub-contracted to either an architect or a specialist sub-contractor, the main contractor will seek to pass liability down the line to the actual designer. This, of course, can only be done if the designer's liability on the sub-contract is at the same level as the contractor's liability on the main contract.

An excellent illustration of the problem, and the strongest authority for subjecting a designer to strict liability, is the case of *Greaves* v. *Baynham Meikle*.[1] The plaintiffs there were employed under a package deal contract to construct a warehouse, the first floor of which was to be used for the storage of oil drums, stacked and moved by fork-lift trucks. The plaintiffs sub-contracted the design of this warehouse to the defendants, a firm of consultant structural engineers, who knew precisely the purpose of the finished building. The defendants' design did not make sufficient allowance for vibrations from the fork-lift trucks; as a result, the floor cracked and became dangerous, and the plaintiffs became liable to the clients for the cost of replacement. The plaintiffs accordingly sued the defendants to recover this cost, claiming that it was an implied term of their sub-contract that the design would be fit for its intended purpose.

It was held by the Court of Appeal that, on these facts, the defendants had been guilty of negligence and were accordingly liable. However, the importance of the case for present purposes lies in the court's ruling that even if there had not been negligence, the defendants would still have been liable for the failure of their design. This was because, while it could not be assumed that *every* designer would be taken to warrant the fitness of his or her design (i.e. as a term implied by law into every design contract), such a term could be implied into *this* contract as a matter of fact. The defendants had always regarded their brief as being the design of a warehouse for a particular purpose, and could be taken to have guaranteed that it would be fit for that purpose when completed.

Notwithstanding this decision, it must be recognized that the traditional legal position favours liability on the part of a 'pure' designer only where there is negligence, a position reaffirmed by the Court of Appeal in *Hawkins* v. *Chrysler*.[2] The first defendants there, having accepted liability to one of their employees who was injured when he slipped in a wet shower-room, claimed against the architects who had designed, specified and supervised the installation of the showers. The Court of Appeal held that there was no reason on these facts to imply any warranty other than that the designers would use reasonable care and skill; there was no warranty that the materials selected would be fit for their intended purpose. While recognizing that this might create an anomalous distinction between a pure designer and a designer/builder, the Court of Appeal did not feel justified in raising 'professional liability' to a new level.

As we have mentioned, this question of the standard of design liability becomes important partly because of the law's readiness to impose strict liability in design and build contracts. This readiness was shown in *Viking Grain Storage* v. *T.H. White*,[3] which concerned a defective grain storage and drying installation designed and erected by the defendants. It was also shown, though less conclusively, by the House of Lords in *IBA* v. *EMI & BICC*.[4] The contract in that case was for the design and erection of a 1250 ft high television mast at Emley Moor, Yorkshire. This was let to EMI as main contractors, and they sub-contracted the work to BICC on terms which were virtually identical. The mast, which was of a novel cylindrical design, collapsed due to vortex shedding (induced by wind) and asymmetric ice loading. It was held by the House of Lords that, at the very least, EMI must be taken to have warranted that BICC's design would not be negligent. Since it *was* negligent, EMI were liable to the clients and BICC were, in turn, liable to EMI. As a result of this finding of negligence, it was unnecessary to decide whether there would have been any strict liability for the defective design. However, their lordships stated that there probably *would* have been such liability.

The implication of a strict 'fitness for the purpose' obligation into design and build contracts will not, it appears, be negatived by the mere fact that the actual design is carried out by a sub-contractor nominated by the employer. However, all the circumstances of the case must be examined. Where it is clear that the employer has placed no reliance whatsoever on the main contractor in respect of design, there will be no implied term. This occurred in the Irish case of *Norta Wallpapers* v. *Sisk*,[5] in which the roof of a factory was supplied and erected by a specialist sub-contractor nominated by the employer. Since the main contractor in this case had no option but to accept this sub-contractor *and to adopt his design*, it was held that no warranty of fitness for the purpose could be implied into the main contract. (In *IBA* v. *EMI*, by contrast, the main contractors were not bound to accept any particular design produced by the nominated sub-contractors.)

Before leaving the 'fitness for purpose or negligence' issue, three other points are worth making. First, while it may indeed be easy for a court to imply the higher standard of obligation into a package deal contract, this cannot override any contrary *express* terms. In this connection, it should be noted that both the JCT Standard Form of Building Contract with Contractor's Design 1981 and the JCT Contractor's Designed Portion Supplement 1981 make it clear that the main contractor's liability goes no further than that which would be incurred by 'an architect or...other appropriate professional designer holding himself out as competent to take on work for such design'. Thus, where these forms of contract are chosen, the contractor's duty is merely to use reasonable care and skill and does not extend to a guarantee of 'fitness for purpose'. The ACA Form of Contract clause 3.1, by contrast, is one under which 'fitness for purpose' *would* be guaranteed.

The second point arises out of the increasingly common practice whereby nominated sub-contractors design their own work. If the main contract is of the design and build type, then the legal situation is as outlined above. However, where the main contract is of a conventional 'build only' type, it is highly unlikely that a court would hold the main contractor responsible for any defect resulting from the nominated sub-contractor's design. In view of this possibility, it is of course most important for the employer, or the employer's professional advisers, to ensure that the sub-contractor undertakes direct responsibility for his or her design, for example, by entering into a collateral agreement.

The third and last point concerns the limitations of professional indemnity insurance. Many of the policies held by architects and other specialist designers do not cover any form of liability stricter than negligence, so that liability under an implied warranty could well be left unprotected. Further, many contractors' liability insurance policies do not cover the 'design' element at all! It is, of course, vital that such matters be checked thoroughly at the start of a project.

7.1.2 Duration of liability

A designer, such as an architect, is often involved in superintending the process of construction. Where this is so, it is clear that the designer's responsibility in respect of that design does not end when the contractor receives the necessary documentation and begins to build what has been designed. The architect remains under a continuing obligation to see that the design will work.[6] As to the precise duration of this obligation, it undoubtedly lasts until the date of practical completion, almost certainly throughout any defects liability period, and probably until the issue of the final certificate.[7] However, a worrying suggestion by a trial judge to the effect that consulting engineers remain under a duty *after completion* to check and recheck their design in the light of new knowledge, and to inform their clients if new sources of danger come to light, has been unanimously rejected by the Court of Appeal.[8]

7.1.3 Techniques and materials

One of the most important aspects of *design* is the selection and specification of materials. In this, as in all other aspects, the designer is required to exercise reasonable care and skill. It should be appreciated that where an architect specifies materials, there will be no implied warranty from the contractor that the materials used will be fit for their purpose (although the contractor's implied warranty as to the 'quality' of the materials will normally be unaffected). It is therefore important for the architect to take such steps as are possible (e.g. testing or examination of other sites) to ensure the suitability of any new product to be specified. It would also be sensible to obtain, wherever possible, some collateral warranty from the supplier as to the product's performance.

As with new materials, so with new techniques. The standard of care demanded of a designer is judged in the light of professional knowledge at the relevant time, what is called the 'state of the art'. However, this does not mean that a designer may simply leap into the unknown without any legal responsibility. Indeed, the very fact that there *is* no general experience and expertise to draw on in relation to a novel form of design may require the taking of *extra* precautions. As has been said in the House of Lords:[9]

> The project may be alluring. But the risks of injury to those engaged in it, or to others, or to both, may be so manifest and substantial and their elimination may be so difficult to ensure with reasonable certainty that the only proper course is to abandon the project altogether...Circumstances have at times arisen in which it is plain commonsense and any other decision foolhardy. The law requires even pioneers to be prudent.

7.1.4 Compliance with statutory requirements

The proper carrying out of a design function clearly includes the task of seeing that the designed works can be carried out lawfully. This means that the works will not contravene Building Regulations, planning law or other relevant legal requirements. In this respect, as with other aspects of design, the law draws a distinction between someone who merely designs and someone who operates under a design and build contract. A mere designer, it appears, impliedly undertakes only to use professional skill and reasonable care, and does not warrant that the design will not contravene any relevant legal principle. Thus, where an architect-designed building failed to qualify for the office development permit which the client wanted, the architect none the less avoided responsibility. The legal rules governing the matter were complicated, and the architect's advice, though wrong, was of a kind which a reasonably competent architect might give.[10]

By contrast, a contractor under a design and build contract will be *strictly* liable to the client for any breach of the Building Regulations. This point was established in *Newham LBC* v. *Taylor Woodrow*,[11] a case which arose out of the collapse of a block of flats at Ronan Point in London.

Responsibility for a building which contravenes the law will usually fall in the final analysis upon the designer rather than the builder, at least where a traditional form of contract is used. Under JCT 80 clause 6.1.1, for example, the contractor is made *generally* responsible for ensuring that all statutory rules are complied with. However, a contractor who has merely worked in accordance with the contract drawings or bills is protected from liability by clause 6.1.5. This protection is subject to the proviso that, upon discovering any discrepancy between these documents and the legal requirements, the contractor immediately notifies the contract administrator.

Not surprisingly, the JCT Standard Form of Building Contract with Contractor's Design 1981 gives no such protection. Clause 6 of that contract provides that the contractor must bear any cost involved in making the work comply with the law. This is so even where it is the Employer's Requirements which are at fault, unless the contract specifically states that these are in accordance with the law.

Quite apart from the designer's potential liability to the client for breach of contract, there is the possibility that defective design may lead to *personal* liability for breach of Building Regulations. This matter is dealt with later in this chapter.

7.2   LEGAL RESPONSIBILITY FOR DESIGN

7.2.1   Liability in contract

Whether a person can be liable for breach of contract in respect of a design fault is, in theory at least, a simple one to answer. It depends upon the terms, express and implied, of the contract under which the design function has been carried out. However, as we shall see, the application of this straightforward principle is not always obvious.

7.2.2   Architect

The overall responsibility for the design of the project will usually be borne by the architect, where one is involved. Indeed, the basic rule is that the architect cannot delegate *any* part of the design work. Such delegation, without authority, will render the architect personally responsible for any defects in the design which arise out of negligence.

It was on this basis that liability was imposed upon an architect in *Moresk Cleaners* v. *Hicks*.[12] The plaintiffs in that case, who wanted an extension to their laundry, employed the defendant architect for the project, which involved designing a reinforced concrete structure on a sloping site. Feeling that this was beyond his competence, the architect gave the job to a contractor on a design and build basis. When the design proved defective, the architect argued that either he had implied authority to delegate specialist design tasks, or he had acted merely as the employer's agent in employing the contractor. However, it was held that the architect was liable in respect of the design, which he had been wrong to delegate. The judge stated that, an architect who finds that part of a design job is too difficult, has there possible courses of action:

- to refuse the commission altogether;
- to persuade the employer to employ a specialist for that part of the work;
- to employ and pay for a specialist *personally*, knowing that any liability for defective design can then be passed along the chain of contracts.

Notwithstanding the basic principle which was applied in *Moresk*, the complexity of modern construction technology has led to an increased dependence on specialists, both at the design and construction stages of a project. As a result, authority for an architect to delegate specified parts of the design will frequently be given by the employer, and it may even be implied from the circumstances of the case. In *Merton LBC* v. *Lowe*,[13] for example, an architect was held entitled to appoint a specialist subcontractor who specialized in the use of a certain proprietary ceiling.

In recommending the appointment of a particular specialist (or for that matter, a particular contractor), architects owe their clients the usual duty to use reasonable care and professional skill. They will not be *automatically* responsible for the defaults of the people they recommend. But if their recommendations are negligent, they may become liable for their clients' losses. In *Pratt* v. *George J. Hill Associates*,[14] for instance, a contractor who was strongly recommended by the defendant architects proved to be highly unsuitable. He became insolvent leaving a trail of defective work. It was held that the defendants were liable to the client for the money which she was unable to recoup from the builder.

Even assuming that architects act reasonably in recommending a specialist, this is not the end of their duty to the client. The legal position has been summed up by the Court of Appeal as follows:[15]

> In relation to the work allotted to the expert, the architect's legal responsibility will normally be confined to directing and co-ordinating the expert's work in the whole. However...if any danger or problem arises in connection with work allotted to the expert, of which an architect of ordinary competence reasonably ought to be aware and reasonably could be expected to warn the client, despite the employment of the expert, and despite what the expert says or does about it, it is...the duty of the architect to warn the client. In such a contingency he is not entitled to rely blindly on the expert, with no mind of his own, on matters which must or should have been apparent to him.

7.2.3 Contractor

As we have already mentioned, traditional systems of construction regard design as the exclusive province of the architect, plus such specialists as are necessary. Design and build or package deal procurement systems may be different, but under normal circumstances the contractor's responsibility is merely to build in strict accordance with the designer's specification. This frequently includes a considerable measure of detail as to the quality and standards of materials and workmanship. Thus one might expect the contractor to be free from any form of responsibility for design.

This indeed does represent the basic legal position, as appears from the case of *Mowlem* v. *British Insulated Callenders Pension Trust*.[16] This concerned a contract let under JCT 63, where a performance specification in the bills of quantities purported to impose a measure of design responsibility on the contractor. It was held that this was ineffective because of clause 12(1) (now clause 2.2.1 of JCT 80), which prevents anything contained in the bills from overriding the contract conditions.

In theory, then, a contractor is not involved in design in any way which may create legal liability. However, in practice, and even under a traditional form of contract, things are not quite so clear-cut. Contractors and sub-contractors tend to take on a measure of design responsibility in the following ways:

- Where the contract documents do not give sufficient fine detail, a contractor who exercises discretion is effectively taking on a design function. This may shade into questions of 'workmanship', or it may be very small scale (e.g. a decision on how far apart to place fixing screws). Whatever, a contractor who uses initiative in such circumstances, instead of seeking an architect's instruction, will incur responsibility for any defects which ensue.
- Contractors and sub-contractors are often asked, as a project progresses, for their opinion as to the best means of overcoming a particular problem which has arisen. There can be no doubt that if such advice is given (at least if the person concerned is a specialist), a duty of care will arise.
- In some, if not all, building contracts it seems that a term will be implied requiring the contractor to warn the employer of any defects in design of which the contractor becomes aware. However, the extent of such an obligation has not yet been worked out by the courts, for instance, it is not clear whether it applies only to those defects which are *dangerous*.
- Where contractors, sub-contractors or suppliers are required to produce drawings for the architect's approval, any matters of design which are included may be a source of liability. This is despite the possibility that the architect may *also* be liable.

Apart from these hidden forms of design liability, there are of course certain situations in which a contractor specifically undertakes responsibility for the design, as well as the construction, of a building. If the parties do indeed intend their relationship to be on a design and build or package deal basis, then it should be appreciated that JCT 80 is a wholly unsuitable form of contract to use since this assumes design by an architect and has no express provisions to deal with design by the contractor. Instead an appropriate form of contract such as the JCT Standard Form of Building Contract with Contractor's Design 1981, the ACA Form of Contract or (where only *part* of the work is to be contractor designed) the JCT Contractor's Designed Portion Supplement 1981 should be adopted. However, as we have already noted, an important drawback from the point of view of an employer is that the JCT forms limit the contractor's design liability to the level of 'reasonable care and skill' – there is no warranty that the design will be fit for its intended purpose.

7.2.4 Sub-contractor

Even more common, perhaps, than cases of 'contractor's design' are cases in which part or all of the design is allotted to a specialist *as sub-*

contractor. Where the main contract is in the JCT 80 form and the specialist in question is a *nominated* sub-contractor, the following points should be borne in mind. First, in the likely event that the sub-contractor enters into a direct warranty agreement with the employer (NSC/2 or NSC/2A), this does not warrant 'fitness for purpose', but merely the exercise of reasonable care and skill. Second, whether or not there is such a direct warranty, clause 35.21 of JCT 80 provides that the main contractor shall not be responsible to the employer for anything which *would* be within it. This means that the main contractor will be liable to the employer for defects in workmanship or materials, but not in respect of the sub-contractor's design.

7.3 TORT OF NEGLIGENCE

We have already noted in Chapter 4 the substantial cutbacks in the application of the tort of negligence to defective buildings. In particular, the decisions of the House of Lords in *D. & F. Estates* v. *Church Commissioners*[17] and *Murphy* v. *Brentwood D.C.*[18] should mean that actions in tort will not now be possible unless the defects cause personal injury or physical damage to 'other property'. Further, even where this condition is satisfied, it would seem that the damages to be awarded will not go beyond what is required to repair the damaged property. Any damage to the defective property itself, or losses consequential on that damage, will be seen as 'pure financial loss' and therefore not recoverable.

The *D. & F. Estates* case was concerned with the liability of a builder, and did not deal specifically with the position of a designer. There seems no logical reason to distinguish the two, although it has been pointed out that the work of a designer could well be treated as a 'statement' rather than as an 'act'. If this is so, then a negligent designer might well be in a worse position than a negligent builder since the law of tort still permits the recovery of damages for pure financial loss where this results from negligent *advice*.[19] Whether a court will be prepared to uphold this rather arbitrary distinction remains to be seen, but it is an argument which appears bound to surface in litigation in the near future.

7.4 LIABILITY UNDER STATUTE

The extent of a designer's *contractual* obligation to ensure that the design complies with all legal requirements has already been considered. A quite separate issue concerns the extent to which a designer may be liable *in tort* for breach of the statute itself. The question is an important one because such liability would, of course, attract the tort limitation period.

Further, and even more important, it would extend beyond the client to future owners and tenants of the property, and possibly even to other third parties. Two forms of potential statutory liability merit particular consideration.

7.4.1 Building Regulations

Whether a tort action for breach of statutory duty (which would not require proof of negligence) will lie against a person whose design of a building contravenes the Building Regulations is a complex question. Those Building Regulations do not specify the persons to whom they apply, and while it would appear likely that a designer is included, there is no actual decision to this effect. The cases so far reported have confirmed only the liability of contractors and building owners.

Even if the Building Regulations *do* apply to designers, it is by no means sure that a civil action may be brought for their breach. It was certainly the opinion of Lord Wilberforce in *Anns* v. *Merton*[20] that such an action would lie, but while his suggestion has been applied in at least one subsequent case it has more commonly been rejected by the courts.

As to the future, section 38 of the *Building Act 1984* makes provision for civil liability for any 'damage' caused by a breach of regulations made under that Act. However, this is not yet in force, and even when it is, it should be noted that the Building Regulations themselves impose no higher duty than that of securing reasonable standards of health and safety. Thus the Building Regulations will not permit a claim to be made in respect of a defect in a building which is not dangerous.

7.4.2 Defective Premises Act 1972

Section 1(1) of this Act imposes a duty on any person taking on work for, or in connection with, the provision of a dwelling (including cases where the dwelling is provided by the erection or by the conversion or enlargement of a building). This duty is owed to any person to whose order the dwelling is provided. It is also owed to every person who subsequently acquires an interest, whether legal or equitable, in the dwelling.

The nature of the duty is to see that the work which has been taken on is done in a workmanlike or professional manner; that proper materials are used; and that the dwelling will be fit for habitation when completed. This provision clearly affects not only builders, but also designers.

The duty imposed by section 1(1) is not a duty of reasonable care, but rather a statutory version of the strict warranty which the common law implies into contracts to build and sell a dwelling. The benefit of this duty, which cannot be contracted out of (section 6(3)), is now extended beyond the contracting party to anyone who subsequently acquires an interest in the property.

On the face of it, this provision seems to be of great potential importance, but its practical value is severely restricted by two factors:

1. Claims under this provision are subject to a shorter limitation period than claims for negligence since they must be commenced within 6 years from when the dwelling is completed.
2. The *Defective Premises Act 1972* applies only to 'dwellings', whereas a claim for negligence at common law may be made in respect of all types of property.

A third restriction on the usefulness of the *Defective Premises Act 1972* is that it does not apply to any dwelling which is subject to an 'approved scheme' (section 2). Until recently, this was the most important restriction of all, for the scheme in question was the one administered by the National House-Building Council, which covered the vast majority of new dwellings. However, the current version of the NHBC Guarantee Scheme (known as the 'Buildmark', and in force since 1988) is not an 'approved scheme' for this purpose. As a result, house or flat purchasers can now have the benefits of the Buildmark, under which the vendor-builder undertakes to remedy defects in the first two years and the Council provides insurance against major structural defects in the next 8 years, and can also make claims under the *Defective Premises Act 1972*.

REFERENCES

1. *Greaves & Co. (Contractors) Ltd* v. *Baynham Meikle and Partners* [1975] 3 All E.R. 99.
2. *Hawkins* v. *Chrysler (UK) Ltd and Burne Associates* (1986) 38 B.L.R. 36.
3. *Viking Grain Storage Ltd* v. *T.H. White Installations Ltd* (1985) 33 B.L.R. 103.
4. *Independent Broadcasting Authority* v. *EMI Electronics Ltd and BICC Construction Ltd* (1980) 14 B.L.R. 1.
5. *Norta Wallpapers (Ireland)* v. *Sisk & Sons (Dublin)* [1978] I.R. 114.
6. *Brickfield Properties Ltd* v. *Newton* [1971] 3 All E.R. 328.
7. *Merton LBC* v. *Lowe & Another* (1981) 18 B.L.R. 130.
8. *Eckersley* v. *Binnie & Partners* (1990) 18 Con. L.R. 1.
9. *Independent Broadcasting Authority* v. *EMI Electronics Ltd and BICC Construction Ltd* (1980) 14 B.L.R. 1.
10. *BL Holdings Ltd* v. *Robert J. Wood & Partners* (1979) 12 B.L.R. 1.
11. *Newham LBC* v. *Taylor Woodrow (Anglian) Ltd* (1981) 19 B.L.R. 99.
12. *Moresk Cleaners Ltd* v. *Hicks* [1966] 2 Lloyd's Rep. 338.
13. *Merton LBC* v. *Lowe* (1981) 18 B.L.R. 130.
14. *Pratt* v. *George J. Hill Associates* (1987) 38 B.L.R. 25.

15. *Investors in Industry Ltd* v. *South Bedfordshire DC* [1986] Q.B. 1034.
16. *John Mowlem & Co. Ltd* v. *British Insulated Callenders Pension Trust Ltd* (1977) 3 Con. L.R. 64.
17. *D. & F. Estates Ltd* v. *Church Commissioners for England* [1988] 2 All E.R. 992.
18. *Murphy* v. *Brentwood DC* [1990] 2 All E.R. 908.
19. *Hedley Byrne & Co. Ltd* v. *Heller & Partners Ltd* [1964] A.C. 465.
20. *Anns* v. *Merton LBC* [1978] A.C. 728.

PART THREE ————————————

Obligations of the Contractor

8

Nature and quality of the contract work

The contractor's obligations begin with the obligation to construct the works. The nature of what is to be built, and the workmanship and quality to be utilized in building it, are fundamental issues in analysing what it is that a contractor has contracted to do.

8.1 NATURE OF THE CONTRACT WORK

The basic obligation of the contractor is to carry out and complete the **contract works**. The works are described in the contract documents, and these documents also lay down the conditions with which the contractor is to comply. Before looking at the general obligations of the contractor, therefore, it is necessary to identify the contract and to examine what precisely is meant by the phrase 'contract documents'.

8.1.1 Standard Forms of Contract

We have examined in Chapter 2 the range of Standard Forms of Contract and their origins. Where a standard form contract is to be used for a particular project, it is very important to select the one which is most appropriate. The choice will usually be made by the employer on advice from an architect or surveyor. Because of this, some building contractors would say that the choice of contract forms is academic where they are concerned since they can do very little to influence the decision about which form to use. However, a contractor who does not have a thorough knowledge of the various forms will be unable to assess the influence which the selected form of contract has on the tender figure. To tender without such knowledge would be very foolish.

A good example of the use of inappropriate forms is provided by the construction industry's resistance to the introduction of JCT 80. Since this was a development of JCT 63 – and because it is so complicated to learn one's way around a standard form contract – many professionals simply buried their heads in the sand and continued to use JCT 63 long after the publication of JCT 80. There is an annual survey undertaken by the RICS Junior Organization which analyses the extent of the use of each of the standard forms.[1] One of the most disturbing results of this survey is the extent to which JCT 63 continued to be used for a long time after it had become obsolete. In 1984, 4 years after it had been superseded, 24% of projects were let under JCT 63. Admittedly, by 1987 the situation had improved considerably, with only 7% of projects being let in this way. Even so, 7 years is a long time to have to wait for some people to finally move over to the 'new' form!

The reasons that professionals should avoid the use of JCT 63 are as follows:

1. JCT 63 contains many provisions which have been corrected or improved upon by JCT 80.
2. Unlike other JCT forms (which are current), JCT 63 is no longer considered to be a negotiated contract. Instead it will be regarded as a set of terms dictated by the employer, which means that anything in the contract which is ambiguous or difficult to interpret will be construed by the courts against the employer. What is more, it may well be treated as the employer's 'written standard terms of business' for the purposes of the *Unfair Contract Terms Act 1977*. If this is so, then certain terms of the contract can only be enforced if a court regards them as fair and reasonable.
3. Because of these problems, it is quite possible that a professional consultant who recommends to a client that JCT 63 is used instead of JCT 80 might be liable to the client for negligence!

The second point about standard forms of contract is that some people think it wise to amend the forms for particular projects, in an attempt to shift the burden of risk on to unsuspecting parties. (Chapter 2 makes it clear why this is an unsound practice from the business point of view.) In addition, if the amendments are substantial, an amended form may be treated as the employer's 'written standard terms of business', because an amended form is not arrived at by negotiation. If so, it will be subject to the same disadvantages as JCT 63 (above).

8.1.2 Contract documentation

Contract documentation is the means by which a designer's intentions are conveyed to the client, the statutory authorities, the quantity surveyor, the contractor and the sub-contractors. In addition, the other design consultants each add their own specialized information to the increasing body of documentation as the project progresses. From a management and administrative point of view, every item in this 'contract documentation' is important because it describes and records all aspects of the project. However, by no means every item comes within the more limited legal definition of **contract documents**, a special term used in construction contracts to describe those documents which define the contractor's obligations. Whichever form of contract is used, the contractor's basic undertaking is to carry out the works in accordance with these contract documents.

As to what the term 'contract documents' includes, nearly all the forms identify the articles of agreement, the conditions of contract, the appendix, the drawings and the bills as key contract documents. However, there are differences between the forms when it comes to such items as programmes, specifications, and the like. *programmes, specifications*

The various elements of documentation will be examined briefly in isolation from each other, before looking at how they relate to each other and how the conditions of contract integrate them.

Articles of Agreement

The Articles of Agreement record in general terms what it is that the parties have agreed to do. They identify the parties to the contract, what is to be built (the contractor's obligation) and what is to be paid (the employer's obligation). They tie these obligations to the conditions and to the other contract documents.

In defining the contractor's obligation, the articles do not descend to any great detail, but merely state, in a section starting with the word 'Whereas', that 'the employer is desirous' of having the briefly described works carried out. Some standard forms also record that tenders have been accepted, that drawings have been prepared, and so on. This section is called the 'Recitals' (although only JCT 80 specifically gives it this name). The purpose of the Recitals is to describe the background to and the purpose of the contract. They help to provide a basis for interpretation of the detailed provisions contained in the contract clauses.

Conditions of Contract

The Conditions of Contract are the highly detailed clauses which follow on from the Articles of Agreement. It has become common practice recently for standard forms to provide a table of contents to help in finding the various clauses. Until 1980 this was a rare occurrence! The

ICE 6 and GC/Works/1 also have indexes which go further in helping people to find their way around the conditions.

The purpose of the conditions is to amplify and explain the basic obligations which the parties undertake by signing the article of agreement. The conditions also provide administrative mechanisms for ensuring that the correct procedures are observed. Effective contract clauses of this kind deal efficiently with minor breaches of contract, and therefore ensure that the contract is kept 'alive'.

As a result of the status of the conditions, certain procedures operate in a grey area which borders on the edge of 'breach of contract'. For example, the conditions which govern the issue of variations orders enable the employer to change parts of the works, even as they are being erected. Without express terms to do this, the employer would definitely be in breach of contract. However, the presence of express terms enabling variations to be made does not give the employer *carte blanche*. Any changes which go 'to the root of the contract' will still constitute a major breach of contract by the employer. This particular aspect is dealt with in more detail in Chapter 11.

Appendix

Certain facts relating to the execution of a building contract will differ from one project to another. To enable standard form contracts to be used in spite of these differences, the facts concerned can be summarized in an Appendix to the contract. Thus, JCT 80 contains two pages, and ICE 6 three pages, which should be filled in when executing the contract. GC/Works/1 achieves the same effect with a document called an 'Abstract of Particulars' which is included with the tender documentation.

It is in the Appendix that the base date, date for completion, defects liability period and amount of liquidated damages are entered. Some of the contractual conditions specify what is to happen if the relevant entry in the Appendix is left blank. Some provisions are not applicable at all unless the Appendix is completed, such as the employer's right to delay possession of the site by up to six weeks.

The contents of the Appendix are of fundamental importance in assessing the amount and duration of responsibility accepted by the parties. It is therefore essential that close attention is paid to the entries in the Appendix to the contract.

Drawings

The production of drawings is generally (although not always) the responsibility of the design team. The technical complexity of most modern buildings makes it essential that this process (including all associated information, as well as the drawings themselves) is properly planned and organized. Detailed guidance on this is available from numerous sources (Chapter 6).

As with all types of communication, clarity is essential. The aim is to transmit the information in a way that can be understood. If this is done adequately, people will have confidence in a designer's ability. On the other hand, lack of clarity in communication will not endear a designer to the client, to other consultants or to the courts!

Drawings have more than one function. These different functions are usually fulfilled by different drawings, but it is well to remind oneself of the exact nature and purpose of each particular drawing.

First, they form a model of the designers' ideas and help to rationalize and predict problems and conflicts with fabrication and with appearances. Isometrics, scheme designs and 'artistic impressions' help to fulfil this function; although there is little information on them which would enable a builder accurately to erect the proposed building, they amplify and explain the basic nature of the required finished building.

Second, drawings are the vehicle by which the designers' intentions are conveyed to the contractor. The detail design drawings contain information which shows how the separate parts of the building interact with one another. The detailed information from specialist sub-contractors and from other designers is co-ordinated and presented through such drawings.

Third, drawings form a record of what has been done. These 'as-built' drawings are essential to the building owner as a basis for future maintenance of the facility, and may not be the same drawings that were used for the purposes of fabrication.

The multiple uses which different drawings are called upon to perform, and the interaction between drawings and other types of documentation, have often been a source of problems for construction projects. A consequence of these problems was the setting up of the Co-ordinating Committee for Project Information (CCPI) which produced a set of guildelines for the production of drawings, specifications and bills of quantities. These currently represent best practice in the industry and should be essential reading for everyone concerned with the documentation of construction projects.[2]

On completion of the work, the architect or building surveyor can insist that all drawings are returned because, according to their conditions of engagement, the copyright for this information is theirs. Neither the contractor nor the client is entitled to use the information again, by constructing an identical building, without first obtaining the permission of the designer.

Schedules

Schedules are tables of information which summarize the quantities and dimensions of certain generic items, for example, windows or iron-mongery. Although they will rarely be cited as contract documents, they will often be bound up and included with the sets of drawings, as they are invaluable in summarizing detailed information. Clearly, a drawing will show all the windows in a building, but it is very useful to extract all the details of sizes and numbers on to one table. Although dimensions can be summarized in tabular form, some information is best conveyed on a dimensioned sketch such as the arrangement of opening lights in a window.

Schedules provide information to quantity surveyors, builders' buyers and others in a form which has advantages over drawings:[3] the checking of mistakes is simplified; the counting of similar items for obtaining estimates and placing orders is simplified; and if the information is set down systematically, the need for prolonged searching through a specification is avoided.

The aim of the schedule is merely to simplify the retrieval of information. It is not intended to supplant the bills of quantity, which will contain the full and final description of the work.

The information in and layout of a schedule cannot be standardized, as schedules must vary with different types of building, but they should normally be designed with the quantity surveyor in mind. With schedules, as with all documentation, one needs constantly to ask: 'Which people are going to use this?' 'What information do they need?'

Specifications

Drawings provide information about the shape, appearance and location of the various components which have to be assembled, but they convey little about the methods to be used, the quality of finishes and the workmanship to be employed. Assuming that such things are to be specifically controlled by the contract, rather than relying on the terms which would be implied at common law, this is a matter for the specification. This has been defined by the Co-ordinating Committee for Project Information as 'the document, or part of a document...[which defines] the materials and products to be used, the standard of work required, any performance requirements and the conditions under which the work is to be executed'.

Where bills of quantity are used for a project, information of this kind will be contained in the bills, and there will be no 'specification' in the

sense of a separate document. However, not all projects need full quantification with bills of quantity; an increasing number of projects are being
let by drawings and specification alone. Where this is done, the specification may be called upon to perform an even wider role.

In order to prepare a useful and accurate specification, it is essential to
be systematic and methodical. There are a variety of choices open to the
specification writer, but the most obvious one is to use the CCPI code of
procedure for writing a project specification.[4]

Bills of quantity

The purpose of bills of quantity, and their status, may vary under different standard form contracts. However, when used, they are almost invariably specified as a contract document.

In the JCT 80 form (clause 14.1) they define the quality and the
quantity of work to be done by the contractor. Under the IFC 84 form, if
bills are used, then their status is the same as under JCT 80. However,
there are alternative forms of documentation which can be used under
IFC 84 (clauses 1.3 and 1.5), so that bills of quantity may not exist in
some projects.

In the ICE 6 form the bills have a more limited role. Quality is
required by clause 36 to be of the kinds described in the contract,
meaning the whole combined documentation. In any event, this is subject
in all cases to such tests as the engineer may require, such tests to be at
the contractor's expense. The quantity of work described in the bills is
only an estimate of what the contractor will have to do to fulfil the
obligations under the contract (clause 55). The contractor is obliged to
undertake as much work as is necessary, and this obligation is not
affected by anything in the bills.

The contracts also govern the preparation of the bills. Clause 2.2.2 of
JCT 80 dictates that the bills must be prepared in accordance with the
RICS Standard Method of Measurement (SMM 7), and IFC 84 form
(clause 1.5) lays down a similar requirement for those projects where bills
of quantity are prepared. Under ICE 6 clause 57, it is the Civil Engineering Standard Method of Measurement (CESMM) which must be used.
Because the bills have such contractual significance, especially under the
JCT series of contracts, it is often necessary to be fully cognizant of what
the relevant Standard Method of Measurement contains. Indeed, JCT 80
explicitly requires that any departure from the principles of SMM 7 must
be expressed quite categorically in the bills, in terms of both the nature of
the change and which items are affected.

The bill of quantities originated as a tendering document; indeed,
engineering contracts still retain this emphasis. In the JCT contracts the

bills of quantity have an increasingly important role to play in the valuation of variations and interim certificates, and in the control of the works. In addition, various other categories of information are often gleaned from the bills, such as locational identification of work and formation of a basis for cost planning. Not surprisingly, bills of quantity are increasingly being seen as hopelessly inadequate for all of these conflicting needs. There are many ways of choosing a contractor, and many ways of fixing a price for the work to be undertaken. To use the bill as the sole vehicle for both these purposes is an oversimplification that can lead to many problems.[5]

The bills consist of preliminaries, preambles and measured works. There is a wide variation in the application of these terms, and it is useful to clarify their meaning.

The **preliminaries** contain the definition of the scope of the works. In the new Common Arrangement of Work Sections,[6] section A is given over to defining the preliminaries and general conditions. It includes, among other things, particulars of the project, lists of drawings, description of the site, scope of the work, details of documentation and management arrangements.

The **preambles** used to be a separate description of the materials and workmanship to be employed in assembling the building, and this was known as the 'specification' section of the bill. In the common arrangement, this is section A33 of the work sections and, as a result, it is likely that 'preambles' will disappear from the vocabulary of building contracts.

The **measured works** are the detailed quantification of the works. This section should be presented according to the rules dictated in the contract.

Two further terms worthy of mention are prime cost and provisional sums. These terms are antiquated and their origins are now obscure, but their use is prevalent and seems likely to continue:

Prime cost (PC) sums are used for works under the building contract which are to be carried out under the direction of the main contractor by certain other persons, namely nominated sub-contractors, nominated suppliers and statutory authorities. The nominated sub-contractors will usually have been selected prior to the selection of the main contractor. Since the contractor has no control over the pricing of this work, an amount of money is simply included in the bills, to which the contractor can add a price for attendance and profit.

Provisional sums are used for work which has not been finalized, or for costs which are unknown, at the time the bills are prepared. They may simply be contingency sums, and their presence does not necessarily imply any obligation on the part of the employer to spend them. In effect, they are simply a method for the employer to express part of the budget for the project. The contract administrator must issue instructions to spend these sums.

The most useful definition of a provisional sum to be found in the major contracts is that in clause 58 of ICE 6. JCT 80 (by amendment 7) contains a definition in clause 1.3 which effectively incorporates the definition found in SMM 7. This, however, only clarifies the status of types of provisional sum; it does not define the concept itself.

Certificates

There are several types of certificate in building contracts. They fall into two main categories: those which certify the quantity of work done to date, on which payment is calculated; and those which certify that an event has taken place. The former are called **interim certificates**, and their use is one of the most distinctive features of building contracts as compared with other contracts.

Interim certificates are used in the great majority of building contracts, because it is not intended that the contractor should have to finance the whole of the building work. The contractor will be paid for the amount of work done at regular periods, usually one month. When each payment is made, a small percentage of the money due to the contractor (called the **retention**) is kept back, and this is released when the work is completed. It is also possible for other amounts of money to be withheld, under a right known as **set-off**, for delay or defective work. The issues of retention and set-off, which are of great practical importance, are dealt with in Chapter 11.

The second category of certificates consists of those which record an event (or non-event). They vary from one form of contract to another, but basically they are:

1. Certificate of practical completion;
2. Certificate of final completion;
3. Certificate of non-completion.

The full effect of these certificates is covered in Chapter 14.

Other documents

Additional contract information is contained in **instructions**, which contain information more detailed than that found in the tender documents. There are also other post-contractual documents (e.g. descriptive schedules, further drawings and setting-out information), and these are described as being 'necessary' or 'required' to execute the work. Clause

5.3.2 makes it clear that this additional information is to impose nothing 'extra' on the contractor. If the contract administrator wishes to impose changes when issuing these instructions, then a variation order must be issued to cover the changes.

JCT 80, ICE 6 and GC/Works/1 all make it incumbent upon the contractor to provide a **programme of work**. Although certain dates in the *contract* are legally binding, the programme is not. All the contracts make it clear that, even though the contractor must provide a programme soon after being awarded the contract, there can be no extra obligations imposed by it. JCT 80 makes it clear that the employer can strike out the requirement for a programme, but this practice is not recommended. The programme is essential as a management control mechanism. In order for it to be effective in this role, it must be updated from time to time, and the contracts make this a requirement.

Interaction between documents

The relationships between the various forms of documentation are worthy of comment. These documents may have to stand on their own for certain purposes, but for the purpose of procuring the building they must interact, and this interaction must be consistent and dependable. One result of JCT 80 being widely used is that the specification is no longer a separate document in its own right because of clause 14.1, which makes the bills of quantity the vehicle for defining both quality and quantity of the work which is included in the contract sum.

Because of this clause, the specification is effectively embodied within the bills. This means that any specification notes on the drawings will have no contractual significance, unless they are incorporated into the bills either directly or by reference. This is a good illustration of the need for proper information co-ordination; it is quite valid to use specification notes on the drawings, but they must be referred to in some way in the bills.

Discrepancies in and between documents

On a construction project of any substantial size, the sheer weight of detail which is found in the contract documentation gives ample scope for discrepancies and inconsistencies. These may arise within one particular document, as where the contract bills contain two inconsistent provisions. They may also arise between two documents, as where something in the bills conflicts with something in the conditions.

The general approach of most standard form contracts to this problem is that, in the event of finding a discrepancy, the contractor should refer it to the contract administrator (JCT 80 clause 2.3; ICE 6 clause 5). The latter must then issue instructions so as to resolve the discrepancy, and if these cause delay or disruption, the contractor will be entitled to an extension of time and to compensation for loss and expense (JCT 80 clauses 25.4.5.1 and 26.2.3; ICE 6 clause 13(3)). Furthermore, if the instructions constitute a variation, the contractor will be paid at the appropriate rate for the work involved.

When called upon to resolve a discrepancy of this kind, the contract administrator should in general apply those principles of law which govern the interpretation of contracts. However, this is subject to the terms of the contract itself, and it is noticeable that these general principles are expressly modified by a number of standard form building contracts. For example, one of the common law rules is that written words prevail over typed words, and that typed words in turn prevail over printed words. That rule is based on the sensible idea that documents which are prepared for a specific job, rather than being taken 'off the shelf', are more likely to reflect the parties' true intentions. If it were to be applied to a building contract, it would mean for example that provisions in bills of quantity would override the printed conditions of contract.

This is emphatically *not* the case, at least where the main standard forms are concerned! While ICE 6 is fairly neutral, stating in clause 6 that all documents are to be taken as mutually explanatory, GC/Works/1 provides categorically in clause 2(1) that the conditions shall prevail over all other documents. Similarly, JCT 80 clause 2.2.1 states that nothing in the contract bills shall override or modify what is contained in the Articles, Conditions or Appendix. This wording does not prevent the bills from imposing *extra* obligations on the contractor. It does mean that where a particular matter is dealt with in the Conditions, any special provisions on that subject in the bills are to be ignored.

In cases dealing with similar wording in JCT 63, the courts have ruled that the clause can operate to defeat what is the clear intention of the parties as expressed in the bills. The most striking example of this is the case of *Gleeson* v. *Hillingdon*,[7] where a contract for the provision of a large number of houses gave single completion date of 24 months after the date for possession. In reality, as the preliminaries bill showed, the parties' intention was that blocks of houses were to be handed over at 3-month intervals from 12 months onwards. When the first blocks of houses were not completed after 12 months, the employer deducted liquidated damages at the contract rate, but this was held to be invalid. The contract made no provision for sectional completion, and it could not be varied by the contract bills.

The moral of this and similar cases is clear. If the parties really do intend to override or modify the printed conditions of the contract, then those conditions must themselves be formally altered to reflect this. If this is not done, the intended changes will be ineffective.

8.2 STANDARD OF WORK

The contractor's basic obligation, so far as the **standard of work** is concerned, is to comply with the terms of the contract. This includes both express terms (such as the requirement of JCT 80 clause 8 that work shall be of the standards described in the bills) and implied terms (such as the principle that all materials shall be of 'merchantable quality').

In addition, there are often provisions in the bills for work to be to the satisfaction of the contract administrator. This might seem to suggest that the contract administrator has an absolute right of rejection of such work, but JCT 80 limits this power to rejection only on reasonable grounds. Clause 2.1 states that where approval of workmanship or materials is a matter for the opinion of the contract administrator, 'such quality and standards shall be to the reasonable satisfaction of the contract administrator'.

As a result of this wording, the contract administrator only has the power to ensure that the work complies with the contract documents. In exercising this function, clause 8 of JCT 80 gives the contract administrator considerable powers to order the opening up of earlier work, so that it can be inspected and/or tested. Generally, the expense of opening up the work is borne by the contractor only if the work is proved to be unfit.

The phrase 'standard of work' in fact contains three separate, though linked, ideas, as follows.

8.2.1 Workmanship

The standard of workmanship may be defined in considerable detail by the contract, for example, by requiring it to comply with an appropriate code of practice. Under JCT 80, such a requirement would appear in the bills of quantity, and it would have contractual force by virtue of clause 8.1.2. This provides that 'all workmanship shall be of the standards described in the contract bills'. The clause goes on to state that where the bills do not set a standard, the workmanship 'shall be of a standard appropriate to the works'. This would, in any case, be implied by law since, in the absence of any express terms covering this issue, the courts will imply a term in the contract that the work will be carried out with proper skill and care – i.e. in a 'workmanlike' manner.

It is at least arguable that 'workmanship' refers only to the standard of the finished item, not to the method used to achieve that standard. If this is so, then the contract administrator has no power to control the manner of working at the time it is being carried out. However, a 1990 amendment to JCT 80 (Amendment 9) gives the contract administrator such power by inserting, as clause 8.1.3, a provision that 'all work shall be carried out in a proper and workmanlike manner'. If this is breached by the contractor, then clause 8.5 empowers the contract administrator to issue whatever instructions are necessary. Even if these constitute a variation, the contractor will not be entitled to any payment or to any extension of time.

It is important to note that the contractor is responsible not only for personally performing unsatisfactory workmanship, but also for that of any sub-contractor, either domestic or nominated.

8.2.2   Standard of materials

Clause 8.1.1 of JCT 80 states that all materials and goods shall, so far as procurable, be of the respective kinds and standards described in the contract bills. This wording allows for the eventuality that some things which were available at the time of tender may become unavailable. ICE 6, IFC 84 and GC/Works/1 all place a similar obligation upon the contractor, but none of them makes allowance for materials which may have become unprocurable.

These express obligations are backed up by an implied term (contained in the *Supply of Goods and Services Act 1982, section 4)* that all goods and materials supplied shall be of 'merchantable quality'. This well-known phrase, which is derived from the *Sale of Goods Act*, means that they are to be as free from any defects as it is reasonable to expect, given such factors as their price and the way they are described.

It has been held by the House of Lords that a contractor will be liable if materials are unmerchantable, even where those materials have been selected by the employer (e.g. by nominating a particular supplier).[8] However, the contractor will *not* be liable for defective materials where forced by the employer to obtain those materials from a supplier who, to the employer's knowledge, excludes or limits liability for defects.[9] This last principle is now expressly provided for by JCT 80 clause 36.5.

8.2.3   Suitability of materials

Even where materials are perfectly 'merchantable', in the sense of being free from defects, they may still not be fit for the purpose for which they are used. Where this is the case, it is again possible for the contractor to be liable, but the term which will be implied here is of a more limited kind. Section 4 of the *Supply of Goods and Services Act 1982* implies a term that goods shall be reasonably fit for the purpose for which they are supplied, but *only* where it is clear that the recipient is relying on the skill and judgement of the supplier. In practical terms, it is only when the contractor has the choice of materials that liability can be imposed if what is selected is unfit for its purpose. However, there will be no such implied term in respect of materials which are specified by the employer or the architect, for here there is no reliance on the contractor.

8.2.4 Suitability of the building

Quite apart from the obligation to provide suitable materials, a contractor may in some circumstances be subject to an implied term that the *building* itself, when completed, will be fit for its intended purpose. Such a term, which will normally be implied only into 'design and build' or 'package deal' contracts, is dealt with in Chapter 7.

REFERENCES

1. RICS JO (QS). Contracts in use. *Chartered Quantity Surveyor*, January 1989, pp. 24–6.
2. Gordon, A. (chairman). *Co-ordinated Project Information: Guide*. Co-ordinating Committee for Project Information, London, 1987.
3. The Aqua Group. *Pre-Contract Practice for Architects and Quantity Surveyors* (7th edn). BSP Professional Books, Oxford, 1986.
4. Gordon, A. (chairman). *Project Specification: A Code of Procedure for Building Works*. Building Project Information Committee, London, 1987.
5. Skinner, D.W.H. *The Contractor's Use of Bills of Quantities*. CIOB Occasional Paper No. 24. Chartered Institute of Building, Ascot, 1981.
6. Gordon, A. (chairman). *Common Arrangement of Work Sections for Building Works*. Building Project Information Committee, London, 1987.
7. *M.J. Gleeson (Contractors) Ltd* v. *Hillingdon London Borough* (1970) 215 E.G. 165.
8. *Young & Marten Ltd* v. *McManus Childs Ltd* [1969] 1 A.C. 454.
9. *Gloucestershire CC* v. *Richardson* [1969] 1 A.C. 480.

9

Obligations as to time

The issue of time is extremely important in building contracts. Commonly, definitions of construction project management give time, cost and quality as the primary objectives and the criteria by which projects are managed.[1] The contract conditions which cover quality we have discussed in Chapter 8. In this chapter we will concentrate on the control of time in the contract.

The scope of this subject may be seen from clause 23.1 of JCT 80, which states: 'On the Date of Possession possession of the site shall be given to the contractor who shall thereupon begin the Works, regularly and diligently proceed with the same and shall complete the same on or before the Completion Date.' This identifies the three basic issues as **commencement**, **progress** and **completion**. In fact there are also two other issues: the contractor's continuing **obligations after completion**, and the **time extension** available to the contractor when the work is delayed by certain specified causes.

9.1 COMMENCEMENT

9.1.1 Possession of the site

An employer who fails to give the contractor possession of the site, may be liable to pay damages for breach of contract.[2] This is so despite provisions in the contract for the contract administrator to postpone all or any part of the works, since it seems that such provisions may not be used to postpone the entire project.[3] However, employers are not deemed to *guarantee* possession, and will not be liable if the contractor is prevented from gaining access by some third party for whose acts they are not regarded as responsible and over whom they have no control, such as unlawful pickets.[4]

Under JCT 80, the contractor is entitled to possession of the *whole* site, even though some parts may not be needed until a later stage of the project. By contrast. ICE 6 only requires the employer to give possession of so much of the site as is required to enable the contractor to commence the works in accordance with the programme. In either case, however, what is given to the contractor must include not only the actual area to be built on, but also enough of the surrounding area to enable the work to be undertaken.

9.1.2 Date for possession

Most building contracts will name a date on which the contractor is to be given possession of the site, after which the contractor may commence the works. If possession is not given on the date specified, the employer will lose the right to recover liquidated damages from the contractor in the event of late completion.[5] ICE 6 gives a little more flexibility by providing that, if no date is specified from the outset, it is for the engineer to notify the contractor of the date for commencement of the works. This notice must be given in writing, and the date itself must be within 28 days of the award of the contract.

If the contract contains no specific commencement provision, then the contractor must be given possession at such a time as will enable him or her to complete the work by the completion date.[6] The contractor is not obliged to start work on the date for possession as such. However, a contractor who does not start reasonably quickly, may be liable for not proceeding 'regularly and diligently' (JCT 80) or 'with due expedition and without delay' (ICE 6).

9.1.3 Deferred possession

Although the contract administrator's power to order the postponement of any work cannot be used by the employer so as to justify delay in giving the contractor possession of the site, there are specific provisions in JCT 80 clause 23.1.2 and IFC 84 clause 2.2 under which the employer may defer the date for possession by up to 6 weeks. In order for this provision to apply, it must be stated in the Appendix to the contract.

9.2 PROGRESS

JCT 80 clause 23.1.1 imposes an obligation on the contractor to proceed with the works 'regularly and diligently'. Therefore, if the contractor does not make regular progress, this will constitute a breach of contract. Under JCT 80, such a breach gives the employer grounds for determination of the contract, under clause 27.1.2. Under ICE 6 clause 46, the contractor's obligation is to proceed at such a speed as will enable completion to take place at the proper time. If progress is too slow for this to be achieved, the engineer has power to order the contractor to take steps to expedite the work.

The obligation to proceed regularly and diligently is modified in JCT 80 by clause 23.2, which gives the contract administrator the power to postpone any part of the works. However, if the whole, or a substantial part, of the works is suspended continuously for more than the period set out in the Appendix to the contract, this gives grounds for determination by the contractor. Provisions which are somewhat similar, though differing in detail, are found in ICE 6 clause 40.

9.3   COMPLETION

9.3.1   Meaning

If a building contract is for the whole of the works, then it is what the law calls an 'entire' contract. This means that the builder undertakes to construct the entire building and is legally obliged to do everything necessary for the completion of the whole of the work as described. Where this is so, then the

> omission of anything indispensably necessary will make the work incomplete so as to render the price not payable, and the builder or contractor liable in damages for non-completion. It makes no difference that such indispensably necessary works are not described in the specification. . . If full particulars are not shown on the drawing, if they are impracticable or are calculated wrongly or their costs or extent underestimated in the specification, the contractor must still perform all the works necessary to perfect completion.[7]

This principle applies whether descriptions are in the bills of quantity or not, and it makes no difference if the bills form part of the contract. However, JCT 80 clause 13.1.1 seems to modify this position because it clearly places an obligation on the contractor to do only that work which is in the contract bills and no more. Any departure from that which is described in the bills is to be treated as a variation.

Although a contractor cannot be said to have totally performed the contract if a single item is missing or defective, to delay the handover of something as complex as a large building for so trivial a breach would be inconvenient and impracticable. As a result, most building contracts provide that the contractor must achieve 'practical completion', that is a state in which any work outstanding is so minimal that it will not affect the employer's use and enjoyment of the building. To take a house as an example, 'completion' implies that it will be ready for immediate occupation.

The point at which a building can be said to be 'practically complete' is a decision for the contract administrator, based on an inspection of the works and the exercise of reason. The resulting certificate means that the final instalment of payment for the work will be made. Furthermore, under JCT 80 the next interim certificate will result in the contractor receiving one-half of the 'retention money' which has been deducted from each payment. The other half will not be released until the contractor has put right any defects which appear during the 'Defects Liability Period' (see below).

9.3.2 Date for completion

A building contract need not specify a date for completion; if it does not, the contractor's obligation is to complete the works within a reasonable time. This, however, is very seldom the position, at least on a project of any appreciable size, for the client will normally need to have some degree of confidence about when to expect completion. In addition, without a specific completion date there can be no provision for 'liquidated damages', that is a fixed sum to be paid by the contractor for every day or week of delay. It is thus usual to name the date by which completion is required. In JCT 80 this is done by means of an entry in the Appendix to the contract.

9.3.3 Completion date

JCT 80 draws a distinction between the 'Date for Completion' and the 'Completion Date', both of which are defined in clause 1.3. The Date for Completion is defined as that date which is fixed and stated in the Appendix. Thus, the Date for Completion can only be that date and no other. The Completion Date, on the other hand, is defined as the Date for Completion *or* any other date fixed under either clause 25 or clause 33.1.3. This means that while the Completion Date can be changed, the Date for Completion cannot.

The practical result of this twin definition is that the contractor's obligation is to complete the building on or before the Completion Date. Thus, if an extension of time has been granted under clause 25, the obligation is to complete on or before the new date. However, even where the Completion Date is moved *forward* in time (e.g. where work has been omitted), clause 25.3.6 makes it clear that the contractor can never be obliged to complete before the original Date for Completion.

The JCT 80 approach to time may be contrasted with that of ICE 6, under which the contractor inserts the time required to carry out the work in the Appendix to the tender. The contractor's obligation is then to complete the works within the stated time (as extended under clause 44, where this is appropriate), calculated from the 'Works Commencement Date'.

9.3.4 Delay in completion

The contractor's obligation to complete the works by the completion date is, like all such obligations, backed up by legal sanctions. If, under the particular contract, time is 'of the essence', then the contractor's failure to complete on time will enable the employer to determine the contract. However, whether or not the contractor's delay has this drastic effect, it will undoubtedly give rise to a liability to pay damages for breach of contract.

As to how such damages are to be measured, it is of course perfectly possible for the contract to say nothing, and to leave the assessment of the employer's loss (including any loss of profit) to an arbitrator or a court. However, it is standard practice in building and civil engineering contracts to state in advance what the damages shall be for delay, and this is usually done by specifying a fixed sum of money to be due for every day, week or month by which the contractor fails to meet the prescribed completion date. Such damages are called 'liquidated' or 'liquidated and ascertained' damages, and they are dealt with in Chapter 22.

9.3.5 Sectional completion and partial possession

If the intention of the parties is that the contract work should be completed and handed over in phases, it is essential that the contract documents make proper provision for this. ICE 6, for instance, enables different sections to be identified in the Appendix, each with its own time for completion and its own liquidated damages. The JCT 80 Standard Form contains no such provision, but there is a Sectional Completion Supplement which makes the necessary modifications and which should always be used. Even this Supplement may not be sufficient for projects in which the starting date of one section is dependent upon completion of a previous section. In such circumstances, if it is intended that an extension of time on phase 1 should delay the start of phase 2, then the contract must be specially amended to provide for this.

If appropriate contractual terms are not drafted, attempts to provide for sectional completion by listing separate phase dates in the bills of quantity will fail, since clause 2.2.1 prevents anything in the bills from overriding or modifying what is in the conditions.[8] Nor, it seems, can a similar effect be achieved by expressing liquidated damages as '£x per week for each uncompleted house', since this is inconsistent with other provisions of the contract.[9]

If there is no provision in the contract for the works to be completed and handed over in sections, the contractor's right to occupy the whole of the site will continue as long as work under the contract is required to be done. However, JCT 80 clause 18 enables this right to be given up by the contractor. If the employer requests it and the contractor agrees (this must not unreasonably be refused), the employer can take possession of those parts of the works which are ready. Where this is done, the contract administrator must issue a written statement identifying the parts taken over and, for most purposes, practical completion of those parts is deemed to have occurred. It should also be noted that, under clause 23.3.2, the employer may be permitted by the contractor to use parts of the site for 'storage of his goods or otherwise', provided that this will not prejudice the insurance position. Once again, the contractor's consent is not to be unreasonably withheld.

9.4   CONTRACTOR'S OBLIGATIONS AFTER COMPLETION

There are further obligations which are imposed on the contractor after completion, notably by JCT 80 clause 17, IFC 84 clause 2.10 and ICE 6 clause 49. Under the JCT contracts, the issue of the 'Certificate of Practical Completion' marks the start of the 'Defects Liability Period', which lasts 6 months if no other period is specified in the Appendix. Any defects, shrinkages or other faults which arise during this period due to defective materials or workmanship must be put right by the contractor at his or her own expense. Further, the contractor is responsible for damage by frost which appears during this period, but only where the contract administrator certifies that the damage was actually *caused* before practical completion.

The contract administrator must issue a schedule of such defects to the contractor not later than 14 days after the end of the defects liability period, and the contractor then has a reasonable time to put them right. Once this has been done, the contract administrator will issue a 'Certificate of Completion of Making Good Defects', following which the contractor becomes entitled to the remaining part of the retention money.

In the ICE form the situation is similar, although the terminology is different. Here the issue of the 'Certificate of Substantial Completion' brings into operation the 'Defects Correction Period'. There is a similar requirement for the engineer to issue to the contractor a schedule of defects within 14 days of the end of the period. If the contractor does not

make good the defects, after being served with a schedule of def
the employer can give notice that the work must be done. If th
tor does not comply with that notice immediately, then the
can employ others to do the work and recover the expense from the
contractor.

Under the ICE conditions, the contractor's obligation goes beyond
repairing and completing those items which are a direct consequence of
the contractor's default. However, work done on other items (i.e. those
which are not due to workmanship or materials being in breach of
contract) entitles the contractor to extra payment.

It should be noted that defects liability clauses do more than simply
impose further obligations upon the contractor. Clearly, if there are
defects in the works, due to the default of the contractor, then the
contractor will be liable in damages to the employer. In order to avoid
this liability, the contractor needs access to the works to put things right.
In this way, the defects liability clause operates to the protection of the
contractor. It gives the contractor the right to repair any defects before
the employer either appoints others to do the repairs at the contractor's
expense or simply sues the contractor for breach of contract. Either of
those courses of action is likely to cost the contractor far more than
simply undertaking the work.

It is also worth noting that defects liability clauses do not act as
exclusion clauses. If a defect is not included on a schedule of defects, and
is not noticed by the contractor or contract administrator before the end
of the period, the contractor is still liable for it. Since the period has
expired, the contractor has no right to return to the site to repair the
defect, but is liable to the employer for damages.

9.5 EXTENSION OF TIME

Most building contracts contain express provisions under which the
period allowed for the contractor to undertake and complete the works
can be extended. These provisions are for delay caused by various events
which are neither the fault or the responsibility of the contractor. Such
provisions obviously benefit the contractor who will not be liable to pay
damages for delay during the period for which time is validly extended. In
addition, and less obviously, the power to extend time is also for the
employer's benefit, for the following reason.

At common law, the contractor's obligation to complete the works by
the specified date is removed if the employer delays the contractor in the
execution of the works. Thus if the contract administrator issues an
instruction which increases the amount of work to be done, or is late

in giving the contractor necessary instructions, the specified completion date no longer applies. In this situation, time is said to be 'at large', and the contractor's obligation is merely to complete the works within a reasonable time. In order to fix what is 'reasonable', all the circumstances of the particular project must be taken into account but, in many cases, it will simply mean that the amount of delay for which the employer is responsible will be added to the old completion date.

The importance of losing the fixed date is that, a contractor who may still be liable to pay damages for delay which is his or her fault, can no longer be made liable for *liquidated* damages. Even where the delay caused by the employer is a very small part of the overall delay, the employer cannot simply discount this and claim liquidated damages for the remainder.[10] The liquidated damages provision fails altogether, and the employer can claim only for losses actually due to the delay. This may be difficult to prove in court and it may, in any event, be less than the amount fixed a liquidated damages. It is therefore very much in the employer's interest to extend time for delays which are his or her fault, thus enabling claims for liquidated damages from the revised completion data.

9.5.1   Grounds for extensions of time

A fundamental point is that the time for completion can only be extended where the contract permits, and strictly in accordance with the contract provisions. If delay is caused by some event which the contract does not cover, then the contractor cannot claim an extension, nor can the employer insist on giving one (in order to keep alive a claim for liquidated damages). For example, it was held that a power to extend time for delays caused by the ordering of extra work only applied where the extra work was *properly* ordered, not where the architect gave the relevant instructions orally instead of in writing, as the contract required.[11]

It is thus important that the likely causes of delay are covered by an extension of time clause, but the courts have made things more difficult by ruling that general words such as 'other unavoidable circumstances' do not cover delay which is due to the fault of the employer.[12] Oddly, although this attitude of the courts is well known, many contracts continue to use general phrases of this kind. ICE 6 clause 44(1), for instance, speaks of 'other special circumstances of any kind whatsoever', while MW 80 clause 2.2 uses 'reasons beyond the control of the contractor'.

A further point which needs to be made is that there is often argument as to what is the actual cause of a particular delay. Suppose, for example, that the employer on a contract for refurbishment work is one week late in giving the contractor access to a particular part of the building, but that the contractor could not have started work anyway, having forgotten to order the necessary materials! Which of them has 'caused' the delay? And what if during the week in question the entire area was several feet deep in snow and work would have been impossible? The answers to such questions are not at all clear since the only guidance from the courts is that it is *not* correct to identify one cause as 'dominant' and hold that cause entirely responsible.[13] It may be that since, in theory at least, it is always the contractor who claims an extension of time, the onus is on him to prove that delay has been caused by an event for which an extension can be granted. Thus, if another sufficient 'cause' also exists, the contractor will fail.

9.5.2 'Relevant Events' under JCT 80

As a good example of the kind of grounds on which time for completion can be extended in building contracts, we can take the list of 'Relevant Events' which is found in clause 25.4 of JCT 80; these are as follows.

Force majeure

The meaning of *force majeure* we have covered already in Chapter 2. As we shall see, many of the events which might come within the definition are specifically covered under JCT 80 by other grounds, and this ground is thus of very limited application.

Exceptionally adverse weather conditions

JCT 63 used the phrase 'exceptionally *inclement* weather'. The problem with this is that it only covered exceptionally *bad* weather such as excessive rain and wind. Since excessively hot and dry weather can also cause problems with progress of the works, the definition was changed in JCT 80 to 'exceptionally adverse weather', a phrase which clearly includes such conditions.

Interestingly, while ICE 6 clause 44(1) uses the same phrase as JCT 80, GC/Works/1 does not recognize any kind of weather conditions as grounds for extensions of time. This means that, under GC/Works/1, the entire 'weather risk' is borne by the contractor (who will presumably price the tender accordingly). Under the other forms of contract, the risk is shared.

In a temperate and varied climate like that of the UK it can be difficult to establish exactly what constitutes 'exceptionally adverse weather'. An examination of local weather records should establish what is normal for the locality. This will provide a definition of what is 'usually adverse' weather and thus help to identify 'exceptionally adverse' weather. However, since the exact nature of the weather is critical in deciding the validity of a claim, Meteorological Office records may be inadequate. It is wise to keep detailed site weather records because weather can vary greatly over short distances, especially where there are hills nearby.

An example of this is the Humber Bridge, where a complex *in situ* cable-spinning process was used to sling the main suspension cables between the towers of the bridge. Since work could only take place on these cables when the wind was low, weather records at the nearby Meteorological Office weather station were examined in detail before work commenced. Unfortunately, the actual site was a few miles from the weather station, and the effect of the hills channelling the wind up the estuary resulted in higher wind speeds than expected and led to excessive delays. However, these higher wind speeds were normal at the location of the bridge.

In considering weather problems, it must always be borne in mind that there can be no extension of time unless the whole project is actually or potentially delayed. If, for example, exceptionally bad weather occurs at a time when most of the work is indoors, this is not a ground for an extension. It is also important to note that it is the *actual* effect of weather on the work which is relevant – thus what matters is the weather at the time when a particular part of the work was in fact carried out, not necessarily at the time when it was programmed to be carried out.

Loss or damage occasioned by the Specified Perils

The 'Specified Perils' are listed in clause 1.3 of JCT 80 and include such matters as fire, lightning, explosion, storm, tempest, flood, bursting or overflowing of water tanks, apparatus or pipes, etc, riot and civil commotion. Clause 25.4.3 allows for an extension of the contract period if loss or damage caused by these things delays the contractor. The wording means that the events do not have to cause delay directly to the contractor; but if the contractor incurs loss or damage because of them, and that loss subsequently delays the contractor, then the contractor can claim for an extension of the contract period.

These perils are the subject of the insurance provisions in clause 22. Even if the loss or damage is brought about by omission or default of the contractor (or those for whom the contractor is responsible), it appears that clause 25.4.3 still applies.[14] Perhaps because of this result (which means that the contractor benefits from his or her own default), the courts tend to interpret the specified perils rather strictly. In one case,[15] for example, a sub-contractor dropped a purlin on to a high-pressure jet of water pipe. The pipe broke and the resulting high-pressure jet of water caused severe damage to the plaintiff's goods. Although the 'bursting of pipes' is a Specified Peril, so that the risk of damage is firmly with the employer, the judge in this case considered that what had happened did not fit into this category. A burst was held to be a disruption from within the pipe, and the cause of damage here was in fact the negligent dropping of a purlin. Thus the sub-contractors were found liable for the damage done.

Civil commotion, strike, lock-out, etc.

This applies to delays caused by industrial action taken by any group of people who are employed on the works, are manufacturing items for inclusion in the works or are involved in transportation of goods to the works. It seems, however, that a strike or industrial dispute which affected, for example, the supply of fuel to the transporters would not be covered by the wording of this clause. Clearly, it makes no difference whether the strike is official or unofficial.

Although a 'go-slow' or a 'work-to-rule' does not constitute a strike, it would presumably be covered by the phrase 'any combination of workmen'.

Compliance with the contract administrator's instructions

JCT 80 gives the contract administrator wide powers to issue instructions to the contractor during the progress of the works. In relation to some, though not all, of these, clause 25.4.5.1 provides that any delay resulting from the contractor's compliance will be a valid ground for an extension of time. Instructions on the following matters fall into this category:

- discrepancy in or divergence between contract documents (clause 2.3);
- variations (clause 13.2);
- the expenditure of provisional sums (clause 13.3);
- the postponement of any work to be executed under the contract (clause 23.2);
- any action to be taken concerning fossils, antiquities and other objects of interest or value (clause 34);
- nominated sub-contractors (clause 35, which itself contains a further list of matters about which instructions can be issued);
- nominated suppliers (clause 36).

It is important to appreciate that, under JCT 80 clause 4.1, the contractor must 'forthwith comply' with *all* instructions which the contract empowers the contract administrator to issue. If the contractor fails to do so, the employer may employ others to do part of the works. In these circumstances, the contractor would not be entitled to claim an extension of time.

Opening up and inspection of defective work

Clause 25.4.5.2 covers a further issue which may result from an instruction from the contract administrator, namely the opening up and testing of work which has been covered up. Delay resulting from this will entitle the contractor to an extension of time, unless the inspection shows the work to be defective.

Delay in the supply of information

The basic position under JCT 80 is that it is the responsibility of the contract administrator to keep the contractor supplied with the information which is needed in order to carry out the work. Failure to supply drawings or details (clause 5.4) or information on levels (clause 7) at the right time will be a breach of contract for which the contractor will be entitled to recover damages. Moreover, this claim for damages does not depend upon the contractor having specifically asked for the information; it is the contract administrator's responsibility to know when information is going to be required and to ensure that it is ready.

Clause 25.4.6 means that, as well as leading to an action for damages, delay in supplying necessary information may in certain circumstances be a ground on which the contractor is entitled to an extension of time. For this purpose, 'information' is defined as 'necessary instructions, drawings, details or levels', and the 'instructions' referred to cover only those matters about which the contract gives the contract administrator power to issue instructions.

In order for a contractor to claim an extension of time under clause 25 (or to determine the employment under clause 27) on the grounds of late supply of information, the information must have previously been requested by the contractor in writing, at a time 'neither unreasonably distant from nor unreasonably close to' the time when it is required. Although it might be argued that the submission of the contractor's original programme to the contract administrator comes at too early a date to constitute a proper request for *all* the information which will be necessary, it has been held in one case[16] that the programme is all that is required. In any event, the insertion of due dates for information, and the regular revision and re-issue of such a programme, will certainly fulfil the requirements of this clause.

Delay on the part of nominated sub-contractors/suppliers

Before we look at the way in which the courts have interpreted this clause, it is worthwhile considering its practical implications. If the main contractor is entitled to an extension of time when delayed by a nominated sub-contractor, it means that there is no liability for liquidated damages to the employer. This, in turn, means that although the contractor may claim damages from the nominated sub-contractor for loss caused by disturbance of the progress of the works, these damages will not include the amount of the liquidated damages because the contractor will not have paid these. As a result, unless the employer has a direct claim against the nominated sub-contractor for the delay (e.g. under NSC/2 or NSC/2a, the JCT standard form of 'collateral warranty'), the employer will simply lose out and the nominated sub-contractor will evade much of the responsibility for the delay which he or she has caused!

The apparent strangeness and unfairness of this result may help to explain why the courts have interpreted clause 25.4.7 in what seems to be an artificially narrow way. It has held by the House of Lords in the case of *Westminster CC* v. *Jarvis*[17] that 'delay on the part of' is not the same thing as 'delay caused by'. This phrase does not refer to any lack of diligence by the sub-contractor, but only to the sub-contractor's failure to achieve his or her own completion date which results in the main contractor being unable to achieve the overall completion date. Thus, in the *Jarvis* case, although the nominated sub-contractor's work was later found to be defective, necessitating a return to the site to put it right, completion had apparently been achieved on the due date. It was accordingly held that there had been no 'delay on the part of' the nominated sub-contractor. As a result, the main contractor was liable to the employer and the sub-contractor was, in turn, liable to the main contractor.

The contractor should closely monitor the progress of nominated sub-contractors to ensure that they remain on programme, and so that the contractor can warn the contract administrator in plenty of time of the likelihood of a nominated sub-contractor delaying the works. Similarly, supplies of goods and materials from nominated suppliers should be closely checked. Contractors who fail in this may lose the right to an extension of time, either through failing to take 'all practicable steps to avoid or reduce' the delay (clause 25.4.7) or, more generally, because they have not constantly used their best endeavours to prevent delay (clause 25.3.4.1).

It is important to note that, if a nominated sub-contractor ceases work altogether (for example, because of insolvency), this is not in itself grounds for the main contractor to claim an extension of time. The position is that the contract administrator has a duty to re-nominate another sub-contractor within a reasonable time, and that only delay in doing so will entitle the main contractor to extra time.[18]

The execution of work not forming part of the contract

Clause 29 allows the employer to undertake parts of the works, either directly or through another contractor, where this is stated in the contract bills. Such work will not form part of the contract, but because of this clause, a delay in that part of the work will give the contractor grounds for Extension of Time.

The supply of materials by the employer

As with the previous clause, the employer may choose to supply some of the materials or goods for incorporation in the works. Once again, however, this must be clearly stated in the bills, since if this is not done, it is the contractor's obligation, and right, to do the entire work set out in the contract documents.

Where the employer is to supply materials, the contractor must make sure that the employer is fully aware of the dates upon which they will be required. If this is not done, the contractor will lose the right to claim an extension of time for any resulting delay.

The exercise by the government of any power, etc.
which directly affects the works

An example of the kind of exercise of government power which would be relevant here is the three-day week which resulted from the miners' strike in 1974. The government at that time decreed that people could only have electricity for three days per week, with a view to preserving coal stocks for as long as possible to try to break the miners' strike.

In order for this clause to be used as a reason for claiming an extension of time, the contractor must have had no knowledge of the matter at the date of tender.

Contractor's inability to secure labour, goods or materials

It must be very difficult to establish the extent to which shortages of materials exist – particularly if paying a higher price than the market rate would secure them. Clearly, the price paid must bear some relationship to what was envisaged at the time of tender, but if the contractor waits for the shortage to finish, the price may never drop.

In order to be able to claim an extension of time under this provision, the contractor has to demonstrate that it could not have 'reasonably foreseen' its inability at the date of tender.

Carrying out of work by statutory power

This ground for extension of time refers only to the carrying out of work by a local authority or statutory undertaking *in pursuance of its statutory powers*. It does not cover the situation where a statutory undertaking is used as a sub-contractor. According to SMM 7, any work to be undertaken by a statutory undertaking should be included in the bills of quantity as a provisional sum.

Failure by the employer to give access over employer's land

This ground only applies when land or buildings adjacent to the site are in the employer's possession and control, there is an undertaking to give the contractor access to the site through that land. It does not refer to the employer's obligation to give the contractor possession of the site itself; nor does it apply to any failure by the employer to obtain wayleaves over other people's property.

Deferment of Date of Possession under clause 23.1.2 (optional)

As we have noted under clause 1.3, above, failure by the employer to give the contractor possession of the site on the agreed date is a serious breach of contract. However, if the optional clause 23.1.2 is used, then the employer may defer the giving of possession for whatever period (not exceeding 6 weeks) is specified in the Appendix to the contract. If possession is deferred in this way, then naturally the contractor is entitled to an extension of time.

9.5.3   Procedures for claiming extension of time

General

A point which is occasionally overlooked is that extensions of time can only be granted in respect of events which are likely to delay *completion*. Thus, if a contractor's schedule is geared to finishing before the completion date, or if the contractor is so far ahead of the contract programme when delay occurs that the 'slack' can be taken up, it appears that no extension should be granted at that stage.[19] However, where the contract permits the contract administrator to review the question of extension of time at a later date, such delay can then be taken into account. This is the position under both JCT 80 (clause 25.3.3) and ICE 6 (clause 44.4).

As a general principle, an extension of time can only be validly granted if the procedures which the contract lays down are strictly followed. In one case,[20] for example, where the contract did not make clear that the architect could extend time retrospectively (i.e. after completion had been achieved), it was held that this was not possible. The purpose of extending time, it was said, was to give the contractor a date to work towards.

This problem does not arise under either JCT 80 or ICE 6 since both contracts clearly permit retrospective extensions. In any event, it may be that the courts today are rather less strict in their interpretation of contractual procedures. For example, although JCT 80 requires the contract administrator to grant an extension within 12 weeks of receiving the contractor's claim 'if reasonably practicable', it has been held by the Court of Appeal that an extension granted outside that period is still valid.[21]

A very important question which has not yet been answered by the courts is whether it is possible to grant an extension of time at a point when the completion date is already past and the contractor is thus in delay. If an extension *cannot* be granted, it could mean that an employer who causes such delay (e.g. by issuing a variation) will lose the right to claim liquidated damages – possibly even having to pay back any liquidated damages which have already been collected ! On the other hand, if an extension *can* be granted, logic suggests that the new completion date must be set in the future, in which case the contractor might escape liability altogether for the earlier breach!

Either result clearly produces difficult problems. Our tentative view is that an extension cannot be granted in such circumstances, but that this will not cost the employer the right to damages; he or she will be entitled to liquidated damages until the event occurs, and to unliquidated damages from the moment its effects cease.

Procedures under JCT 80

JCT 80 clause 25 lays down a specific procedure which must be followed in order to ask for the time for completion to be extended. This procedure can be utilized more than once during the contract; indeed, it should be used on every occasion that delay occurs. Furthermore, clause 25.3 provides that the contract administrator shall within 12 weeks of practical completion make a final decision on extensions of time, whether or not notice has been given by the contractor, and may at that stage review earlier decisions.

A contractor who wishes to claim an extension of time must show that he has at all times used its 'best endeavours to prevent delay in the progress of the works, however caused'. Subject to this, the procedure laid down by clause 25 is as follows:

1. Whenever it becomes reasonably apparent that the progress of the works is being or is likely to be delayed for any reason (not just by an event listed in clause 25), the contractor is required to give written notice to the contract administrator. This notice should specify the cause or causes of the delay, and identify any 'relevant event'. Any nominated sub-contractor referred to, must be sent a copy of the notice.

2. In respect of any 'relevant event' mentioned in the contractor's notice, the contractor must as soon as possible write to the contract administrator, giving particulars of the likely effects and an estimate of the expected delay. The contractor must from that time keep the contract administrator up to date with any developments. Again, a relevant sub-contractor must be sent a copy of the information.

3. When he receives this information, the contract administrator is required to decide whether completion of the works is likely to be delayed beyond the completion date by one or more 'relevant events'. If the contract administrator decides that this is the case, then he or she must fix a new completion date, giving such extention as is fair and reasonable, and notify the contractor in writing. If the contract administrator decides against the contractor, this too must be notified in writing. In either case, the decision is to be notified within 12 weeks 'if practicable', or before the completion date if this is less than 12 weeks away.

4. In fixing a new completion date on second or subsequent occasions, the contract administrator is entitled to bring the date forward to take account of any work which has been ordered to be omitted. However, it is *never* possible to fix a completion date earlier than the original Date for Completion stated in the Appendix to the contract, no matter how much work is omitted.

REFERENCES

1. Charmer, K. Definitions of project management. *Bulletin of the Association of Project Managers*, 2(7), March 1990, 18–19 and 3(1), June 1990, 13–14.
2. *Rapid Building Group Ltd* v. *Ealing Family Housing Association Ltd* (1985) 29 B.L.R. 5.
3. *Whittal Builders Co.* v. *Chester-le-Street DC* (1987) 40 B.L.R. 82.
4. *LRE Engineering Services Ltd* v. *Otto Simon Carves Ltd* (1981) 24 B.L.R. 127.
5. *Holme* v. *Guppy* (1838) 3 M. & W. 387.
6. *Freeman* v. *Hensler* (1900) 64 JP 260.

7. Anderson, A.J. *et al.* *Emden's Construction Law*, Butterworths, London (1990) p. II: 168.
8. *M.J. Gleeson (Contractors) Ltd* v. *Hillingdon London Borough* (1970) 215 E.G. 165.
9. *Bramall & Ogden Ltd* v. *Sheffield CC* (1983) B.L.R. 73.
10. *Dodd* v. *Churton* [1897] 1 Q.B. 562.
11. *Murdoch* v. *Luckie* (1897) 15 N.Z.L.R. 296.
12. *Peak Construction (Liverpool) Ltd* v. *McKinney Foundations Ltd* (1970) 1 B.L.R. 111.
13. *H Fairweather & Co. Ltd* v. *Wandsworth LBC* (1987) 39 B.L.R. 106.
14. *Surrey Heath Borough Council* v. *Lovell Construction Ltd* (1988) 42 B.L.R. 25; *Scottish Special Housing Association* v. *Wimpey Construction (UK) Ltd* [1986] 2 All E.R. 957.
15. *Computer & Systems Engineering plc* v. *John Lelliott (Ilford) Ltd* [1989] C.S.W. July 6.
16. *London Borough of Merton* v. *Stanley Hugh Leach* (1985) B.L.R. 55.
17. *Westminster City Council* v. *Jarvis and Sons Ltd* [1970] 1 All E.R. 943.
18. *North West Metropolitan Regional Hospital Board* v. *TA Bickerton Ltd* [1970] 1 All E.R. 977; *Percy Bilton Ltd* v. *GLC* [1982] 2 All E.R. 623.
19. *Hounslow BC* v. *Twickenham Garden Developments Ltd* [1971] Ch. 253.
20. *Miller* v. *LCC* (1934) 50 T.L.R. 479.
21. *Temloc Ltd* v. *Errill Properties Ltd* (1987) 39 B.L.R. 30.

10

Other obligations of the contractor

The most important **obligations of the contractor** under a construction contract are those which govern the standard of work and the time within which it is to be carried out. These obligations we have dealt with in Chapters 8 and 9. However, the detailed conditions of standard form contracts impose other duties upon a contractor, and these are very numerous – one textbook identifies more than 70 such duties in JCT 80! It is not possible for us to deal in detail with all of these, but in this chapter we identify some of the more important categories into which these other duties can be divided.

10.1 STATUTORY OBLIGATIONS

10.1.1 Contractor's duties

Most, if not all, construction contracts provide expressly that in carrying out the works the contractor must comply with all relevant statutes and statutory instruments, which includes giving whatever notices they may require. The most important provisions controlling building work are likely to be the Building Regulations 1985 and the *Health and Safety at Work Act 1984*, but the contractor's obligation extends much wider than these. JCT 80 clause 6.1.1 makes it clear that there must be compliance with local authority by-laws, and also with regulations made by statutory undertakers such as electricity, gas and water boards, to whose systems the works are to be connected.

The reason for contractual provisons such as clause 6 is that where the contract works are carried on in such a way as to breach a statute, the effect may well be that the employer becomes liable to criminal prosecution or to civil actions brought by third parties who are adversely affected. By placing the primary obligation of compliance on the contractor, the contract seeks to ensure that in such circumstances the employer will be entitled to claim an indemnity from the contractor.

In relation to any fees, charges, rates or taxes which become payable in respect of the works, JCT 80 clause 6.2 again places the primary obligation of paying these upon the contractor. However, the ultimate cost will be borne by the employer, for the amounts are to be added to the contract sum.

The position outlined above is in general terms followed by ICE 6 in clauses 26 and 27. However, no doubt because the nature of civil engineering projects makes it more likely that work will be done in streets or other highways, the clauses cover these eventualities in considerable detail.

10.1.2   Divergence between statutory requirements and contract

The obligations of the contractor described above are subject to an important qualification under JCT 80 clause 6.1.5. If the reason why there is a breach of statute is that the work, as designed, does not conform to statutory requirements, then responsibility for this falls upon the employer and not upon the contractor. The contractor's only obligation is to notify the contract administrator of any divergence between the contract documents and the statutory requirements which it actually discovers. Provided the contractor does this (and it is to be noted that, somewhat strangely, the contract does *not* require a positive to search for such divergences), the contract administrator must then within 7 days issue instructions so as to bring the works into line with the statutory requirements. Such instructions will be treated as a variation, which means that the contractor will be paid for the work involved. Further, where compliance with the instructions causes delay or disruption, the contractor will be entitled to claim an extension of time and for loss and/or expense.

The treatment of divergences described here applies to most JCT contracts and also to ICE 6. However, the JCT form of contract With Contractor's Design 81 is very different. Except where the Employer's Requirements are specifically stated to be in accordance with statutory requirements, it is the contractor's responsibility to ensure that the work as designed and built does not contravene the law. As a result, any divergence must be put right at the contractor's own expense.

10.1.3   Emergency work

JCT 80 clause 6.1.4 makes provision for the circumstance where emergency work is necessary to ensure the continuing safety of people and property; for example, where a neighbouring property has become unsafe and may collapse on to the site. The contractor must immediately (i.e. without waiting for instructions from the contract administrator) undertake such limited work and supply such limited materials as are necessary to ensure compliance with statutory obligations. Provided that the emergency is then shown to have arisen because of a divergence between the contract documents and the statutory requirements, the contractor's work will then be valued as a variation.

The ICE 6 form does not mention emergency work at all, which suggests that the cost of such work is to be borne entirely by the contractor. Where the emergency arises because of a divergence between the contract documents and statutory requirements, the engineer must issue a variation instruction and the contractor will be paid for this work. However, even here it is arguable that the contractor will remain uncompensated both for the earlier abortive work and for the cost of removing it.

10.2 CO-ORDINATION AND MANAGEMENT

Apart from the main contractor's role as builder (which may be very limited where extensive use is made of sub-contractors, or even non-existent under a management contract), the main contractor has an important part to play in managing the site and the persons who work on it. This covers a number of issues, which are dealt with below.

10.2.1 Control of persons on the site

It is the main contractor's responsibility to programme the overall project and to co-ordinate the contributions made by various other persons and organizations, notably sub-contractors. As to the extent to which the contractor bears responsibility for the defaults of such sub-contractors, even when they are nominated, this is dealt with in Chapters 16–18.

Apart from sub-contractors, an important group of participants in construction projects consists of statutory undertakers. There are two types of these: those who exercise some sort of power over the works, and those who have to undertake work on the site. Examples of the first type are the public bodies which exercise supervision over the design, quality or safety of the works by the enforcement of planning legislation or building regulations. Examples of the second type are those public bodies whic provide utility services such gas, water, electricity and drainage. With those of the second type, the contractor will have to co-ordinate and connect its own work to theirs, but will not have the same powers of control as over sub-contractors.

In the UK it is often the case that statutory undertakings will undertake work which is not part of the statutory powers. For example, an electricity board may be employed to carry out sub-contract works. In this case, they are not treated as a statutory undertaking, but are in the same position as any other sub-contractor (nominated or domestic). It is obviously of great importance to know in what capacity a statutory undertaking is operating in any particular case, but unfortunately this is not always clear, especially where they exceed their powers.[1]

Although overall responsibility for the way in which work is carried out lies with the contractor, the contract administrator has a supervisory role to play. To enable this to take place, JCT 80 clause 11 provides that the contractor must allow the contract administrator to have access to the works and to the contractor's workshops at all reasonable times. The contractor is also required to ensure that such access is also possible to the workshops of sub-contractors. Furthermore, if the employer exercises the right to appoint a clerk of works (Chapter 14) to act as inspector under the directions of the contract administrator, JCT 80 clause 12 requires the contractor to afford every reasonable facility for the performance of that duty.

It may finally be noted, as a practical feature of the contractor's responsibility for management and co-ordination, that JCT 80 clause 10 specifically requires the contractor to keep constantly upon the works 'a competent person-in-charge'.

10.2.2   Exclusion of persons from the words

All the main standard forms of contract give power to the contract administrator to order the exclusion from the works of specified persons. Under clause 8.5 of JCT 80, such an instruction, which must not be issued 'unreasonably or vexatiously', extends to beyond the contractor's own employees to include the employees of sub-contractors. The fact that this clause is found immediately after the contract provisions in respect of bad workmanship suggests that its purpose is to exclude persistent bad performers, although this is not made explicit. The strict wording would appear to entitle the contract administrator to exclude militant shop stewards, and the like, but this would probably be a mis-use of the provision. However, the question of unreasonableness, or vexation, is one which can only be decided by an arbitrator.

Under ICE 6, clause 16 requires the contractor to employ only those people who are properly skilled and undertake their duties with an appropriate level of care. The engineer has the power to order the removal from site of any of the contractor's employees, but only for lack of diligence or workmanship.

The equivalent clause in GC/Works/1 clause 26 gives the project manager extremely far-reaching powers to exclude any individual from the site. No reason need be given, and the contractor cannot question the exclusion. This is clearly and unambiguously disconnected from workmanship and diligence and appears to be a matter of security.

10.2.3 Antiquities

Contractual provisions dealing with the discovery of interesting objects – new or old – during the course of the work are necessary for various reasons. One important reason is that the removal or disturbance of such objects may actually destroy their worth. A recent example of this was the discovery of Shakespeare's Globe Theatre in London, where an archaeological find of great importance held up a very large and expensive development project for a considerable period of time. More generally, fossils may be valuable, and some types may completely degrade on exposure to atmosphere for any length of time. Further, one of the most significant features of a fossil is the exact location in which it is found. It must be left in place, for a random fossil is of little use to a paleontologist without data about its location. A third problem relates to treasure trove. What happens if the contractor digs up £100 000 worth of gold doubloons?! Who owns them?

JCT 80 clause 34 contains extensive provisions to cover these issues, beginning with a general statement that: 'All fossils, antiquities and other objects of interest or value which may be found on the site or in excavating the same during progress of the Works shall become the property of the employer.' This provokes three comments:

1. The phrase 'all fossils' is a rather unfortunate one because, if the site is on chalk or limestone, it will be very difficult to excavate a single shovelful of material *without* finding a fossil of some sort!
2. The phrase 'other objects of interest or value' means that this clause does not only apply to old objects; it can equally apply to new things, provided that they are 'of interest or value'.
3. It is important to appreciate that this clause only settles the issue of ownership as between the employer and the contractor. It can have no bearing on the relative rights of, say, landlord and tenant, where the site is held under a lease. In such circumstances, it is necessary to refer to the general law which governs the right to objects which are found.

The remainder of clause 34 (which is followed in general terms by ICE 6 clause 32) lays down detailed provisions as to what shall happen where such an object is discovered. The contractor is not to disturb the object, but must take all necessary steps to preserve it in the exact position and condition in which it was found. The contract administrator is to be informed forthwith of the discovery, so that instructions can be given as to what to do. If this results in a delay to progress of the works, then the contractor is entitled to an extension of time under clause 25.4.5.1. Any loss/expense incurred by the contractor is also reimbursable, but the provisions in clause 34.3.1 are notably different from the other loss/expense provisions in clause 26. Here the initiative is placed entirely with the contract administrator who has to form an opinion and 'shall himself ascertain...the amount of such loss/expense'. There are no rules laid down as to how this sum of money is to be calculated.

Apart from the contractual provisions governing antiquities, attention must be paid to the *Ancient Monuments and Archaeological Areas Act 1979*. This empowers the Secretary of State and local authorities to designate areas of archaeological importance, which will be registered under the *Local Land Charges Act 1979*. Under the Act, if any operations are to be undertaken on a designated area which would disturb the ground, an 'Operations Notice' must first be served on the local authority. The Department of Environment then has a power to delay the building work, and no compensation is payable unless the archaeologists damage the site. If the provisions of this Act are contravened, criminal penalties may be imposed, and there is also power to issue injunctions preventing any further contravention.

These statutory provisions are not covered by clause 34, which only applies to objects found during the progress of the works. JCT 80 simply makes no specific provision for what is to happen if the powers given by the Act are exercised. Presumably, if the operations are suspended for the period stated in the Appendix, then the contractor can claim that the contract has been suspended by *force majeure*, in which case there is a power of determination under clause 28.3.1.

10.3 TRANSFER OF MATERIALS

10.3.1 General Position

At common law, the rules governing the transfer of ownership in materials from contractor to employer are fairly straightforward, and will operate as implied terms in any contract where they are not overridden by express provisions. These rules provide that as soon as any materials or goods are incorporated into a building, they cease to belong to the contractor and become the property of the employer.[2] Until the materials are built in to the works, however, even though they have been delivered to site, they remain the property of the contractor. Even the fact that the employer has paid the contractor for the materials will not make a difference, unless (as is usually the case) the contract makes express provision for this.

The point at which the question of whether ownership lies with the employer or the contractor becomes most important is where one of the parties becomes insolvent. As a general principle, all the creditors of an insolvent person or company are entitled to share equally in the remaining assets, and these will include all property which is owned by the insolvent person at the time. Thus, if the contractor becomes insolvent, materials which are on site but which have not yet passed to the employer may be seized by the contractor's receivers. What is more, unless the contract provides otherwise, this will hold good even where the value of those materials has been included in interim certificates.[3]

Somewhat strangely, the courts have not always applied the same principle to cases where it is the employer who becomes insolvent. It has, for instance, been held that although the ownership of building materials may have passed to the employer under a 'vesting clause', the contractor's continuing rights to use those materials in constructing the building are strong enough to override the claims of the employer's creditors.[4]

10.3.2   Contract provisions

JCT 80 does not alter the principle that the ownership of materials is transferred when they are incorporated into the building, but clause 16 provides a method by which the ownership may pass to the employer at an earlier stage. The value of unfixed materials and goods intended for the works, whether they are on or off site, may be included in an interim certificate. If this is done, then the ownership of those materials and goods will pass to the employer as soon as the amount is duly paid.

The provisions of ICE 6 depart further from the common law position. Clause 53 states baldly that 'All Contractor's Equipment Temporary Works materials for Temporary Works or other goods or materials owned by the Contractor...shall when on Site be deemed to be the property of the Employer'. This rather drastic statement is then watered down by provisions that the contractor shall have exclusive use of all the materials; that the contractor may remove the materials when they are no longer required for the works; and that the ownership of the materials so removed shall then revert to the contractor. As for materials which have not been delivered to the site but which are ready for incorporation in the works, clause 54 enables the contractor to transfer ownership in these to the employer. Once this is done and the engineer gives written approval to the materials, the contractor is entitled to be paid for them.

Note

10.3.3 Retention of title

The contract may deal satisfactorily with questions of ownership as between the employer and the contractor; however, problems may arise in cases where the contractor brings on to the site materials which are still in the ownership of a supplier. In particular, many suppliers operate under standard conditions of sale, which provide that they shall retain the ownership of goods until full payment is made.

There is here an obvious possibility of conflict between the terms of the main contract and those of the contract of supply.[5] The problems which can then arise are dealt with in Chapter 17.

10.4 GENERAL COMPLIANCE

10.4.1 Contract documents

As we have seen in Chapter 8, the contractor's overriding obligation is to comply with the contract documents, as defined by the particular form of contract. The definition of the work to be done is in the contract documents, and the form of the documents is as defined by the contract. About this nothing more need be said at this point, except to repeat that, under JCT 80, nothing in the contract bills can override or modify the Articles, Conditions or Appendix.

10.4.2 Contract administrator's instructions

Because construction projects are usually complex, and also because they frequently last for a considerable time (so that conditions may change), it is recognized that it may not be possible to deal in advance with every eventuality which may possibly arise. In consequence, most standard form contracts give the contract administrator extremely wide powers to issue instructions, with which the contractor must comply. These are discussed in Chapter 14, so at this point it is necessary only to state that:

- An instruction need only be complied with if the contract specifically empowers the contract administrator to issue it.
- An instruction need only be complied with if it is issued by the correct person and in the correct form.
- A contractor who complies with a valid instruction will normally be entitled to claim an extension of time and compensation for loss/ expense.

REFERENCES

1. *Henry Boot Construction Ltd* v. *Central Lancashire New Town Development Corporation* (1980) 15 B.L.R. 1.
2. *Sims* v. *London Necropolis Co.* [1885] 1 T.L.R. 584.
3. *W. Hanson (Harrow) Ltd* v. *Rapid Civil Engineering Ltd and Usborne Developments Ltd* (1987) 38 B.L.R. 106.
4. *Beeston* v. *Marriott* (1864) 8 L.T. 690.
5. See *Dawber Williamson Roofing Ltd* v. *Humberside CC* (1979) 14 B.L.R. 70; *Archivent Sales and Developments Ltd* v. *Strathclyde Regional Council* (1984) 27 B.L.R. 98.

PART FOUR

Obligations of the Employer

11

Payment

The provisions relating to **payment** concern the way in which the contractor is paid by the employer. The consideration which is given by the employer to the contractor is not always a fixed amount of money. However, there are only certain circumstances in which the contract sum can be altered. The most important of these is where there are variations. This chapter addresses these issues, and also the way in which mechanisms such as retention and set-off affect payment to the contractor.

11.1 EMPLOYER'S OBLIGATION TO PAY

The primary obligation upon the employer is to give the contractor the sum of money which forms the consideration for the contract.

11.1.1 Contract price

The contract **price** is dealt with in different ways by different contracts. Under JCT contracts, with bills of quantity, the bid by the contractor is based upon the work which is described and quantified in the contract bills. If any quantities are altered because of variations in the client's requirements, then the contract sum must be altered. Otherwise, the contractor is entitled to be paid the amount of the tender. This is by stark contrast with ICE 6, which is known as a 're-measurement', or 'measure and value' contract. This means that even though there may be quantities in the bills which the contractor priced, their purpose is purely to assist the tendering process. The price to be paid for the works will not be fully established until the works are complete.

These two types of contract are basic types, although naturally there are variations on the themes. The difference between them is of fundamental importance to any employer when considering what type of contract is appropriate for a particular project.

There are numerous provisions within the contractual conditions to ensure that the contract remains 'entire', that is a contract where the contractor undertakes to do the whole of the work for the whole of the money. The simple fact that the money is actually paid in stages does not alter the essential nature of the contract in terms of its entirety. This is a theme which is followed through in the contracts by the fact that it is only the final certificate which is ever conclusive as to workmanship or quality of materials.

11.1.2 Time of payment

The price to be paid by the employer is not usually to be withheld until the contractor has fulfilled the entire contract. The employer is obliged by JCT 80 to pay to the contractor the contract sum by instalments. Similar arrangements for stage payments exist in ICE 6, IFC 84 and all but the smallest contracts. The amount of money due in each instalment is recorded by the contract administrator in an 'Interim Certificate'. The issue of such a certificate by the contract administrator imposes upon the employer a strict obligation to make payment (subject only to certain exceptions discussed in section 11.6 of this chapter).

JCT contracts oblige the employer to pay within 14 days the amount of money shown on an interim certificate. This is by contrast with ICE 6 clause 60(2), which requires the contractor to submit a monthly statement to the engineer. Within 28 days of the submission of this statement, the engineer shall certify, and the employer shall pay, the relevant amount of money.

In the event of the main contractor defaulting, there are usually provisions for the employer to make direct payments to sub-contractors (this is dealt with more fully in Chapter 17).

11.1.3 Effect of certificates

Interim Certificates exist simply as a mechanism for confirming that an instalment of the consideration is due to the contractor. JCT 80 and IFC 84 are based on a contract administrator's valuation of work done each month. ICE 6 is based on a contractor's claim for payment which is evaluated by the engineer. GC/Works/1 is based on a graph of expected progress.

Whichever method is used to calculate the amount of money due, an 'interim certificate' is not conclusive about anything. It says nothing about the quality of materials or workmanship, nor does it indicate satisfaction with the work done to date. Anything which has been included in such a certificate may yet be the subject of a later certificate. It is only the final certificate which can be conclusive. As a result, the *only* obligation which arises from a certificate is an obligation on the employer to make a payment within the stated time. Failure to do so is a serious breach of contract.(Certificates are considered in more detail in Chapter 14.)

11.2   THE CONTRACT SUM

11.2.1   Definition

In JCT contracts, the **Contract sum** is defined in the Articles of Agreement as the amount of money which the employer will pay to the contractor. It is exclusive of VAT. Article 2 states that the contract sum is this amount of money or such other sum as shall become payable under the conditions, at the times and in the manner specified in the conditions. It is clear therefore that, under JCT terms, the sum is specified at the outset although it may be altered as work proceeds.

In ICE 6, by contrast, the 'contract price' is defined in clause 1(1) as the sum to be ascertained and paid in accordance with the provisions. This concept of contract sum is very different from that in JCT contracts. Under the ICE form, the sum can only be ascertained when the contract is concluded. Although the employer covenants to pay the contract price, it is not a specified amount of money at the time the contract is signed.

Because of the intrinsic differences between JCT and ICE contracts in this respect, we shall concentrate in this chapter on JCT contracts, in order to explore fully the detailed provisions relating to payment. The ICE conditions can then be understood by comparison.

In JCT 80 the contract sum is fixed by clause 14.2, which states that it cannot be altered or adjusted in any way other than by the conditions. An equivalent provision appears as clause 4.1 of IFC 84. This also states that any errors in the computation of the contract sum, whether arithmetic or not, are deemed to be accepted by both parties. The effect of this clause is that the contract sum can only be changed when the conditions allow adjustments.

Clause 3 of JCT 80 states that any changes to the contract sum, in the sense of amounts to be deducted or added, must take effect immediately. This means that as soon as such a change has been computed or ascertained it must be added to or deducted from the next interim certificate.

11.2.2   Permissible changes

The contract sum may be changed for a variety of reasons, which can be divided into three groups as follows:

1. Reimbursement of the contractor for certain expense caused by the contract administrator, employer or certain events outside the control of the contractor. These matters are covered by clauses such as JCT 80 clause 26 under which the contractor can claim for 'loss and/or expense'.
2. Payment for extra work brought about by an instruction of the contract administrator.
3. Reimbursement of extra expense brought about by market fluctuations affecting the contractor's inputs.

The loss/expense provisions will be covered in Chapter 12, and the present chapter concentrates on the second and third categories.

11.3 VARIATIONS

11.3.1   The need for variations

Clearly, buildings are so complex as to require changes to be made before they are completed. Additionally, it is rare for design to be completely detailed at the time of tender; a result of this is that changes have to be made in order simply to make the building work. If there were no provision in the contract for varying the work to be done, then (subject to what is said below) any attempt by the employer to vary it could simply be refused by the contractor. If the employer then refused to pay unless the contractor complied, this would probably amount to a repudiatory breach by the employer, which would entitle the contractor to terminate the contract. Therefore, in effect, the lack of a provision for variation would effectively enable the contractor to negotiate a new price for the whole contract every time the employer tried to make a change.

It should be conceded that this difficulty may not be quite so rigorous as it sounds. The absence of a **variations clause** undoubtedly makes it difficult to vary the terms of the contract, but it is at least possible that the courts would imply a term allowing *minor* variation to be made. In any event, it would of course be most unusual for a contractor either to refuse to carry out small changes, and even less likely that the contractor would go to court over an attempt to impose them.

By inserting a clause which allows for changes to be made to the works as they are being built, the employer, through the contract administrator, can alter the works as and when necessary. The purpose of the variation clauses is to allow such changes to be made, and also to permit any consequential changes to be made to the contract sum.

It must be borne in mind that the existence of a variations clause does not entitle the employer to make large-scale and significant changes to the nature of the works, as these are defined in the 'Recitals' to the contract.

In particular, variations which 'go to the root of the contract' are not permissible. If the Recitals state that 8 dwelling houses are to be built, then a variation altering this to 12 would possibly be construed as going to the root of the contract. However, if the Recitals state that the contract is for 1008 houses, then a variation changing this to 1012 would not go to the root of the contract because it would be a minor change in quantity. If the quantity of work is not indicated in the Recital, then the question does not arise in the same way. What is probably more important is that if the contract is for the erection of a swimming-pool, a variation which attempts to change it to a house would clearly be beyond the scope of the contract.

The case of *Blue Circle* v. *Holland Dredging*[1] illustrates the distinction between a variation and work which is beyond the scope of the contract. It was there stated that a variation is something which bears some relationship to the work of which it is a variation. If the work could not have been in the contemplation of the parties at the time they made their contract, then it must fall outside the scope of a variations clause.

One possible disadvantage of a variations clause is that it may encourage the design team to be less than specific at the time of tendering, in terms of what is to be built. The fact that things may be varied as the contract proceeds means that the design team may not have to finalize their design until a very late stage. This is bad practice and should be discouraged as far as possible. The variations clause should only really be used for unforeseen changes.[2]

11.3.2 Definition of variations

The following discussion concentrates on the principles contained in JCT 80 and IFC 84, which have very similar provisions for variations. Oddly, however, the provisions are ordered differently. IFC 84 begins by giving power to issue variations (more concisely than JCT 80) and then defines what variations are. JCT 80, on the other hand, starts with the definition and follows with the power! Why this should be is not at all clear.

The definitions of 'variation' in the two contracts are identical in all respects except one. This is that JCT 80 specifically excludes the nomination of sub-contractors. Since IFC 84 is not intended for use where sub-contractors are nominated, this exclusion is not required in IFC 84.

The definition of variation in JCT 80 clause 13.1 is a wide one, applying to both the content of the work and the method of doing it. Indeed, at first glance the definition appears almost unlimited in scope since it makes repeated reference to 'any' work. However, bearing in mind what was said earlier about the recitals, and not changing the nature of the contract, this is clearly not the true position.

We may now look in more detail at the JCT 80 provisions.

Alteration of the work

The basic definition includes any 'alteration or modification of the design, quality or quantity of the works as shown on the contract drawings and described by or referred to in the contract bills'. The clause clarifies this further by stating that such alteration or modification includes additions, omissions or substitutions.

The inclusion of substitutions within the definition is somewhat strange since a substitution normally involves omitting one thing and adding another. For this reason, it is by no means clear why the phrase 'substitution of any work' is there at all. However, it is possible that this refers to the situation where a thing is varied after it has been completely built.

This part of the definition of a variation specifically includes the alteration of the kind or standard of any of the materials or goods to be used in the works. Such changes necessarily involve the contractor's head office in expenditure such as the additional time needed to cancel orders, find alternative suppliers and re-order materials and goods. Detailed records may be needed to prove this type of expenditure; or alternatively, it may be calculated on a pro-rata basis.

The third aspect of this part of the definition is the removal from the site of work or materials which are there for the proper purposes of the contract. This is by contrast with clause 8.4, which deals with the removal of things which are *not* in accordance with the conditions.

Alteration of working methods

In addition to allowing the works themselves to be altered, clause 13.1 allows for variations in the means of achieving those works. The means available to the contractor may be seriously affected by access to the site, working space, hours of work or the sequence in which work is to be carried out. Unlike the permitted variations to the works, however, these definite and specific matters of working *method* are fairly limited in the way in which they can be varied. In particular it must be borne in mind that exercising restrictions on these things could result in substantial money claims by the contractor under clause 26.1.

The final aspect of the definition, as briefly mentioned earlier, is that a variation under JCT 80 may not include the nomination of a sub-contractor for measured work already priced by the contractor. In accordance with the common law position,[3] the contract provides specifically that none of the contractor's work can be taken away and given to others while the contract is current.

Variations under ICE 6

The ICE definition of a variation appears in clause 51. It includes additions, omissions, substitutions, alterations, changes in quality, form, character, kind, position, dimension, level or line, and changes in any specified sequence, method or timing of construction. This list, which contains a number of synonyms, means in effect the engineer may issue variations about almost anything. The clause also makes it clear that a variation order need not be issued merely for the purposes of altering quantities in the bills. This is because the bills are not intended as a full description of the work, but only as a mechanism for selecting the contractor.

11.3.3 The issue of variations

In the JCT forms of contract, the definition of variations is distinct from the power to issue them. A variation for this purpose is an instruction issued by the contract administrator. Hence, in order for such an instruction to be valid under the contract it must be issued in accordance with clause 4 (clause 3.5 of IFC 84). This means, for example, that it must be in writing. It also means that the contractor has the right to object on reasonable grounds to a variation.

As well as issuing an instruction which may require a variation, the contract administrator may sanction a variation that has been made by the contractor. The contractor normally has no authority whatsoever to vary anything (except for the execution of emergency work by clause 6.1). For example, the contractor cannot substitute higher-quality work or materials than those specified. A contractor who *does* vary anything can be instructed to remove it under clause 8.4.[4] This power for the contract administrator to sanction an unauthorized variation by the contractor is thus an important one since it allows the contract administrator easily to pick up and deal with minor items which are varied by the contractor, or which are directed by the Clerk of Works and not confirmed by the contract administrator.

All the contract forms state that 'no variation required by the architect/ contract administrator or subsequently sanctioned by him shall vitiate this contract'. This in fact is an unnecessary and somewhat misleading statement, which adds nothing at all to the general legal position. Even without such a clause, an attempt by the employer to vary the contractor's obligations in a minor way would not 'vitiate the contract'; the contractor would simply be entitled to refuse. On the other hand, an alteration great enough to 'vitiate the contract' will continue to do so notwithstanding this clause because such an alteration will go beyond the contractual definition of a 'variation'!

In JCT contracts variations can only apply to firm quantities and to provisional sums; they cannot relate to approximate quantities. By amendment 7 to JCT 80, the With Quantities forms can now be used when some of the quantities are approximate. If this is done, the 'firming up' of those approximate quantities does not require the contract administrator to issue a variation instruction. Likewise, under ICE contracts variations are not used to alter or firm up any of the quantities.

Both JCT forms contain a clause under which the contract administrator issues instructions as to the expenditure of provisional sums, and JCT 80 extends this to provisional sums in sub-contracts (JCT 80 clause 13.3, IFC 84 clause 3.8). It should be noted that this is a *duty* of the contract administrator, as well as a power. Under JCT 80, such instructions may well consist of nominating a sub-contractor or supplier, but this is not necessarily the case. It will depend upon why the particular provisional sum was included in the contract bills. The definition and various uses of provisional and 'prime cost' sums is discussed in Chapter 8.

11.3.4 Valuation of variations

General principles

JCT 80 clause 13.5 and IFC 84 clause 3.7 each provide for certain work to be valued by the Quantity Surveyor in accordance with the Valuation Rules. The work in question includes any work executed as a result of a variation, work sanctioned as if it were a variation and work done as consequence of an instruction on the expenditure of a provisional sum. In fact this is not compulsory; it is perfectly legitimate for the employer and the contractor to make a specific agreement about a price for the varied work. However, in the absence of such an agreement, each contract lays down a set of rules for calculating the value of the work. There is little difference between the two forms in this respect; what follows is based on JCT 80.

In considering the valuation of variations under JCT 80, two vital preliminary points must be made. First, clause 13.5.6 makes it clear that if a particular case does not fit into any of the specific rules provided, then the contractor is entitled to 'a fair valuation'. This is very wide ranging in scope, and is intended as a residual or 'catch-all' clause. Indeed, it may be noted that this provision is even wide enough to bring about a *reduction* in the contract price, if limitations on the contractor's working methods are removed under clauses 13.1.2.1 to 13.1.2.4.

The second preliminary point arises out of clause 13.5.5. This states that if compliance with an instruction results in a consequential change to the conditions of any other work, then all that other work shall also be valued as if it were a variation. In other words, if the conditions of work are altered because the contractor has to comply with an instruction, then the provisions of clause 13 will apply to all that work as well.

Valuation rules

It will be seen that JCT 80 effectively divides work to be **valued** into three categories: work which can be valued by measurement; omitted work; and work which cannot be measured. We shall look at these categories in turn. First, however, attention should be given to three general points which are made in clause 13.5.3. These points relate to work which can be valued by measurement and to omitted work; they do *not* apply to work which cannot properly be valued by measurement. The points in question are:

1. In relation to measurable work and omitted work, any measurement is to be carried out in accordance with the same principles as those used for the preparation of the contract bills. This cross refers to clause 2.2.2.1, which lays down which Standard Method of Measurement (SMM) is to be used. The effect, therefore, is that all measurements taken to define the varied work must be taken in accordance with the relevant SMM.
2. Allowance is to be made for any percentage or lump sum adjustments in contract bills. Such an allowance is necessary because it is common practice for contractors when tendering to allow for overheads and profit by a lump sum or percentage addition to the sum of the preliminaries, instead of allowing a proportion in each and every measured item. This provision allows the lump sum to be adjusted in line with the variation.
3. An appropriate allowance is to be made in respect of certain preliminary items, the use of which would not be attributable in whole to the varied item, but which would be needed in a different way if items are varied. For example, changing the way in which brickwork is to be finished may involve keeping scaffolding on site for an extra period. The Standard Method of Measurement contains further examples of preliminary items which may be affected in this way.

We may now turn to the three categories of work to be valued which were identified above.

- *Measured work* The basic rule applying to 'additional or substituted work which can properly be valued by measurement' is that the rates and prices in the contract bills shall apply. However, this only applies to work which is of similar character, is executed under similar conditions and does not significantly change the quantity given in the bills. There is of course room for argument over exactly what is meant by such words as 'similar' and 'character'; none the less, most variations would be expected to fall within this principle.

If the varied work is of a similar character to work already in the contract bills, but is executed under different conditions and/or there is a significant change in the quantity, a different method of valuation must be used. Once again, the rates in the bills must be used as a basis, but here the valuation must include 'a fair allowance' for the difference in conditions and/or quantity. The new rate, which is thus derived from a bill rate by making this fair allowance, is known as a 'star rate'.

Examples of 'different conditions' under this clause would include winter instead of summer working; night instead of day working; differences in levels (such as storey heights, etc.) at which work is carried out; and the discovery of antiquities under clause 34. It is also worth making the point that changes in quantity alone must be 'significant' in order to justify the adoption of 'star rates'.

Work which does not fit into either of the previous two categories, because it is *not* of a similar character to work priced in the bills, is to be valued at 'fair rates and prices'. It is not easy for a contractor to invoke this clause after the work has been done. The contractor should make it clear to the contract administrator before undertaking the work that it should be valued under this rule. If this is not done, the contract administrator can claim that the contractor's lack of protest shows that the work falls into one of the previous two categories, so that no further allowance need be made.

- *Omitted work* It should be noted that this refers only to work which is being *intentionally* excluded under clause 13.1.1.1 from what was stated in the bills, and not to work *accidentally* left out by virtue of clause 2.2.2.2! Here the bill rates can and should be used for valuing the work omitted. IFC 84 does not expressly cover this point, but it would in any case be implied.[5]

- *Unmeasurable work* In respect of 'additional or substituted work which cannot properly be valued by measurement', valuation may be on a 'dayworks' basis. It is important to note that a decision as to whether or not this method should be adopted is for the Quantity Surveyor to make; it is not for the contractor to insist on valuation according to dayworks.

The clause lays down details as to how the dayworks items are to be calculated, both for the main contractor and for specialists. Certain 'official' definitions are used to determine the prime cost, and to this is added the relevant profit percentages set out in the bills. There are strict procedures requiring the contractor to produce vouchers specifying the time spent each day on the work, the names of the workers employed on it and details of the plant and materials used. All these vouchers must be given to the contract administrator by the end of the week following that in which the work was executed. If these administrative procedures are not followed to the letter by the contractor, the claim for valuation on a dayworks basis will probably fail.

11.4   FLUCTUATIONS

We may now look briefly at *fluctuations*, which are the third mechanism by which the contract sum may validly be adjusted. The purpose of a 'fluctuations clause' is to provide a mechanism for reimbursing contractors for changes in input prices over which they have no control at all. The JCT 80 fluctuations provisions are printed in a separate booklet from the main form of contract because these clauses are to an extent optional. The Appendix must state which of the fluctuations clauses apply.

In JCT 80, clause 37 (which is part of the main form) simply brings into operation the fluctuations clauses. It does this by stating that fluctuations shall be dealt with according to whichever of three alternatives are identified in the Appendix. These alternatives are clauses 38, 39 and 40. In the absence of any entry in the Appendix, the basic minimum provision for fluctuations contained in clause 38 is stated to apply.

The three fluctuation schemes are as follows:

- *Clause 38*:   Contributions, levy and tax fluctuations. This clause applies to items which are affected by the government and are thus completely beyond both the control and the prediction of the contractor. The elements to which the clause applies fluctuations are labour, materials and goods, electricity and fuels, but only to the extent that they are affected by tax, etc. In some cases, they are only covered as far as they have been listed in the contract documents. There are no methods for calculation set out in the clause, but obviously it would be necessary to take into account man-hours, quantities of materials and other directly ascertained costs. It is not intended that this clause should change the amount of contractor's profit.
- *Clause 39*:   Labour and materials cost and tax fluctuations. This clause includes all the government-related items that are covered by clause 38; it adds in labour and materials fluctuations. This covers the market costs of inputs such as wage rates and prices of materials.
- *Clause 40*:   Use of price adjustment formulae. This is a completely different type of calculation. It incorporates by reference a set of formula rules which define a technical financial calculation based on a wide variety of categories. The whole of the works is divided up into

financial categories and a monthly published bulletin gives indices by which each sum should be multiplied. In order for this to work, it is necessary for the contract bills to reflect the categories used by the fluctuation categories. Since the index numbers reflect the market situation each month, they are deemed to include the matters covered by clauses 38 and 39, and so only one of the clauses has to apply. The purpose of this method is to reduce the amount of calculation which has to be undertaken by the project team.

These different types of fluctuations are referred to as 'limited fluctuations' (clause 38) and 'full fluctuations' (clauses 39 and 40). In addition, it is of course possible to have no fluctuations provisions at all, by crossing out clause 37. Such a procedure would, however, only be suitable for a small project under steady conditions.

ICE 6 approaches the question of fluctuations in a similar way to JCT 80. Again, the fluctuations clauses are optional, are printed separately from the remainder of the contract and are based on published indices. However, to bring them into force requires a Special Condition in the contract, rather than an entry in the Appendix.

11.5 RETENTION MONEY

11.5.1 Nature and purpose of retention

It is common practice under a building contract of any appreciable size to make provision for what is called *retention*. This means that the employer retains a small percentage of each sum of money to which the contractor becomes entitled during the project, usually as the contract administrator issues interim certificates. The 'retention fund' thus created is intended to be available to the employer for the purpose of rectifying, or inducing the contractor to rectify, any defects in the work appearing during the 'Defects Liability Period'. As we have seen in Chapter 9, this period runs from the date of Practical Completion as certified by the contract administrator for whatever length of time is specified in the Appendix to the contract: 6 months is a common period.

JCT 80, in clauses 30.2 and 30.4, provides an illustration of the typical operation of a retention scheme. The effect of those provisions is that on the issue of every interim certificate the employer is entitled to deduct the agreed 'retention percentage'. This is deducted from the value of work which has not yet reached practical completion and from the value of any materials included in the certificate. The employer is also entitled to make equivalent retention from sums due to nominated sub-contractors.

It is further stated that the retention percentage referred to will be whatever figure the parties have entered in the Appendix to the contract. The default figure is 5%, although a footnote to the contract suggests that, if the contract is expected to exceed £500000, it should not be more than 3%. Further, it is common to provide a 'ceiling' beyond which no more will be retained, although JCT 80 itself contains no such provision.

After the contract administrator certifies that practical completion has been achieved, but before the issue of a certificate of 'Making Good Defects', the deduction which the employer is entitled to make is reduced by one-half. In effect, this means that the first interim certificate issued after practical completion will result in the release of one-half of the retention money currently held by the employer. The remainder will be released by the interim certificate required under clause 30.1.3, issued either at the end of the Defects Liability Period or upon the issue of the Certificate of Completion of Making Good Defects, whichever is the later.

11.5.2 Status and treatment of the retention

It is important to ensure that retention money is protected in the event of the employer's insolvency, so that contractors and sub-contractors can claim it in priority to the employer's general creditors. Clause 30.5.1 accordingly provides that 'the employer's interest in the retention is fiduciary as trustee for the contractor and for any nominated sub-contractor (but without obligation to invest)'. The idea is to make the retention money a trust fund, though without imposing upon the employer all the investment and accounting duties of a trustee. If successfully achieved, this would mean that a liquidator of the employer would be obliged to hand over the retention fund in full to the contractors and sub-contractors involved.

There are, however, practical problems. The provisions of clause 30.5.1 are not in themselves sufficient to enable a claim to be made; it is necessary for the money in question to be appropriated and set aside as a separate trust fund, usually in a separate bank account. Accordingly, the Private editions of JCT 80 provide, in clause 30.5.3, that any interested contractor or sub-contractor can obtain a court order for this to be done albeit leaving the employer to keep whatever interest is earned. Indeed, it seems that a contractor or sub-contractor would be entitled to take such action, even without a specific provision in the contract. This was laid down in *Rayack* v. *Lampeter Meat Co.*,[6] a startling case where the retention level was 50% and the Defects Liability Period lasted for 5 years! However, it is necessary to move quickly, for it has been held that an application to court will be too late once liquidation proceedings against the employer have actually been started.[7]

Notwithstanding the employer's status as a 'trustee' in relation to retention money, it is specifically provided by JCT 80 clause 30.1.1.2 that any rights of deduction or set-off available to the employer may be exercised against that fund. As a result, where the contract administrator has issued a certificate of delay and thus entitled the employer to liquidated damages in excess of the retention, the employer will not be compelled to pay such money into a separate account. This will be so, even if the contractor is seeking to challenge the certificate.[8] However, an employer can only adopt this course of action where the right of set-off is clear, for example, where it is backed by a certificate. Where the employer's claims, although arguable, are speculative and unsubstantiated, an order to pay the money into a separate account *will* be made.[9]

The complex rules which govern retention money are given a further dimension where nominated sub-contractors are involved. The problems which arise in such cases are discussed in Chapter 17.

11.6   SET OFF

11.6.1   The legal background

Set-off, in the construction context, concerns the right of an employer to refuse payment to the contractor on the basis that the employer has some counter-claim which would reduce or even extinguish what is owed. It is equally relevant to sub-contracts, where it concerns a main contractor's refusal on similar grounds to pay the sub-contractor.

Without such a right, an employer must simply make payment in accordance with the contract terms and then take the counter-claim to court or to arbitration. And if the contract provides (as many do) that no such claim can be arbitrated until the project is completed, the employer may have to wait several years for reimbursement. It can thus be readily appreciated, given the sheer size of many claims which arise out of large projects, that this is a topic of immense practical importance.

It is interesting to note that the early common law knew nothing of set-off. If a builder was promised a sum of money for building a house, then the money would have to be paid as soon as the work was complete. Even if the house had already fallen down, the client would have no defence to the builder's action, but merely a right to claim damages in a separate lawsuit!

Such an inconvenient rule could not possibly survive for long, and various inroads were made into it. First, it was provided by statute that a defendant could use as a defence any claims against the plaintiff arising out of the same transaction, *provided that they were already liquidated and ascertained debts* when the proceedings commenced. Second, common law began to recognize a right for a buyer to *abate the price* where goods were shown to be defective.[10] Third, and most important, the courts of equity began to permit the setting off of claims wherever they were so closely linked that 'neither of these claims ought to be insisted upon without taking the other into account'.

The general availability of set-off as a defence in construction disputes was confirmed by the Court of Appeal in *Hanak* v. *Green*.[11] In that case the employer and contractor were virtually at war throughout the contract period and, at the end, the employer sued the contractor for defective work. In answer to this action, the contractor raised claims for extra work, disruption caused by the employer's refusal to allow one of the workmen into the house and the loss of certain tools which the employer had thrown away! It was held that all these claims could properly be raised as defences since they arose directly under and affected the contract on which the employer relied.

It can now safely be said that, unless a particular contract excludes the right of set-off, it will apply in the following circumstances:

- Where there are mutual *debts*. This means that the amount owing is already ascertained and liquidated.
- Where defects in work are relied on to abate (i.e. reduce) a claim for the price of that work.
- Where the contract in question expressly permits it.
- Where the 'set-off' arises out of a breach of the same contract as that under which the claim for payment is made. Thus, for example, an employer who has a valid claim for damages for delay may set this off against the contractor's claim for payment.[12]
- Where the set-off arises out of a *separate* contract, but the two contracts are so closely linked that it would be unfair to deal with one claim without, at the same time, dealing with the other.[13]

This last category is the most difficult one. The courts are usually reluctant to hold that two separate contracts are close enough to permit a set-off.[14] For example, in *Anglian* v. *French Construction*[15] a contractor's claim against a supplier for defects in concrete beams used on the M3 motorway could not be set off against the supplier's claim for payment for beams used on the M4 and M6. Further, where the two contracts are not even between the same parties, the likelihood of successfully claiming a set-off is even more remote. Thus it seems that an employer cannot refuse to pay the main contractor in respect of work done by a nominated sub-contractor, on the ground that the employer has a claim against that sub-contractor under a direct warranty agreement for defective work.[16]

11.6.2 Certified sums

Can an employer exercise a right of set-off against sums which the contract administrator has certified as due for work properly executed? Or does the contract administrator's decision effectively override the employer's claim? This vital question has occupied the courts from 1971.

In *Dawnays* v. *Minter*[17] the Court of Appeal held that a main contractor could not set off a claim for a sub-contractor's delay against sums certified as due to the sub-contractor. The actual decision was based on the precise wording of the 'green form' of sub-contract, which was used for nominated sub-contractors under JCT 63, but the court clearly regarded the maintenance of cash flow as of general importance. As Lord Denning, MR, put it: 'An interim certificate is to be regarded virtually as cash, like a bill of exchange. It must be honoured. Payment must not be withheld on account of cross-claims, whether good or bad, except so far as the contract specifically provides.'

The approach adopted in the *Dawnays* case was applied by the Court of Appeal in several subsequent cases. Most of these likewise concerned sub-contracts, but the principle was also applied as between an employer and a contractor under a *main* contract.[18] However, this whole line of cases was heavily criticized by the House of Lords in the leading case of *Gilbert-Ash* v. *Modern Engineering*.[19] That case again concerned a sub-contract, but the terms of this one were very different. It was specifically stated that the main contractor could set off from certified sums 'any bona fide contra account and/or other claims'. Not surprisingly, it was held that this clause entitled the main contractor to set off claims for delay and defective workmanship.

Because the wording of the sub-contract in the *Gilbert-Ash* case was so clear, it is possible to argue that the *Dawnays* principle still operates. However, the better view is that the courts now regard that principle as having been overruled. As a result: 'In order to exclude the right to assert cross-claims admissible as equitable set-offs...it is necessary to find some clear and express provision in the contract which has that effect'.[20] To this statement should be added the qualification that, just occasionally, the right of set-off may also be excluded *by implication*. This happened, for example, in *Mottram* v. *Sunley*,[21] where a contractual clause giving a right of set-off was actually deleted by the parties before the contract was signed. It was held by the House of Lords that this showed the parties' intention not to have any such right.

11.6.3 Current standard form contracts

It appears from the decision of the Court of Appeal in *Pillings* v. *Kent Investments*[22] that the payment clauses currently found in JCT main contracts do not exclude the employer's right of set-off. It further seems likely that a similar view would be taken of ICE 6, which does not deal specifically with set-off at all. And, indeed, both GC/Works/1 and the ACA form of contract expressly *preserve* the employer's right.

On turning to sub-contracts, a rather different situation is found. As currently drafted, all JCT sub-contracts specify certain rights of set-off which the main contractor may exercise; they then provide that the rights of the parties in respect of set-off are fully set out in the sub-contract, and that no other rights whatsoever shall be implied. This attempt to outflank the *Gilbert-Ash* decision was held to be successful in *BWP* v. *Beaver*.[23] As a result, a main contractor who failed to comply with the procedures for a *contractual* set-off was not allowed to set off his claim at common law.

Since then, however, an important qualification has emerged. In *Acsim* v. *Dancon*[24] it was held by the Court of Appeal that a contractor who has lost the right of *set-off* may still show that the sum claimed by the sub-contractor is not really due. Thus, where a main contractor had not given notice of an intended set-off to the sub-contractor, as required by the contract, the main contractor was still permitted to defend by showing that the value of the sub-contractor's work was less than the amount claimed.

This decision is of considerable practical importance because most forms of sub-contract lay down strict procedures which must be followed in order to exercise a right of set-off. Claims have failed, for example, for lack of an architect's certificate of delay;[25] failure by the main contractor to give written notice;[26] and failure to quantity the set-off claim in sufficient detail.[27] However, none of these restrictions apply to the *common law* right of set-off.[28] Consequently, it may be expected that many contractors, having failed to comply with the contractual procedures, will simply fall back on their common law rights.

REFERENCES

1. *Blue Circle Industries plc* v. *Holland Dredging (UK) Ltd* (1987) 37 B.L.R. 40.
2. Wainwright, W.H. and Wood, A.A.B. *Variation and Final Account Procedure*. (4th edn). Hutchinson, London, 1983.
3. *North West Regional Hospital Board* v. *T.A. Bickerton & Son Ltd* [1970] 1 All E.R. 1039.
4. *Simplex Concrete Piles Ltd* v. *St Pancras MBC* (1958) 14 B.L.R. 80.
5. *Commissioner for Main Roads* v. *Reed & Stuart Pty Ltd* (1974) 12 B.L.R. 55.
6. *Rayack Construction Ltd* v. *Lampeter Meat Co. Ltd* (1979) 12 B.L.R. 30.

7. *Re Jartay Developments Ltd* (1982) 22 B.L.R. 134.
8. *Henry Boot Building Ltd* v. *Croydon Hotel & Leisure Co. Ltd* (1985) 36 B.L.R. 41.
9. *Concorde Construction Co. Ltd* v. *Colgan Co. Ltd* (1984) 29 B.L.R. 120.
10. *Mondel* v. *Steel* (1841) 8 M. & W. 858.
11. *Hanak* v. *Green* [1958] 2 Q.B. 9.
12. *Rapid Building Group Ltd* v. *Ealing Family Housing Association Ltd* (1984) 29 B.L.R. 5.
13. *Redpath Dorman Long Ltd* v. *Tubeworkers Ltd* (1984, unreported).
14. *A.B. Contractors Ltd* v. *Flaherty Brothers Ltd* (1978) 16 B.L.R. 8.
15. *Anglian Building Products Ltd* v. *W. & C. French (Construction) Ltd* (1972) 16 B.L.R. 1.
16. *George E. Taylor & Co. Ltd* v. *G Percy Trentham Ltd* (1980) 16 B.L.R. 15.
17. *Dawnays Ltd* v. *F.G. Minter Ltd* [1971] 2 All E.R. 1389.
18. *Frederick Mark Ltd* v. *Schield* (1971) 1 B.L.R. 32.
19. *Gilbert-Ash (Northern) Ltd* v. *Modern Engineering (Bristol) Ltd* [1974] A.C. 689.
20. *C.M. Pillings & Co. Ltd* v. *Kent Investments Ltd* (1985) 30 B.L.R. 80.
21. *Mottram Consultants Ltd* v. *Bernard Sunley & Sons Ltd* (1974) 2 B.L.R. 28.
22. *C.M. Pillings & Co. Ltd* v. *Kent Investments Ltd* (1985) 30 B.L.R. 80.
23. *BWP (Architectural) Ltd* v. *Beaver Building Systems Ltd* (1988) 42 B.L.R. 86.
24. *Acsim (Southern) Ltd* v. *Danish Contracting and Development Co.Ltd* (1989) 47 B.L.R. 55.
25. *Brightside Kilpatrick Engineering Services* v. *Mitchell Construction (1973) Ltd* (1973) 1 B.L.R. 62.
26. *Pillar PG Ltd* v. *D.J. Higgins Construction Ltd* (1986) 34 B.L.R. 43.
27. *BWP (Architectural) Ltd* v. *Beaver Building Systems Ltd* (1988) 42 B.L.R. 86.
28. *NEI Thompson Ltd* v. *Wimpey Construction UK Ltd* (1987) 39 B.L.R. 65.

12

Contractor's claims for loss and expense

A contractor is, of course, entitled under the contract to be paid for work done, including where appropriate the ascertained value of any variations which are ordered. In addition, the contractor may be able to make other claims against the employer. In Chapter 9 we considered those claims which relate to an extension of the contractual *time* for completion. We now turn to claims which, if successful, will result in the employer having to pay *money* to the contractor.

12.1 CONTRACT CLAIMS AND DAMAGES

Most of the standard form construction contracts and sub-contracts currently in use (with the exception of those designed for small-scale projects such as MW 80 and GC/Works/2) contain detailed provisions under which the contractor or sub-contractor can claim against the other party for any losses suffered through disruption of the work due to certain specified causes. These provisions tend to bear a greater or lesser resemblance to those under which an extension of time may by claimed, but it is important not to confuse the two issues. As we have already noted, clauses under which extensions of time for completion may be granted are included in the contract for the benefit of *both* parties, in that they not only protect the contractor from liability for delay, but also safeguard the employer's right to claim liquidated damages. As a result, they frequently apply to various 'neutral' events such as adverse weather, as well as to those which are the employer's responsibility. By contrast, the vast majority of contractual provisions which compel an employer to pay compensation to the contractor are based on causes of disruption for which the employer may reasonably be blamed.

This feature of claims provisions means that, in many cases, an event which enables a claim to be made would also found an action for damages for breach of contract. In particular, it may amount to a breach of the employer's implied obligation of co-operation with the contractor, which we shall discuss in Chapter 13. Where this occurs, the contractor may either sue for breach of contract or make a claim under the appropriate clause in the contract. The contractor's right to choose which remedy to pursue will only be removed by clear words in the contract itself, and this would be most unusual – indeed, JCT contracts specifically preserve the contractor's common law rights.

In deciding which remedy to pursue, it should be noted that the amount of money which is likely to be awarded will not be affected. As we shall see, the courts have ruled that 'direct loss and/or expense' (the words used in most contracts to describe what can be claimed in such cases) is to be assessed on exactly the same basis as damages for breach of contract. However, there are certain respects in which the two remedies *are* different, and these differences must be borne in mind when a claim is under consideration.

The main distinctions between making a contractual claim and bringing a legal action for damages are as follows:

- Although there is a broad similarity between the grounds on which a contractual claim may be made, and the conduct of an employer which amounts to a breach of contract, the two things are not identical. For example, while the disruption caused by an architect's instruction to postpone any part of the work may give rise to a claim under JCT 80, the giving of such an instruction would seldom amount to a breach of contract. Conversely, failure by the employer to provide continuous access to the site as promised is a clear breach of contract, but by no means all standard form contracts make this the subject of a claim. In fact JCT 80 *does* permit a claim to be made for this, providing that the access concerned is through adjoining land in the employer's possession and control.
- As a general rule, a claim under a specific provision of the contract can be made as soon as the relevant event occurs and the loss is suffered. Indeed, it may even be possible to claim *before* any loss is suffered, provided that this is clearly going to happen. By contrast, a contractor who sues for breach of contract will normally have to wait until completion to go to court or to arbitration. This, of course, is likely to have a damaging effect upon the contractor's cash flow.
- A claim under the contract will be settled by the contract administrator, sometimes with the assistance of the quantity surveyor, and will be paid through the normal contractual machinery, that is on the next

interim certificate to be issued after the claim is settled. By contrast, any damages must be awarded by a court or an arbitrator, and the judgment is then enforced in the normal way. The only exception to this is where the contract administrator is given express power to deal with claims for breach of contract; this is most unusual, although the ACA form of contract gives such power.

- The two preceding points are very much in favour of claiming under the contract in those circumstances where the contractor has a choice. However, an important limitation on contractual claims is that any specific procedural provisions in the contract (such as the giving of written notice, or the furnishing of sufficient supporting information) must be strictly complied with. If they are not, then the contractor is thrown back on to common law rights and can only sue for damages.

12.2 GROUNDS FOR CONTRACTUAL CLAIMS

It cannot be too strongly emphasized that any *contractual* claim made must be based upon some specific provision of the contract in question. The mere fact that unexpected difficulties have been encountered, or that the work is proving far more expensive than was foreseen, gives no shred of entitlement to a contractor. Naturally, there is considerable variation among construction contracts as to the grounds of claim which they permit; however, some general flavour may be obtained from a brief consideration of some of the more important standard forms.

12.2.1 JCT 80

A claim for compensation under JCT 80 clause 26 requires the contractor to prove two things:

1. that the contractor has incurred or is likely to incur direct loss and/or expense which would not otherwise be reimbursed under the contract; and
2. that this loss arises either:
   (a) from deferred possession of the site, where this is permitted under clause 23.1.2; or
   (b) 'because the regular progress of the Works or of any part thereof has been or is likely to be materially affected by any one or more of the matters referred to in clause 26.2'.

As to this effect on regular progress, two points must be made. First, it should be noted that the contractor's entitlement to claim is in no way linked to delay in completion of the work; all that matters is that the contractor's 'regular progress' has been disrupted in a way which causes loss or expense. Second, where loss and/or expense results from a number of causes, but it is practically impossible to identify separately the contribution made by each, then it has been accepted that a 'global' claim may be accepted.[1] However, this is only possible where *all* the causes are qualifying events under the contract and where the impossibility of separating them is not itself due to the contractor's delay in claiming.

The 'matters referred to in clause 26.2' are as follows:

1. The late receipt of instructions, drawings, details or levels from the contract administrator (26.2.1). However, this is dependent upon the contractor having specifically applied in writing for the information at a reasonable time, neither too late nor too early. As to what is a 'reasonable' time, it was held in a civil engineering case[2] that this must have regard to the interests of the engineer, as well as to those of the contractor.
2. The opening up for inspection of any work, or the testing of any work, materials or goods (including making good afterwards), under clause 8.3. Naturally, there can be no claim where such inspection or testing reveals a breach of contract by the contractor (26.2.2).
3. Any discrepancy in or divergence between the contract drawings and the contract bills (26.2.3).
4. The execution or non-execution of work outside the contract by the employer, or by persons engaged by the employer under clause 29 (26.2.4.1). This provision does not cover work done by sub-contractors, whether nominated or domestic, nor does it apply to work done by statutory undertakers, for example, in laying mains. However, it *does* apply to work which such statutory bodies undertake under a contract with the employer.[3]
5. The supply or non-supply of materials which the employer has undertaken to provide (26.2.4.2).
6. The postponement of any work in accordance with an instruction from the contract administrator (26.2.5). The generally accepted view is that this provision does not empower the contract administrator to postpone *all* the work, so as to enable the employer not to give possession of the site at the agreed time. It is concerned rather with instructions which alter the order in which the works are to be carried out, for instance, to accommodate a sub-contractor. Such a procedure may, of course, cause the contractor loss through the need to reprogramme.
7. Any failure by the employer to give access to the site or any part thereof through adjoining land which is in the employer's possession

and control (26.2.6). This ground of claim only applies if such access is specified in the contract bills or drawings, and if any required notice has been given by the contractor to the contract administrator.

8. Any variations or contract administrator's instructions as to the expenditure of provisional sums under clause 13 (26.2.7). It should be noted that the variation itself will be valued and paid in accordance with clause 13; the present provision deals only with any disruption which is caused to the contractor by compliance with the contract administrator's instruction.

12.2.2   Other contracts

As to the grounds of claim under other JCT contracts, IFC 84 follows closely the wording of JCT 80; however, it adds a clause to deal with certain kinds of disruption to the main contractor which may arise out of the provisions of that form of contract relating to 'named sub-contractors'. As regards JCT 63, the grounds are broadly similar, although there are significant differences of wording. However, this earlier contract contains no provisions to deal with work carried out by the employer's own staff (as opposed to the employer's 'artists and tradesmen'), materials supplied by the employer, or failure by the employer to give access to the site.

In the case of GC/Works/1, clause 46(1) enables the contractor to claim if certain listed events result in 'the regular progress of the Works or any part of them being materially disrupted or prolonged', where this means that the contractor 'properly and directly incurs any expense'. The relevant events do not cover a very wide area, although they *do* include such things as delay in providing drawings or other information and delays caused by other contractors. Furthermore, while claims under clause 46(1) can only be made where there is 'disruption or prolongation', any expense involved in complying with the project manager's instructions may qualify for payment under clauses 42 and 43. And it should be noted that this may in certain circumstances effectively entitle the contractor to be compensated in respect of 'unforeseeable ground conditions' (clause 7).

The approach adopted by the ACA form of contract is a more generally worded one. Clause 7 entitles the contractor to claim in respect of any 'damage, loss and/or expense' suffered when 'any act, omission or default or negligence of the employer or of the architect disrupts the regular progress of the Works or of any Section or delays the execution of them in accordance with the dates stated in the Time Schedule'. However, this does not include delay or disruption resulting from compliance with the architect's instructions, something which is separately dealt with under clauses 8 and 17.

Finally, the approach adopted by ICE 6 may be noted. This makes no attempt to collect under a single clause the various grounds on which 'additional payment' may be claimed, although the *procedural* matters which apply to all of them are found in clause 52(4). The grounds themselves are too varied to be summarized, but taken in total they appear to cover a wider area than the grounds under other forms, which means that more risks are borne by the employer. On the other hand, the ICE form makes widespread use of the formula 'which could not reasonably have been foreseen by an experienced contractor' in limiting the circumstances in which successful claims may be made.

12.3   CLAIMS PROCEDURES

Every form of contract which permits the contractor to make money claims lays down certain procedural steps which must be followed if a claim is to succeed. These naturally very between the forms, and space does not permit us to deal with all the variations. We shall therefore concentrate mainly on the provisions of JCT 80, merely drawing attention to some aspects of other contracts which are significantly different.

12.3.1   JCT 80

The procedure in chronological order for making a claim for 'loss and/or expense' under JCT 80 is laid down by clause 26.1. It is as follows:

1. The contractor considers that regular progress of the work has been or is likely to be materially affected by a relevant matter. The contractor further considers that because of this (or because late possession of the site has been given), there is a likely, or actual incurrence of direct loss and/or expense which would not otherwise be reimbursed under the contract.

2. The contractor makes written application to the contract administrator, stating the above. No particular form of application is required (although presumably the matter relied upon should be identified), but the application must be made 'as soon as it has become, or should reasonably have become, apparent' to the contractor that regular progress has been or is likely to be affected. It is vital to appreciate that any notice which does not comply with this time limit may simply be ignored by the contract administrator, in which case the contractor will be left to claim damages for any breach of contract which can be established.

3. The contract administrator must then decide whether or not the contractor's claim is well founded. In deciding this question, the contract administrator may request from the contractor any further information which is reasonably necessary, and the contractor must comply with any such request.

4. If in agreement, in principle with the contractor's claim, the contract administrator must then ascertain or instruct the quantity surveyor to ascertain the amount of loss and/or expense incurred. Again, the contractor may be requested to furnish such details as are reasonably necessary.

5. Any amount duly ascertained under clause 26 is added to the contract sum and will therefore feature in the next interim certificate.

12.3.2 IFC 84

Not surprisingly, the claims machinery under IFC 84 clause 4.11 is closely modelled on that in JCT 80. However, it is possible (though the wording is not altogether clear) that a written application under IFC 84 must *automatically* be accompanied by such supporting information as is reasonably necessary to enable the contract administrator and/or the quantity surveyor to carry out their duties. On the other hand, such an application need not be made *as soon as* disruption appears likely, but only *within a reasonable time* of this becoming apparent.

12.3.3 JCT 63

A crucial difference between the claims machinery of JCT 63 and that of JCT 80 is that written applications under clause 11(6) and 24(1) of JCT 63 are to be made within a reasonable time *after the contractor has been involved in direct loss and/or expense*. As a result, a contractor who incurs loss and/or expense of a continuing nature must either make a series of applications or wait until the loss ceases and deal with it in one application.

As to what constitutes a valid notice, it has been held that the vital question is whether or not it sufficiently identifies the issue on which the architect's decision is required.[4] Naturally, in cases where the architect already knows the relevant facts a very brief and uninformative notice will suffice. Assuming that this requirement is satisfied, it is up to the architect or quantity surveyor to request from the contractor any further information which they need in order to carry out their duties.

There appears to be one important exception to the general rule that the loss and/or expense which gives rise to a claim need not be particularized in any detail. It has been held by the Court of Appeal that where a contractor wishes to claim in respect of financing charges (a continuing loss), this must be mentioned in the notice which is given to the architect.[5]

12.3.4 GC/Works/1

This form of contract makes it abundantly clear that, unless a contractor complies strictly with the claims procedure laid down, there will be no entitlement to anything at all under the contract. Clause 46(3) makes it a condition precedent to an increase of the contract sum for disruption or prolongation expense that:

1. The contractor gives notice to the project manager *immediately* on becoming aware of likely disruption, specifying its cause and stating that an increase in the contract sum is being sought; and
2. The contractor furnishes details and documentary evidence of the expense *as soon as reasonably practicable* after it is incurred.

12.3.5 ACA form of contract

This form of contract, too, imposes strict procedural burdens on a contractor who wishes to claim because the regular progress of the work has been disrupted. Notice must be given to the architect *immediately* it becomes apparent that a claimable event has occurred *or is likely to occur*. Furthermore, the contractor must, when next applying for an interim payment under the contract, submit a written estimate, supported by appropriate documentary evidence, of the damage, loss and/or expense so far incurred. If the architect accepts the estimate, or if it can be settled by negotiation or under the contractual adjudication procedure, then the contract sum is adjusted 'and no further or other additions or payments shall be made' in respect of the claim.

The contract specifically provides that, if the contractor fails to comply with the above procedure, there will be no entitlement to any adjustment of the contract sum until final certificate. Further, even when such an adjustment is made, it will not include any interest or financing charges for the intervening period.

12.3.6 ICE 6

The claims provisions of the ICE contract (and of the FIDIC Conditions for Civil Engineering Contracts, 4th edn, which are modelled on it) appear to have overcome some at least of the problems caused by the tortuous wording of earlier editions. It is now clear that if a contractor wishes to make a claim under any clause of the contract other than those which deal with variations, the contractor must give written notice to the engineer 'as soon as may be reasonable and in any event within 28 days after the happening of the events giving rise to the claim'. The contractor must thereafter keep contemporary records to support any subsequent claim. The initial notice is to be followed 'as soon as is reasonable in all the circumstances' by an account containing full and detailed particulars of the amount claimed.

The case law on early versions of the ICE conditions made it clear that any failure to comply with the provisions as to giving notice would be fatal to a contractor's claim. However, the 6th edition contains two provisions which mitigate the strictness of this principle. First, it is provided that, despite the contractor's failure, the engineer may still uphold the claim 'to the extent that the engineer has not been prevented from or substantially prejudiced by such failure in investigating the said claim'. Second, it is made clear that where the contractor seeks interim payment on a claim but has submitted insufficient particulars, the engineer may none the less authorize payment 'of such part of the claim as the particulars may substantiate to the satisfaction of the engineer'.

12.4 QUANTIFICATION OF CLAIMS

12.4.1 Nature of 'loss and/or expense'

When it comes to turning a contractor's claim into money, the courts have made it clear that 'direct loss and/or expense', and similar phrases found in other standard form contracts, require an assessment process equivalent to that for an award of damages for breach of contract.[6] This means that, notwithstanding the use of the word 'direct', the vital question will be whether any particular item of loss falls within the normal rules of remoteness of damage in breach of contract cases. Indeed, the courts appear to have adopted a fairly liberal approach to this question. In *Croudace* v. *Cawoods*,[7] for example, a contract to supply masonry blocks to the main contractors on a school project stated that the suppliers should not be liable for any 'consequential loss or damage' caused by late delivery or defects. Notwithstanding this clause, in an action for delay and defects the Court of Appeal awarded damages to the main contractors to cover loss of productivity, inflation costs resulting from delay and the cost of meeting a claim brought against them by sub-contractors.

It should at this point be stressed once again that a claim for 'loss and/or expense' is based *not* on delay in completion of the works, but on the fact that the regular progress of those works has been disrupted. It is true that most cases do in fact concern delayed completion, and indeed some types of loss can *only* arise where this is so, but this must be seen as coincidental. Where, despite finishing a job on time, a contractor incurs additional expenses, such as the cost of management time to deal with difficulties caused by the contract administrator's instructions, or loss of productivity due to the unexpected operations of other contractors on the site, the contractor is fully entitled to claim for these losses.

12.4.2 'Immediate' costs

Where a job is prolonged or disrupted, certain types of loss are instantly recognizable as likely to occur. For example, where working conditions are rendered more difficult (e.g. because what was intended to be a summer job has now become a winter one), it may be necessary for the contractor to employ additional labour, use extra materials or hire extra plant, simply in order to achieve the same result. Similarly, the prolongation of a contract may mean that materials which would have lasted for the original period deteriorate during the overrun, requiring either replacement or expensive protective measures. Yet again, the natural effect of inflation may mean that the outlay on both labour and materials is increased because of a delay. Finally, it is fairly obvious that 'site overheads', that is those general expenses exclusively referable to the contract in question, will be greater if the contract period is lengthened.

All these items may in principle be made the subject of a claim. However, three cautionary notes should be sounded:

1. It must be shown that the loss in question has actually been suffered. Thus, for example, any claim for increased labour or materials costs must give full credit for anything received under the operation of a fluctuations clause in the contract.
2. The loss must *as a matter of law* have resulted from the claim-provoking event. Thus an employer must pay for turning a summer contract into a winter one, but is not responsible if the contractor is then caught by some totally independent and unforeseeable disaster, even though this would not have affected the project if the works had been completed on time.
3. Where the contractor's own plant stands idle in a period of delay, the courts will not normally uphold a claim based on current hiring rates, but will limit the contractor to a claim based on depreciation and maintenance costs.[8]

12.4.3 Head office overheads and profit

Any disruption to the regular progress of work under a contract may lead the contractor to incur administrative costs, such as the diversion of managerial time and effort, at head office. If so, these costs may justifiably be claimed, but it will not be assumed that such losses have been suffered; if they are to be recovered, they must be specified and properly supported by the evidence.[9]

Where the completion of a contract is *prolonged* by something for which the employer is contractually responsible, the contractor may also seek to claim in respect of *general* head office overheads. The contractor's argument here is either that the contract is making a smaller contribution to these business expenses than it should, or that the organization is being tied up so as to prevent it from earning the necessary contribution to head offices expenses elsewhere. Further, precisely the same arguments are used to support a claim for lost or diminished profits which, it is claimed, should have arisen out of the contract in question.

In practice, because of the enormous difficulties of accurate quantification, contractors' claims under this heading tend to adopt a 'formula' approach. A notional daily or weekly contribution from the contract in question to general business overheads and profits is identified, and then multiplied by the number of days or weeks for which the contractor is entitled to claim. While the defects of such an approach are obvious, it is regarded by the courts as generally acceptable, provided that any formula used is not applied blindly and without reference to the realities of the situation. Moreover, it is important to emphasize that the onus is on the contractor to prove that actual loss has been suffered. As a result, it was ruled in *Peak* v. *McKinney*[10] that the contractor must be able to show that the organization *could* have worked elsewhere during the period of delay (i.e. that the industry as a whole had work on offer).

As mentioned, a 'formula' approach to this aspect of a claim is centred on the identification of a 'head office overheads and profit contribution' from the delayed contract. Where the three best-known formulae differ is in their method identifying the appropriate percentage:

1. The *Hudson* formula[11] reads as follows:

$$\frac{\text{Overheads/Profit Percentage}}{100} \times \frac{\text{Contract Sum}}{\text{Contract Period}} \times \text{Period of Delay}$$

What this means is that the claim is based on the allowances actually made by the contractor in tendering for the contract, notwithstanding that these may of course have been unreasonably optimistic or pessimistic. This formula has been applied in a Canadian case,[12] and was also apparently approved by an English court in *Finnegan* v. *Sheffield CC*.[13]

2. The *Emden* formula[14] reads:

$$\frac{\text{Total Overheads/Profit}}{\text{Total Turnover}} \times \frac{\text{Contract Sum}}{\text{Contract Period}} \times \text{Period of Delay}$$

Here the figure used is the percentage which is relevant to the contractor's whole organization, found by dividing *total* overhead cost and profit by *total* turnover. This approach, which of course ignores the question whether the particular contract was more or less profitable than usual, has been accepted by an English court in *Whittall Builders* v. *Chester-le-Street*.[15] Ironically, it was also actually applied in the *Finnegan* case,[16] although the judge there approved the *Hudson* formula!

3. The *Eichleay* formula, which is named after the US case in which it was first expressed, reads:

$$\frac{\text{Contract Invoices}}{\text{Total Invoices}} \times \text{Total Overheads/Profit} \times \frac{\text{Contract Sum}}{\text{Contract Period}} \times \text{Delay}$$

This approach is widely used in the USA but does not yet seem to have appeared on this side of the Atlantic. Although more refined than the *Emden* formula, it is subject to the same criticism of ignoring any special features of the particular contract.

12.4.4 Interest and financing charges

The common law has always refused to permit a creditor to claim either damages or interest for the mere fact of being kept out of money owing by late payment.[17] As a result, it was for a long time open for a debtor to pay the bare amount of a debt at any time before judgment was awarded, and thus to avoid any further liability.

The worst of this rule has now been removed by statute in respect of both litigation (*Supreme Court Act 1981*, section 35(a)) and arbitration (*Arbitration Act 1950*, section 19(a)). These provisions enable interest to be awarded wherever a debt was still unpaid when proceedings for its recovery were commenced. However, where payment is made late but before proceedings are launched, it has been reluctantly confirmed by the House of Lords that the common law rule still applies; the plaintiff in such circumstances is not entitled to either damages or interest.[18]

Rather questionably, perhaps, the lower courts have for some time been prepared to ignore the basic rule in cases where a plaintiff can show 'special damage' from late payment, for instance, by having to pay interest on an overdraft which could have been cleared or reduced if the debtor had paid up. This escape route has now been seized upon in construction cases to justify claims by contractors, as part of 'direct loss and/or expense', for what are termed 'financing charges'. Such a claim has been upheld by the Court of Appeal.[19] This was on the ground that since 'the loss of interest which he has to pay on the capital he is forced to borrow and on the capital which he is not free to invest would be recoverable for the employer's breach of contract', it was accordingly also recoverable under JCT 63. It may be noted that, because of the wording of JCT 63, the loss was recoverable only up to the date of the contractor's written application; JCT 80 has removed this need for multiple applications by enabling claims to cover also predicted future losses.

Whether or not this decision is truly consistent with the general common law rule, it was approved by the Court of Appeal in *Rees & Kirby* v. *Swansea CC.*[20] The court in that case also came to the realistic conclusion that such a claim should be assessed on the basis of compound rather than simple interest.

12.4.5   Costs of preparing a claim

In modern times, contractors' money claims have become of enormous, practical importance, and something of a 'claims industry' has grown up to assist in the preparation and presentation of such claims. Where 'claims consultants' are employed in this way, their services may themselves constitute a considerable cost to the contractor, and a question which has arisen is whether these costs can then form part of the claim.

The answer in principle appears to be that, since a contractor is not required under most standard form contracts to make a detailed claim for loss and/or expense, any costs incurred in so doing should not themselves be recoverable.[21] However, where compliance with the contract administrator's or quantity surveyor's request for further evidence involves an unusually heavy amount of managerial time, this can probably be recovered.[22]

REFERENCES

1. *J. Crosby & Sons Ltd* v. *Portland UDC* (1967) 5 B.L.R. 126; *Merton LBC* v. *Stanley Hugh Leach Ltd* (1985) 32 B.L.R. 51.
2. *Neodox Ltd* v. *Swinton & Pendlebury UDC* (1958) 5 B.L.R. 34.
3. *Henry Boot Construction Ltd* v. *Central Lancashire New Town Development Corporation* (1980) 15 B.L.R. 1.
4. *Merton LBC* v. *Stanley Hugh Leach Ltd* (1985) 32 B.L.R. 51.
5. *Rees & Kirby Ltd* v. *Swansea CC* (1985) 30 B.L.R. 1.
6. *Wraight Ltd* v. *P.H. & T. (Holdings) Ltd* (1968) 13 B.L.R. 26; *F.G. Minter Ltd* v. *Welsh Health Technical Services Organisation* (1980) 13 B.L.R. 1.
7. *Croudace Construction Ltd* v. *Cawoods Concrete Products Ltd* (1978) 8 B.L.R. 20
8. *B. Sunley Ltd & Co* v. *Cunard White Star Ltd* [1940] 1 K.B. 740.
9. *Tate & Lyle Food and Distribution Co. Ltd* v. *GLC* [1981] 3 All E.R. 716.
10. *Peak Construction (Liverpool) Ltd* v. *McKinney Foundations Ltd* (1970) 1 B.L.R. 111.

11. Wallace, I.N.D. *Hudson's Building and Engineering Contracts*, 10th edn, Sweet and Maxwell, London, 1970, p. 599.
12. *Ellis-Don Ltd* v. *Parking Authority of Toronto* (1978) 28 B.L.R. 98.
13. *J.F. Finnegan Ltd* v. *Sheffield CC* (1988) 43 B.L.R. 124.
14. Powell-Smith, V. and Sims J. *Building Contract Claims*, 2nd edn, BSP Professional Books, Oxford, 1988, p. 133.
15. *Whittall Builders Co. Ltd* v. *Chester-le-Street DC* (1987) 40 B.L.R. 82.
16. *J.F. Finnegan Ltd* v. *Sheffield CC* (1988) 43 B.L.R. 124.
17. *London, Chatham & Dover Railway Co.* v. *South Eastern Railway Co.* [1893] A.C. 429.
18. *President of India* v. *La Pintada Cia Navegacion SA* [1985] A.C. 104.
19. *F.G. Minter Ltd* v. *Welsh Health Technical Services Organisation* (1980) 13 B.L.R. 1.
20. *Rees & Kirby Ltd* v. *Swansea CC* (1985) 30 B.L.R. 1.
21. *James Longley & Co. Ltd* v. *South West Thames RHA* (1983) 127 S.J. 597.
22. *Tate & Lyle Food and Distribution Co. Ltd* v. *GLC* [1981] 3 All E.R. 716.

13

Other obligations of the employer

The most important of the employer's obligations under a construction contract are monetary: to pay the contractor what is due for work done and, in certain circumstances, to compensate the contractor for loss and expense. These obligations we have discussed in detail in Chapters 11 and 12.

The present chapter considers a number of other obligations which are imposed on the employer. We look, first, at those obligations which will be implied by law wherever they are not overridden by some express term of the contract. Second, a brief account is given of the obligations which are expressly imposed upon the employer under JCT 80. These obligations are few in number, but extremely important to the effective discharge of the contract.

The reason why the employer appears to have relatively few express contractual obligations, and to play a merely passive role, is that the contract allocates numerous duties to the contract administrator. In truth, many of these duties are the employer's responsibility in the sense that, if the contract administrator fails to perform, the contractor may claim against the employer for breach of contract. The extent of the employer's responsibility is also considered in this chapter, although the actual content of the contract administrator's duties is dealt with in more detail in Chapter 14.

The fact that so many of the employer's obligations are carried out by the contract administrator leads to an important practical point. It is that an employer who tries to circumvent this relationship, and to communicate directly with the contractor, runs a serious risk of causing confusion and resulting problems. A wise contractor will decline to accept instructions from the employer, requesting instead that they be channelled through the contract administrator. In any event, the contractor should always ask the contract administrator for written confirmation of the employer's direct instructions.

13.1 IMPLIED OBLIGATIONS

13.1.1 The duty to co-operate with the contractor

It was acknowledged in *Merton* v. *Leach*[1] that two general obligations on the part of the employer are to be implied into all building contracts; they are expressed as follows:

1. The employer will not hinder or prevent the contractor from carrying out his or her obligations in accordance with the terms of the contract and from executing the works in regular and ordely manner.
2. The employer will take all steps reasonably necessary to enable the contractor so to discharge his or her obligations and to execute the works in a regular and orderly manner.

Although they are expressed as two separate obligations, these are in reality the positive and negative aspects of the same thing. Together they make it the employer's duty to *co-operate with the contractor* in all aspects of the contract work. In considering what this means in practice, we shall accordingly not attempt to divide our examples into those which involve 'non-hindrance' and those which require 'co-operation'.

13.1.2 Specific examples of non-hindrance and co-operation

It is obvious to everyone that it is the *duty* of the contractor under a construction contract to carry out and complete the contract works. What is sometimes overlooked is that it is also the contractor's *right* to do this. Unless the contract provides otherwise, the contractor is entitled to carry out the whole of the contract works within the contract period, and the employer must co-operate to enable this to be achieved.

One aspect of the contractor's right to do the work tendered for is that the employer cannot order the omission of work from the contract, with the intention of giving this work to another contractor.[2] This, indeed, is so fundamental that such conduct could well constitute a repudiatory breach by the employer (Chapter 23), which would entitle the contractor to terminate the contract.[3] It is thought that the employer is likewise unable to take work for which the main contractor has priced and instead nominate a sub-contractor to carry it out.

The contractor's right to carry out the work also means that, as a general rule, the employer cannot unilaterally decide to abandon the project altogether. This is certainly the position under JCT 80, where the employer's right to determine the contractor's employment (considered in Chapter 23) arises only in certain very limited circumstances. However, some other standard form contracts (such as GC/Works/1 and MC 87) do contain an express clause allowing the employer to terminate the project at any time without reason. Naturally, under such a contract, an employer who abandons the project will not be liable for damages to the contractor. It is important for a contractor to ensure that, where the main contract contains a unilateral termination clause, the sub-contract contains a similar provision. If this is not done, the contractor will be liable to the sub-contract when the project is abandoned, without being able to pass responsibility for this on to the employer.[4]

As with abandonment, so with temporary suspension of the work, although it is far more common to find an express term of the contract giving the employer certain powers in this respect. The question of suspension is considered in more detail in Chapter 14.

As seen in Chapter 9, the employer's duty of co-operation involves giving the contractor possession of the site at whatever time the contract states. If the contract is silent on this matter, then the employer's implied obligation requires the contractor to be given possession at such a time as will enable the work to be finished by the specified completion date.[5]

Whether or not the employer's obligation extends to the obtaining of any official permits for the proposed work, such as planning permission, depends essentially on the terms of the contract. Under JCT 80, for example, the effect of clause 6 is that the employer is responsible for ensuring that the works as designed comply with all statutory requirements; it is thereafter the contractor's responsibility to serve whatever notices and obtain whatever permissions are necessary. By contrast, many design and build contracts, such as CD 81, place the entire responsibility on the contractor, except in so far as the 'Employer's Requirements' are specifically guaranteed to comply with the statutory requirements.

An important part of the employer's duty of co-operation concerns the appointment of a contract administrator and, where appropriate, the nomination of sub-contractors. These matters are usually covered by express terms of the contract, but if not, the implied obligation certainly extends to them. Indeed, where the contract envisages the use of an architect or an engineer to supervise the works and act as the employer's agent, it is a condition precedent to the performance of the contractor's obligations that the appointment is made.[6] This means that a contractor can refuse to carry out any work until the employer makes such an appointment. If, however, the contractor proceeds without the appointment of a contract administrator, then this would constitute a waiver of the right to insist on an appointment.[7]

Similarly, where the contract makes provision for sub-contractors or suppliers to be nominated, the employer must make these nominations within a reasonable time. Further, should it become necessary to re-nominate (or to reappoint a contract administrator), this too must be done within a reasonable time.

As far as the general running of the project is concerned, the duty of co-operation may be breached on the employer's behalf by a number of other parties. For example, the employer will be liable to the contractor for breach of contract if the contract administrator delays unreasonably in giving necessary instructions; if materials which the employer has undertaken to supply are delivered late; or if the contractor's work is impeded by other contractors working directly for the employer. However, the employer is *not* responsible in this way for the defaults of nominated sub-contractors or suppliers; any responsibility which the employer has for such defaults must be based on an express term of the contract (e.g. JCT 80 clause 25.4.7).

Before leaving the subject of the employer's implied obligations, it is important to note that these do not require co-operation to an extent which enables the contractor to do *more* than the contract specifies. Thus, while it is the contractor's right to complete *on or before* the contractual completion date, the employer's duty of co-operation extends only to ensuring that the completion date is achieved. A contractor who seeks to finish early cannot force the employer to assist.[8] Similarly, where a sub-contractor undertakes to carry out work 'at such time or times as the contractor shall direct or require', there is no implied term requiring the main contractor to make sufficient work available to the sub-contractors to enable them to work in an efficient and economic manner.[9]

13.2   EXPRESS OBLIGATIONS UNDER JCT 80

In addition to the implied obligations described above, the express terms of any construction contract will undoubtedly impose duties on the employer. Some of these (e.g. the duty to give possession of the site) will go no further than the term which would in any event be implied; others (e.g. duties to insure) break completely fresh ground. Naturally, the range and content of the employer's express obligations will vary from one form of contract to another, and it would be impossible here to deal with all the possibilities. We shall therefore look at those obligations contained in JCT 80, in order to give some idea of what is commonly found.

13.2.1   Payment

Undoubtedly the most important of all the employer's express obligations is to pay the contractor the sum of money which forms the consideration for the contract, known as the **Contract Sum**. The extent of this obligation, and the way in which the contract sum is assessed and can be altered, are all matters dealt with in Chapter 11.

13.2.2 Necessary nominations

Article 3 of JCT 80 names the 'Architect or Contract Administrator' who is to be responsible for performing all the functions which the contract conditions allocate to such a person. Similarly, if a 'Quantity Surveyor' is to be appointed, this is done by Article 4. The relevant article provides in each case that, if the person named dies or ceases to act, it is the employer's duty to nominate a replacement. This renomination must take place within a reasonable time, which must in any event not exceed 21 days. It is also made clear that, as a general rule, the contractor has a right of objection on reasonable grounds to the renomination. However, there is no right of objection where the employer is a local authority and the architect, contract administrator or quantity surveyor is an employee of that authority.

Where a nominated sub-contractor drops out (usually through insolvency), it is the duty of the employer to nominate an alternative within a reasonable time. This principle was first established in two important decisions of the House of Lords on JCT 63,[10] and is now made express by clause 35.24 of JCT 80. The working of this provision, and its financial effects upon the employer and the contractor, are discussed in Chapter 18.

13.2.3 Site obligations

As we have seen in Chapter 9, the need to give the contractor possession of the site at the right time is fundamental to the contract. Failure to do so will cause the employer to forfeit any claim for liquidated damages on late completion.[11] It will also render the employer liable to pay damages to the contractor.[12] Given the importance of this matter, it is odd that JCT 80 does not specifically state that it is the employer's duty to give possession of the site. What the contract actually says in clause 23.1.1 is that 'on the Date of Possession possession of the site shall be given to the contractor', without saying by whom it shall be given!

Unless otherwise agreed, the employer's obligation under JCT 80 is to give possession of the whole site from the outset, and not just those parts where work is to begin immediately. It is further accepted that the contractor must be given not only the actual area to be built on, but also sufficient surrounding space to enable the work to be properly undertaken.[13] This would include, for example, room to erect temporary buildings and compounds, to store equipment, and so on. However, the employer will only be obliged to provide access to the site across adjoining land where this is specifically stated in the bills.

13.2.4   Insurance

As we shall see in Chapter 15, clause 22 of JCT 80 offers a choice of insurance arrangements, depending among other things on whether the work consists entirely of new buildings or whether existing buildings are involved. All that need be said here is that, if the clause chosen for inclusion in the contract is either 22B or 22C, then it is the employer's duty to procure the necessary insurance.

13.2.5   Non-assignment

Clause 19.1.1 of JCT 80 provides that 'neither the employer nor the contractor shall, without the written consent of the other, assign this contract'. It has been held that this wording prohibits the employer not only from assigning the whole contract to a third party, but also from assigning a right to sue the contractor for a specific breach of the contract (e.g. for defective work).[14] However, it was also held *not* to prohibit the employer from assigning any claim against the contractor *in tort*.

13.2.6   CONFIDENTIALITY

One final obligation imposed upon the employer by JCT 80 is found in clause 5.7. This forbids the employer to divulge or use any of the rates or prices in the contract bills, except for the purposes of the contract.

13.3   RESPONSIBILITY FOR CONTRACT ADMINISTRATOR

It has been emphasized above that many construction contracts allocate to the contract administrator the performance of what are really the employer's obligations. These will be considered in more detail in Chapter 14; our interest for the moment is on the extent to which the employer can be held responsible to the contractor for the contract administrator's actions.

It is crucial, in this context, to distinguish between two separate aspects of the contract administrator's role. First, there are the numerous things which are done in the capacity of agent of the employer (e.g. supplying information, giving instructions as and when necessary, and so on). In *Merton* v. *Leach*[1] it was held that the employer impliedly guarantees that these functions will all be performed 'with reasonable diligence and with reasonable skill and care'. This means that any negligence on the part of the contract administrator will render the employer liable for breach of contract to the contractor. The employer will then, of course, be able to claim against the contract administrator for breach of the terms of engagement.

The second aspect of the contract administrator's role concerns certain 'independent' or 'discretionary' functions such as adjudication or certification. As to these, it was said in *Merton* v. *Leach*[1] that the employer 'does not undertake that the architect will exercise his discretionary powers reasonably; he undertakes that, although the architect may be engaged or employed by him, he will leave him free to exercise his discretion fairly and without improper interference by him'.

In spite of this dictum, there are circumstances in which the employer's duties in respect of the contract administrator's 'discretionary powers' go further than mere non-interference. In *Perini Corporation* v. *Commonwealth of Australia*[15] an employer became aware that the architect was acting improperly, by refusing to deal at all with applications for extension of time (as opposed to merely making incorrect decisions on applications). The Australian court held that it was the employer's obligation in such circumstances to order the architect to carry out his duties under the contract and, if that failed, to dismiss and replace him. In *Perini*, the architect was an actual employee of the employer, a government department, but it is thought that the same principle would apply in cases where the architect is 'independent'.

13.4 RESPONSIBILITY FOR SITE CONDITIONS

A question which has arisen many times over the years concerns the extent to which an employer who initiates a project bears legal responsibility in respect of its feasibility. In particular, if site conditions such as the subsoil turn out to be unexpectedly adverse, or the proposed method of working proves impracticable, is there any way in which the contractor can claim redress? The answer to these questions naturally lies within the terms of the contract, but a fairly clear overall picture emerges from the leading cases.

13.4.1 Contractor's risk

As a basic principle, it is clear that the risk of adverse site conditions rests with the contractor. This was firmly established in *Bottoms* v. *York Corporation*,[16] which concerned the carrying out of sewerage works. Because the soil was softer than anticipated, the contractor had to carry out considerable extra work. When the engineer refused to authorize extra payment for this work as a variation, the contractor left the site and claimed a reasonable sum for the work done. No boreholes had been sunk in advance by either party, but the employer had received reports before signing the contract that the contractor was certain to lose money in the type of ground to be expected. It was none the less held that the employer owed no duty to disclose these reports to the contractor, whose claim accordingly failed.

The principle that adverse site conditions are a contractor's risk is not altered merely because the employer provides plans or specifications at the time of tender. The mere fact that these are provided does not imply any warranty by the employer as to their accuracy. In *Sharpe* v. *San Paulo Railway*,[17] for example, a contractor undertook to build a railway in Brazil for a lump sum. The engineer's plans proved to be hopelessly inadequate and, as a result, the contractor was forced to excavate about twice as much as had been anticipated. It was held that since the accuracy of the plans was in no way warranted, the contractor was not entitled to any extra payment in respect of this work.

As with site conditions, so with working methods. In *Thorn* v. *London Corporation*,[18] a contract was let for the demolition and replacement of Blackfriars Bridge. The plans and specifications prepared by the engineer (whose directions the contractor was required to obey) featured the use of caissons to enable work to be done whatever the state of the tide. Unfortunately, these caissons proved to be useless, with the result that the contractor suffered considerable delay and extra expense. Once again, however, it was held that there was no implied warranty that the bridge could be built in the manner specified, and so the risk lay on the contractor.

13.4.2 Employer's responsibility

Notwithstanding the general principle outlined above, there may be situations in which an employer incurs liability when the project proves to be unexpectedly difficult or expensive to carry out. The major ways in which this occurs are as follows:

- *Implied warranty*. Although the mere fact that an employer provides tendering information does not mean that its accuracy is guaranteed, it may occasionally be possible for a warranty of accuracy to be implied. In *Bacal* v. *Northampton DC*,[19] for example, a contractor tendered to design and build six blocks of dwelling houses, under instructions to design the foundations on certain hypotheses as to ground conditions. These hypotheses, which were based on borehole data, subsequently proved inaccurate. It was held that, in these circumstances, the employer must be taken to have warranted that the ground conditions would be as they were hypothesized to be.
- *Misrepresentation*. Even where there is no *warranty* as to site conditions, a contractor may be able to show some *misrepresentation* by or

on behalf of the employer. This will certainly be the case if there is any deliberate fraud in covering up the true conditions.[20] In the absence of fraud, it is no doubt possible to base a claim on a *negligent misrepresentation*.[21] However, this will not be easy to establish, given the common contractual provision that it is the contractor's responsibility to check such matters.[22]

• *Standard method of measurement*. Building contracts frequently state that the bills of quantity on which they are based have been prepared in accordance with a specified Standard Method of Measurement. For example, JCT 80 clause 2.2.2.1 refers to SMM 7, and ICE 6 clause 57 refers to CESMM. Where this is so, a contractor who unexpectedly encounters rock may claim that this should have been a separate item in the bills and that the employer must therefore pay the extra cost. Such claims have been described as without foundation and without merit,[23] but there is some legal authority to suggest that they are valid.[24]

REFERENCES

1. *Merton LBC* v. *Stanley Hugh Leach Ltd* (1985) 32 B.L.R. 51.
2. *Commissioner for Main Roads* v. *Reed & Stuart Pty Ltd* (1974) 12 B.L.R. 55.
3. *Carr* v. *J.A. Berriman Pty Ltd* (1953) 27 A.L.J. 273.
4. *Smith & Montgomery* v. *Johnson Brothers Co. Ltd* [1954] 1 D.L.R. 392.
5. *Freeman* v. *Hensler* (1900) 64 J.P. 260.
6. *Coombe* v. *Green* (1843) 11 M. & W. 480.
7. *Hunt* v. *Bishop* (1853) 8 Exch. 675.
8. *Glenlion Construction Ltd* v. *Guinness Trust* (1987) 39 B.L.R. 89.
9. *Martin Grant & Co. Ltd* v. *Sir Lindsay Parkinson & Co. Ltd* (1984) 29 B.L.R. 31.
10. *North West Regional Hospital Board* v. *T.A. Bickerton & Son Ltd* [1970] 1 All E.R. 1039; *Percy Bilton Ltd* v. *GLC* [1982] 2 All E.R. 623.
11. *Holme* v. *Guppy* (1838) 3 M. & W. 387.
12. *Rapid Building Group Ltd* v. *Ealing Family Housing Association Ltd* (1985) 29 B.L.R. 5.
13. *R* v. *Walter Cabott Construction Ltd* (1975) 21 B.L.R. 42.
14. *Linden Gardens* v. *Lenesta Sludge Disposals Ltd* (1991) C.S.W. 24 January.
15. *Perini Corporation* v. *Commonwealth of Australia* (1969) 12 B.L.R. 82.
16. *Bottoms* v. *York Corporation* (1892) H.B.C., 4th edn, ii, 208.
17. *Sharpe* v. *San Paulo Brazilian Railway Co.* (1873) L.R. 8 Ch. App. 597.
18. *Thorn* v. *London Corporation* (1876) 1 App. Cas. 120.
19. *Bacal Construction (Midlands) Ltd* v. *Northampton Development Corporation* (1975) 8 B.L.R. 88.
20. *S. Pearson & Son Ltd* v. *Dublin Corporation* [1907] A.C. 351.
21. *Morrison-Knudsen International Co. Inc.* v. *Commonwealth of Australia* (1972) 13 B.L.R. 114.

22. *Dillingham Ltd* v. *Downs* [1972] 2 N.S.W.L.R. 49.
23. Wallace, I.N.D. *Construction Contracts: Principles and Policies in Tort and Contract.* Sweet and Maxwell, London, 1986.
24. *Bryant & Sons Ltd* v. *Birmingham Hospital Saturday Fund* [1938] 1 All E.R. 503.

PART FIVE

Contract Administration

14

Role of the contract administrator

The purpose of employing an architect, engineer or other professional person on a building project is to give the employer the benefit of that professional's skill and experience. Traditionally, the person appointed has taken responsibility for two separate functions: translating the employer's needs into drawings, specifications, and the like, through the processes of briefing and design, and then supervising the work of actual construction. This is done to ensure that the work complies with the intentions and satisfies standards of workmanship and quality.

Although the functions of design and contract administration are still frequently performed by the same person, this is by no means essential. Indeed, under some forms of building procurement such as construction management, it is unlikely to be the case. In any event, however, the *functions* of a contract administrator (whether described, as 'Architect', 'Engineer', 'Supervising Officer', 'Project Manager' or whatever) are completely separate from those of a designer.

We have considered design responsibilities in Chapter 7, and this chapter is concerned with contract administration as such. As we shall see, a 'Contract Administrator' fulfils two rather different roles. First, there are those duties (e.g. providing necessary information to the contractor) which are carried out as agent of the employer. Second, there are certain decision-making functions (e.g. the certification of work properly carried out) in which the contract administrator is required to act fairly between the parties and exercise independent judgment.

14.1 CONTRACT ADMINISTRATOR AS THE EMPLOYER'S AGENT

A contract administrator who is employed to supervise the carrying out of building works may, in certain respects, be regarded as an agent of the employer. A number of important issues flow from this, concerning especially the extent to which the contract administrator can bind the employer by actions, and the scope of the duty of care and skill owed by the contract administrator to the employer.

14.1.1   Extent of powers

Contracts and variations

An agent can, of course, be *expressly* authorized to do anything on behalf of a client. However, the important question of law concerns the extent of authority which will be *implied* where nothing specific is said. This is important because, where a contract administrator acts without any authority, the employer will not be bound by what is done. In such a case, the third party concerned may sue the contract administrator personally for damages for breach of warranty of authority.

As a general rule, the courts take a rather restricted view on this question. In particular, it has been consistently held that, except in very unusual circumstances, a contract administrator has no authority to create a direct contract between the employer and a sub-contractor. Thus, where an architect promised a sub-contractor that the employer would pay directly for the work, it was held that the employer was under no obligation so to do.[1]

A similarly cautious approach is seen in cases concerning the alteration of an existing contract. Unless the contract administrator acts within the terms of a variations clause, there is no power to change what was originally agreed. In *Cooper* v. *Langdon*,[2] for instance, a contractor deviated from the plans with the architect's permission. The contractor was none the less held liable to the employer for breach of contract, as the architect had no authority to vary the works in this way. Likewise, in *Sharpe* v. *San Paolo Railway*,[3] where the plaintiffs had contracted for a lump sum to perform all the works necessary for the construction of a railway in Brazil, it was held that the engineer had no authority to order as extras any work which was already impliedly included in the job.

As mentioned above, a contract administrator who exceeds his or her authority risks being held personally liable when dealing with a third party. In addition, the law of agency contains another trap for the unwary. This is that any agent who signs a written contract on behalf of a client will be treated as a party to it and thus personally liable, unless the contract itself makes it clear that it is signed merely 'as agent'. In *Sika Contracts* v. *Gill*,[4] for example, where a letter accepting a supplier's tender was signed: 'BS, Chartered Civil Engineer', the engineer was held personally liable to the supplier for the price, even though the latter *knew* that he was only acting as an agent!

Suspension of work

As a general principle, neither the employer nor the contract administrator has any legal right to order the contractor to suspend work. Once the contract work has commenced, it is the contractor's right and duty to carry it through in a regular fashion, and the employer's duty to do nothing which will hinder the contractor in this. As a result, an unjustified order to suspend work, given by the contract administrator, will amount to a breach of contract for which the contractor may claim damages. Further, if the circumstances of the suspension are such as to show an intention no longer to be bound by the contract, this may constitute a 'repudiatory breach' (discussed in Chapter 23).

This general principle is substantially modified by most of the major standard form contracts. ICE 6 clause 40, for example, gives the engineer an unfettered discretion to order the suspension of the whole or any part of the works. Depending on the reason for this order, the contractor may, or may not, be entitled to claim any costs incurred as a result of it. Once such a suspension has lasted for 3 months, the contractor is entitled to require permission to resume. If this permission is not given within 28 days, then the contractor may treat the suspended part as omitted from the contract or, if the suspension order relates to the *whole*, may treat the contract as repudiated.

JCT 80 does not use the word 'suspension' in this context, but all JCT contracts except MW 80 empower the contract administrator to 'issue instructions in regard to the postponement of any work to be executed'. If such postponement relates to the whole of the contract works, it is effectively a suspension order. In these circumstances, the contractor is entitled to an extension of time under clause 25 and to reimbursement of any direct loss and/or expense clause 26. Further, if the suspension lasts for long enough, it becomes a ground for determination of the contractor's employment under clause 28.

It is perhaps worth mentioning that both GC/Works/1 and the ACA form of contract permit the employer or contract administrator to suspend all or part of the work. However, while both forms give the contractor rights to an extension of time and to financial compensation where this occurs, neither makes any provision for the contractor to determine in the case of a long suspension. In such circumstances, a contractor wishing to bring the contract to an end must show that the employer's conduct amounts to a repudiatory breach.

As far as subcontracts are concerned, these will almost invariably give the main contractor a power of suspension which parallels the power of the employer or architect under the head contract. It is, indeed, essential for the protection of the contractor that this should be so, for if it is not, the contractor may incur liabilities to the subcontractor which cannot be passed on. This is what happened in the Canadian case of *Smith and Montgomery* v. *Johnson Bros*,[5] which concerned a sub-contract for tunnelling work. The main contract there empowered the engineer to order work to be stopped, in which case the main contractor's only claim would be for an extension of time. When the engineer ordered the tunnelling work to be stopped and the main contractors repeated this instruction to the subcontractors, the latter successfully sued for damages. The court held that the main contract terms had not been incorporated into the subcontract, so that the suspension order was a breach by the main contractors.

Delegation of authority

As a general principle, an agent is expected to act personally for a client, and not to delegate the task to a sub-agent. However, authority to delegate may be given expressly or by implication. In particular, it seems that where a contract administrator is instructed to invite tenders for the contract work on the basis of bills of quantity, authority to appoint a quantity surveyor will be implied.[6] What is not clear, however, is whether this creates a direct contract between the employer and the quantity surveyor, or whether it simply means that the contract administrator can recover from the employer sums paid to the quantity surveyor. Similar authority to appoint may be implied wherever the building contract provides that variations are to be measured by a quantity surveyor. In such circumstances, it is clear that different parts of the 'contract administration' are to be carried out by different people.

These implications aside, the RIBA Conditions of Engagement (1971 edn) made express provision for the appointment of a quantity surveyor by the employer after consultation with the architect. Interestingly, the 1982 version has dropped all reference to quantity surveyors, who are presumably treated like any other 'consultant' (i.e. they may be nominated and employed by either the employer or the architect, but only with the other's agreement).

At this point, mention should also be made of the possibility that an employer will wish to appoint a clerk of works, who will be permanently on site to act as the 'eyes and ears' of the contract administrator. Since such a person is almost invariably appointed by the employer directly, the division of supervisory duties between contract administrator and clerk of works can cause problems.

The general principle is that while matters of detail may be left to a properly briefed clerk of works, the contract administrator remains responsible for seeing that important matters of design are properly carried out. Thus, where a clerk of works for corrupt purposes allowed the contractor to deviate from the design in laying concrete in a way which led to dry rot in the ground floor, the architect was held liable to the employer.[7] It was said that the architect might justifiably have supervised the laying of concrete in the first building and then left the remainder to the clerk of works; here the architect had not supervised or inspected at all, however.

Notwithstanding this decision, it is clear that failure of proper supervision by a clerk of works is something which may rebound on the employer. In *Kensington* v. *Wettern*,[8] for example, a clerk of works negligently failed to notice defects in the way that artificial stone mullions were fixed. As a result, the damages which the employer was awarded against the architects for negligence were reduced by 20% on the ground of contributory negligence for which they were responsible.

14.1.2 Functions and duties

In carrying out 'administrative' functions under a building contract, the contract administrator naturally owes a duty of reasonable care and skill to the employer. Two areas of special importance relate to advice and to supervision of the work.

Advice to the employer

The kind of matters on which it is reasonable to expect a contract administrator to give advice will naturally vary with the type of project, the professional background of the contract administrator, and so on. However, two cases in which architects were held to have been negligent may give some indication. In the first of these,[9] the architect greatly underestimated the extent of work required to reinstate an old property. As a result the client, having purchased the property, could not afford to refurbish it. In the second case[10] the architect, in preparing estimates of the cost of a project, completely overlooked the effects of inflation. Once again, the client was forced to abandon the project. In both these cases, it was held that the architect was not entitled to any fees since their work was worthless.

In addition to matters of cost, a contract administrator may well advise the employer on the appointment of particular contractors or subcontractors. This is especially likely where a tendering process has taken place. In such circumstances, a duty of care is owed, once again. Thus, where an architect recommended a particular contractor as 'very reliable', the architect was held liable for losses suffered by the employer when the contractor executed defective work and then became insolvent.[11]

Instructions to the contractor

There is no general right under building contracts for contract administrators to issue instructions to contractors. It is only where there is an express condition that this can happen. However, in practice standard form contracts always contain such a clause. This is because the duration and complexity of construction projects are such that conditions are likely to change, and it is recognized that it may thus not be possible to deal in advance with every eventuality which may arise.

Contractual clauses dealing with this matter are often very widely drafted. GC/Works/1, for example, lists in clause 40 a large number of matters on which the project manager may issue instructions, before concluding with 'any other matter which the PM considers necessary or expedient'! ICE 6 clause 13(1) is hardly more limited; having restated that the basic obligation is to build in accordance with the contract, it compels the contractor to 'comply with and adhere strictly to the Engineer's instructions and directions on any matter connected therewith (whether mentioned in the contract or not)'.

The position under JCT 80 is more restricted, for the contractor's duty of compliance under clause 4.1.1 only applies to written instructions which the contract administrator is expressly empowered by the conditions to issue. If there is any doubt about this, the contractor can ask the contract administrator to specify in writing the provision under which the instruction is issued, following which any further dispute can be taken immediately to arbitration. Assuming that an instruction *is* justified, the contractor must comply with it within 7 days, failing which the employer is entitled to have it carried out by someone else at the contractor's expense. On the other hand, where compliance with an instruction involves the contractor in delay, it is possible for an extension of time to be claimed. As to any extra cost involved, the contractor will normally be reimbursed for this either through the provisions for valuing variations or through those relating to loss/expense.

Information to the contractor

Apart from issuing instructions, the contract administrator has an important function as a source of relevant information to the contractor. Under JCT 80, this is recognized by clause 5.2, which obliges the contract administrator to furnish the contractor with one copy of the contract documents certified on behalf of the employer, two further copies of the contract drawings and (where relevant) two copies of the unpriced bills of quantity. These documents are to be furnished immediately after the execution of the contract. Clause 5.3 adds an obligation to provide 'so soon as is possible' two copies of any further information necessary to enable the contractor to complete the works in accordance with the conditions.

Having thus started the contractor off with the basic information required, the contract administrator must keep this information up to date. Clause 5.4 provides that 'as and when from time to time may be necessary' the contract administrator shall provide such further drawings or details as are reasonably necessary either to explain the contract drawings or generally to enable the contractor to carry out the work.

One important aspect of the provision of information is dealt with separately under clause 7 of JCT 80. This concerns the determination of any levels which may be required for the execution of the works. The contract makes this the responsibility of the contract administrator, who has further to furnish the contractor with sufficient accurately dimensioned drawings to enable the works to be set out at ground level. Provided this is duly done, the responsibility for any errors in setting out rests on the contractor. This will normally involve amending the errors, but the contract empowers the employer and contract administrator to deal with the matter instead by means of an 'appropriate' deduction from the contract sum.

Where the contract administrator supplies inadequate information for setting out, a contractor may be tempted simply to go ahead as accurately as possible. While this may seem appealing in the first instance in order to get the job going, it is an extremely dangerous course of action for the contractor to take.[12]

Inspection and supervision

Where a qualified architect is appointed to be contract administrator, it is likely that the terms of engagement used will be those contained in the RIBA Conditions of Appointment 1982. These make it clear that, while the architect will visit the site at intervals, there is no requirement to make 'frequent or constant inspections'. If such inspections are necessary, a clerk of works or resident architect is to be appointed. Indeed, if the latest version of the RIBA Conditions is taken literally, it appears to exclude altogether the architect's liability for failure to supervise. This is because it provides that the employer will hold the contractor or consultant (and *not the architect*) responsible for the proper execution of their respective work. However, it is felt that a court would not let this interpretation override the architect's traditional duty to check general compliance.

Quite apart from specific terms of appointment, the limited nature of an architect's obligation to supervise is in any event well recognized by the English courts.[13] By contrast, an Australian court held an architect liable for the collapse of concrete which was poured between site visits, which took place on a twice-weekly basis.[14] This strict view of the architect's duties should also be compared with the case of *Clayton* v. *Woodman*, which is discussed below.

JCT 80 clearly recognizes that the contract administrator will inspect all work executed. The contractor's basic obligation, imposed by clause 2.1, is to produce the building according to the contract documents. While the contract administrator will naturally wish to check that this is indeed being done, the actual *need* to inspect relates only to those matters which are required to be to the contract administrator's satisfaction. In this context, it may be remembered that any such stipulation means that work must be to the *reasonable* satisfaction and not the *absolute* satisfaction of the contract administrator.

As part of the function of inspecting the contractor's work, the contract administrator is given considerable powers under clause 8 to carry out tests of any materials and to order that work which has been covered up by other work should be opened up for inspection. The cost of making good and restoring the covering work, and any work found to be defective, depends on the status of the inspected work. If no defects are discovered, then the contractor must be paid for the cost of opening up and making good as if this was due to a variation. If the inspected work is defective, then this is to be made good at the contractor's expense. What is more, once defects have been discovered, clause 8.4 entitles the contract administrator to demand further tests. Provided that any such demands are in accordance with the JCT Code of Practice, the cost of them is borne by the contractor, *whether or not any further defects are discovered.*

The contract administrator clearly owes a duty of care and skill to the employer to detect bad workmanship and defects.[15] However, due to the limited nature of the duty to inspect, it cannot be said that every failure of detection will amount to negligence. Further, while it is sometimes said that a similar obligation is owed to contractors, this seems unlikely; they are responsible for their own monitoring of quality. The most that can be said is that where the state of the work is positively *dangerous*, there may be an obligation to warn the contractor of this.[16] Of course, common sense suggests that, regardless of the strict legal position, a contract administrator who is aware of some defective work should certainly communicate this to the contractor.

Mention of danger leads to the more general question of who is responsible for site safety. This, in turn, raises the issue of whether the contract administrator has power to control the contractor's *method* of working. A power of this nature is undoubtedly given to the engineer by clause 13(2) of ICE 6. However, JCT contracts contain no such provision, and this has an important effect on the allocation of responsibility in case of accidents, as is shown by two contrasting cases.

In *Clayton* v. *Woodman*[17] the plaintiff bricklayer was injured by the collapse of a wall in which he was cutting a groove to take a concrete floor. The architect had insisted that this existing wall be incorporated into the new structure, rather than being demolished and replaced as the bricklayer had suggested. It was held that it was not the architect's duty under the RIBA form of contract to advise the builder on what safety precautions to take or how to conduct his operations (which specifically included shoring up and supporting walls and floors). As a result, the architect was not liable.

By contrast, in *Clay* v. *Crump*,[18] an architect agreed that demolition contractors preparing a site should leave a particular wall standing. This was at the suggestion of the demolition contractors, and the architect did not personally inspect the wall. The wall subsequently collapsed, killing two men and injuring the plaintiff, an employee of the main contractors. On this occasion, it was held that the main contractors were entitled to assume, from the very fact that the wall had been left, that it had been inspected and declared safe. The architect was accordingly liable in negligence to the plaintiff.

Quantity surveying functions

As we have mentioned, certain aspects of contract administration are frequently delegated to a qualified quantity surveyor. Indeed, whether or not delegation takes place, these tasks must be performed with the skill and care which a quantity surveyor would bring to them. As to what this involves, there is little legal authority, although a quantity surveyor in an old case escaped liability for negligence where an error of £118 in a £12 000 contract was due to an arithmetical slip by a normally competent clerk.[19] On the other hand, where a local authority's quantity surveyor had accepted ridiculously high rates for work from a contractor, this was held negligent. As a result, when the contractor went into liquidation and the overpaid money was lost, the district auditor was entitled to surcharge the quantity surveyor.[20]

14.2 CONTRACT ADMINISTRATOR AS INDEPENDENT ADJUDICATOR

14.2.1 Certification

As we have mentioned at the beginning of this chapter, a contract administrator has a significant part to play in exercising judgement and reaching decisions on various matters under the contract. In so doing, the contract administrator acts not as the agent of the employer, but as an independent professional.

The most important aspect of these decision-making powers relates to the issue from time to time of what are called **certificates**. These have been defined by Hudson[21] (in a definition approved by the Court of Appeal[22]) as 'the expression in a definite form of the exercise of the judgment, opinion or skill of the engineer, architect or surveyor in relation to some matter provided for by the terms of the contract'. However, this does not mean that every expression of opinion or decision given by the contract administrator will amount to a certificate. It will only be a certificate if it is so described in the contract, or can be so treated by implication.

The general law of building contracts does not require a certificate to be given in any particular form. Indeed, it may be given orally unless the contract provides otherwise. Interestingly, neither JCT 80 nor ICE 6 specifically states that certificates are to be issued in writing. However, since both forms of contract require certificates to be sent to the employer, with a 'copy' to the contractor, the implication seems clear enough.

Types of certificate

There are three main types of certificate found in construction contracts:

1. *Interim certificates.* These are issued at intervals as the work proceeds, and their issue entitles the contractor to be paid a certain proportion of the contract price. Under JCT 80 clause 30.1, the period between interim certificates is whatever is stated in the Appendix to the contract. If none is stated, then it is one month, which is the usual period.

   The amount to be included in an interim certificate under JCT 80 should cover the value of work done and materials delivered to date, plus the value of certain off-site materials. The contract places the responsibility for carrying out interim valuations upon the quantity surveyor. However, it is important to note that the quantity surveyor should not do more than merely carry out the valuations; it is for the contract administrator to calculate what is due and to issue the interim certificates.

2. *Final certificates.* The final certificate can signify the contract administrator's satisfaction with the work, or the amount which is finally due to the contractor, or both of these things. The extent of its effect depends on the terms of the contract, but under JCT 80 it clearly applies to both these issues. Under JCT 80 clause 30.8, the obligation is in general to issue the final certificate within 2 months of the end of the defects liability period.

3. *Certificates recording an event.* In addition to confirming that a sum of money is due to the contractor, certificates may be needed to confirm that a certain event has occurred (or has not occurred). The use of this kind of certificate varies from one form of contract to another, but a good example of their use and importance may be drawn from JCT 80. Under that form, the contract administrator is required to issue the following certificates:

- *Certificate of non-completion.* Issued under clause 24.1, this records the contractor's failure to complete the works by the completion date. Its importance is that it triggers the contractor's liability to pay liquidated damages.
- *Certificate of practical completion.* Issued under clause 17.1, this records the contract administrator's opinion that practical completion of the works has been achieved. The contractor's liability for liquidated damages ceases, one-half of the retention money is released and the Defects Liability Period begins.
- *Certificate of completion of making good defects.* Issued under clause 17.4, this records the contract administrator's opinion that defects appearing within the defects liability period and notified to the contractor have been duly made good. The contractor is then · entitled to the remainder of the retention money.

Conclusiveness of certificates

One of the most important issues concerning certification in building contracts is whether the certificate is binding upon the parties as to what it certifies. This question of conclusiveness depends upon the terms of the particular contract, but it would be extremely unusual to find any certificate except the final certificate treated in this way. JCT 80, for example, makes it clear in clause 30.10 that nothing in any other certificate is conclusive evidence that work or materials are in accordance with the contract. This means that it is open to the employer to show that, despite the certificate, the contractor is not entitled to payment. It also means that any interim certificate can be corrected by the contract administrator when the next interim certificate is issued.

As mentioned, the issue of conclusiveness arises in practice only in relation to final certificates. The first point to make about this is that an arbitration clause such as JCT 80 clause 41, which permits the arbitrator to 'open up, review and revise any certificate', inevitably destroys the conclusiveness of the certificate, at least to that extent. However, the limits of such arbitration clauses may be tightly drawn. In JCT 80, for example, arbitration proceedings involving a challenge to the contract administrator's final certificate can only be launched within 28 days of its issue. If this time limits is not met, then clause 30.9 makes the final certificate 'conclusive evidence' of the following four matters:

1. that where materials or workmanship have to be to the reasonable satisfaction of the contract administrator, they are so (though this does not necessarily mean that they are of merchantable quality);
2. that all appropriate additions and deductions have been made to the contract sum (though clerical or arithmetical errors can still be corrected);
3. that all extensions of time are correct; and
4. that all the contractor's money claims have been properly accounted for.

The question whether the final certificate is truly 'conclusive', even to this extent, is bound up with the question of how, if it is not conclusive, it might be challenged. As to this, the Court of Appeal ruled in the notorious *Crouch* case[23] that where a contract gives power to an arbitrator to 'open up, review and revise' certificates, this means that a *court* has no such power. Hence, if the strict time limits for going to arbitration are not complied with, the certificate becomes in effect unchallengeable. Indeed, as we shall see in Chapter 25, some subsequent cases have gone further, by ruling that a court cannot overturn a final certificate where there is a less wide-ranging arbitration clause[24] or even no arbitration clause at all.[25] However, these extensions are probably wrong,[26] and the basic principle itself has been heavily criticized. Unfortunately, in view of the practical importance of this matter, the law remains unclear.

It should finally be noted that, even where a certificate is conclusive and unchallengeable *on its merits*, there are still grounds on which it can be set aside. The most important circumstances in which this will occur are:

1. where the certificate is not issued in the correct form at the correct time by the correct person;
2. where the contract administrator has 'certified' on something on which the contract gives no power to certify;
3. where there is fraud or collusion between the certifier and one of the parties; and
4. where the employer has improperly pressurized or influenced the certifier.

Recovery without a certificate

Is a contractor entitled to demand interim payments in the absence of an interim certificate? Is the employer entitled to deduct liquidated damages without a certificate of failure to complete the works on time? The answers to these questions depend on whether the issue of the relevant certificate by the contract administrator is a 'condition precedent'.

The general principle adopted in such cases is that, where the contract provides for payment of money following the issue of a certificate, this is indeed a condition precedent. Thus, where a certificate of non-completion is followed by the grant of an extension of time, a further certificate of non-completion must be issued before it is lawful for the employer to deduct liquidated damages.[27] Conversely, a contractor who feels that work has been undervalued on an interim certificate should either demand a further certificate from the contract administrator or seek arbitration under the contract. Such an undervaluation does not justify the contractor in leaving the site.[28]

Notwithstanding this general principle, a contract administrator's refusal or failure to issue a certificate is no more conclusive and binding upon the parties than the issue of one would be. Thus, if the circumstances are such that the *issue* of a certificate could successfully be challenged, it seems that its *non-issue* can equally be bypassed. This means that the points mentioned in the previous section on the conclusiveness of certificates, such as the availability of arbitration, fraud or collusion, are equally relevant.

In. accordance with these principles, contractors have succeeded in recovering where an employer improperly ordered the architect not to certify more than a certain amount,[29] and where the certifier based a decision on whether work had been done *economically* (a question not within the certifier's remit).[30]

14.2.2 Other decision-making functions

Although the issue of certificates is the most important aspect of the contract administrator's 'independent' role, it is not the only one. Construction contracts may also use other forms of words, such as requiring the contract administrator to 'make decisions' or to 'give opinions'. It seems reasonable to assume that the principles outlined above as to 'conclusiveness' and 'conditions precedent' in relation to certificates would apply equally to these similar functions.

An example of 'certification by another name' is provided by JCT 80 clause 18.1, which states that the employer may take possession of part of the works before practical completion is achieved. Where this occurs, the contract administrator is required to issue a 'written statement' identifying the part taken into possession. This statement is then treated for most purposes as if it were a certificate of practical completion for the relevant part.

An extremely important function of this kind is found in clause 66(3) of ICE 6. This provides that any dispute whatsoever between the employer and the contractor arising out of the contract or the work must be referred in writing to the engineer for settlement. The engineer must then give a decision in writing on the dispute. Only when this has been done (or when the engineer has failed to give a decision within a prescribed period) can the matter be taken to arbitration. This provision has caused serious problems because the contract does not lay down any particular form which the engineer's 'decision' must take, and it can sometimes be difficult to know whether a decision has been given or not. This matter is discussed further in Chapter 25.

14.2.3 Liability for negligent decision-making

Liability to the employer

It was for many years believed that in issuing certificates a contract administrator acts in a 'quasi-judicial' capacity. By this is meant that, in exercising judgement about the quantity of work done, and making decisions about how much the contractor should be paid, the architect is acting in a manner similar to that of an arbitrator. This led to the conclusion that the contract administrator should enjoy the same immunity from claims in negligence as an arbitrator (which is itself based on the immunity of a judge).

The principle that a contract administrator could not be sued in negligence by the employer was laid down by the Court of Appeal in 1901.[31] However, in the important case of *Sutcliffe* v. *Thackrah*[32] this principle was overturned by the House of Lords. In that case the architect apparently over-valued a series of certificates and the employer duly paid the contractor. Unfortunately, the contractor then went into liquidation before the job was completed, with the result that the employer could not recover the money which had been overpaid. It was held by the House of Lords that the architect was not acting in a quasi-judicial capacity and had no immunity from liability. The architect was accordingly liable to compensate the employer for the money lost.

The decision of the trial judge in the *Sutcliffe* case[33] is of considerable interest in examining the practical implications of a duty of care in respect of certification. In particular, it appears that the contract administrator must notify the quantity surveyor in advance of any work which is regarded as not properly executed, so that it can be excluded from the quantity surveyor's valuation.

Liability to the contractor

Once it was held that a contract administrator could be liable to the employer for negligent *over-certification*, the question which naturally arose was whether there would be an equivalent liability to the contractor for negligent *under-certification*. This, it was said, would cause serious losses because, even if the contractor ultimately recovered the correct amount from the employer, there would still be an expensive interruption of the contractor's cash flow.

The idea that a contract administrator would owe a duty of care *in tort* to the contractor was suggested by Lord Salmon in *Sutcliffe* v. *Thackrah* itself, and this view attracted some support in subsequent cases.[34] However, it was disapproved by the Court of Appeal in the important case of *Pacific Associates* v. *Baxter*.[35] That case arose out of a dredging contract, made in a standard form (FIDIC 2nd edn), under which the plaintiff contractors undertook work for the ruler of Dubai. The contract entitled the contractors to extra payment if they encountered hard material which could not have been reasonably foreseen by an experienced contractor, and provided that any claims on this basis should be decided by the engineer. The contract also contained an arbitration clause (which meant that any decision of the engineer could be challenged) and a special condition stating that the engineer should not incur personal liability for 'acts or obligations under the contract'. In the course of dredging the contractors encountered a great deal of such material, but the engineer consistently rejected their claims (a total of £31 million). The contractors duly settled in arbitration against the employer for £10 million and sued the engineer in negligence for the shortfall.

An engineer in this situation could undoubtedly foresee that negligence in making a decision might cause loss to the contractors. However, the Court of Appeal held that it would not be 'just and reasonable' to impose a duty of care upon the engineer. This was because, given the contractual background, it could not be said that the engineer had 'voluntarily assumed responsibility' to the contractors, nor that the contractors had 'relied' on him. If any extra responsibilities were to be undertaken, this could have been done by means of a collateral agreement at the time that the contract was negotiated. In the absence of any such agreement, and given that the contractors were fully aware of the contract provisions when tendering for the job, the court would not allow the law of tort to import additional obligations into a carefully structured contractual environment.

Precisely how far this decision extends is not clear, because all three judges in the Court of Appeal stressed the importance of both the arbitration clause and the exemption condition. It *might* be, then, that the absence of one or both of these factors would lead to a contrary decision. None the less, the court clearly did not favour tort claims in such circumstances, as a matter of general principle. In any event, the case has since been used to justify a decision that an architect owes no duty of care whatsoever to a contractor in relation to certification duties under the contract.[36]

REFERENCES

1. *Vigers Sons & Co. Ltd* v. *Swindell* [1939] 3 All E.R. 590.
2. *Cooper* v. *Langdon* (1841) 9 M. & W. 60.
3. *Sharpe* v. *San Paolo Railway* (1873) L.R. 8 Ch. App. 597.
4. *Sika Contracts Ltd* v. *B.L. Gill Ltd* (1978) 9 B.L.R. 15.
5. *Smith and Montgomery* v. *Johnson Bros* [1954] 1 D.L.R. 392.
6. *Waghorn* v. *Wimbledon Local Board* (1877) HBC, 4th edn, ii, 52.
7. *Leicester Board of Guardians* v. *Trollope* (1911) 75 J.P. 197.
8. *Kensington & Chelsea & Westminster AHA* v. *Wettern Composites Ltd* [1985] 1 All E.R. 346.
9. *Ralphs* v. *Francis Horner & Sons* (1987, unreported).
10. *Nye Saunders and Partners* v. *Bristow* (1987) 37 B.L.R. 92.
11. *Pratt* v. *George J. Hill Associates* (1987) 38 B.L.R. 25.
12. Chappell, D. *Understanding JCT Standard Building Contracts*, chap. 4. International Thomson, London, 1987.
13. *East Ham BC* v. *Bernard Sunley & Sons Ltd* [1966] A.C. 406; *Sutcliffe* v. *Chippendale & Edmondson* (1971) 18 B.L.R. 157.
14. *Florida Hotels Pty Ltd* v. *Mayo* (1965) 113 C.L.R. 588.
15. *Imperial College of Science & Technology* v. *Norman & Dawbarn* (1987) 8 Con. L.R. 107.
16. *Oldschool* v. *Gleeson (Construction) Ltd* (1976) 4 B.L.R. 103.
17. *Clayton* v. *Woodman & Son (Builders) Ltd* [1962] 2 Q.B. 533.
18. *Clay* v. *A.J. Crump Ltd* [1964] 1 Q.B. 533.
19. *London School Board* v. *Northcroft* (1889) HBC, 4th Ed., ii, 147.
20. *Tyrer* v. *District Auditor for Monmouthshire* (1973) 230 E.G. 973.
21. Wallace, I.N.D., *Hudson's Building and Engineering Contracts* (10th edn). Sweet and Maxwell, London, 1979.
22. *Token Construction Co. Ltd* v. *Charlton Estates Ltd* (1973) 1 B.L.R. 50.
23. *Northern Regional Health Authority* v. *Derek Crouch Construction Co. Ltd* [1984] Q.B. 644.
24. *Oram Builders Ltd* v. *Pemberton* (1985) 29 B.L.R. 23.
25. *Reed* v. *Van der Vorm* (1985) 35 B.L.R. 136; *J.F. Finnegan Ltd* v. *Sheffield CC* (1988) 43 B.L.R. 124.
26. *Benstrete Construction Ltd* v. *Hill* (1987) 38 B.L.R. 115.
27. *A. Bell & Son (Paddington) Ltd* v. *CBF Residential Care & Housing Association* (1989) 46 B.L.R. 102.
28. *Lubenham Fidelities & Investments* v. *S. Pembrokeshire DC* (1986) 33 B.L.R. 39.
29. *Hickman & Co.* v. *Roberts* [1913] A.C. 229.
30. *Panamena Europea Navegacion* v. *Leyland & Co. Ltd* [1947] A.C. 428.
31. *Chambers* v. *Goldthorpe* [1901] 1 K.B. 624.
32. *Sutcliffe* v. *Thackrah* [1974] A.C. 727.

33. *Sutcliffe* v. *Chippendale & Edmondson* (1971) 18 B.L.R. 157.
34. *F.G. Minter Ltd.* v. *WHTSO* (1979) 11 B.L.R. 1; *Shui On Construction Ltd* v. *Shui Kay Co. Ltd* (1985) 4 Const. L.J. 305; *Salliss & Co.* v. *Calil* (1988) 4 Const. L.J. 125.
35. *Pacific Associates Inc* v. *Baxter* [1989] 2 All E.R. 159.
36. *Leon Engineering & Construction Co. Ltd* v. *Ka Duk Investment Co. Ltd* (1989) 47 B.L.R. 139.

15

Insurance and bonds

As we have seen in Chapter 2, one of the primary functions of a construction contract is to allocate certain *risks* to one or other of the parties. This may be done by providing that one party (X) shall be *liable* to the other (Y) if a particular kind of loss or damage occurs, thus placing the risk of that loss or damage on X. It occurs equally under a provision that X shall *not* be liable to Y for a particular kind of loss since this effectively places the risk of that kind of loss on Y.

In view of the enormous size of some of these risks in financial terms, it is obvious that the party to whom a risk is allocated may want to cover it by means of insurance. What is not so obvious, however, is that a party to whom a risk has *not* been allocated may still insist on insurance backing for that risk. This is simply because, while the contract may say for instance that the contractor shall be liable to the client for certain kinds of damage, the client's right to sue the contractor will be of little use if the contractor cannot afford to pay any damages awarded. In such circumstances, the client will only be protected if the contractor has 'liability insurance' or if the performance of the contractor is 'guaranteed'.

In this chapter we discuss briefly the legal principles on which insurance is based and the main types of construction insurance policy, using the insurance provisions of JCT 80 as illustrations. We also consider professional indemnity insurance and the use of **bonds** or **guarantees** as a means of protection against contractual failure.

15.1 INSURANCE

15.1.1 General principles

It is essential from the start to understand the difference between two types of insurance. Under a **liability insurance policy**, an insurer undertakes that, if the insured person (the client) becomes legally liable to someone else, the insurer will indemnify *the client* against the damages and legal costs which he or she has to pay. A familiar illustration of this type of policy is 'third-party' insurance for a car driver. By contrast, under a **loss insurance policy**, the insured person is entitled to be compensated by the insurers for loss or damage which *that person* has suffered, whether this is caused accidentally or by someone else's negligence. Such a policy may even provide cover in respect of loss or damage caused by the insured person's own negligence, although this is sometimes excluded or restricted by special terms in the policy. A 'comprehensive' motor insurance policy is an example of this type of policy.

Liability insurance

Examples of liability insurance commonly found in the context of construction would include **public liability policies** for contractors, and **professional indemnity policies** for architects and other professionals. What must be clearly understood is that, where an insurance policy is of this kind, the insurer's legal duty is owed to the client and *not* to the 'victim'. Indeed, the insurer is theoretically not responsible at all until the insured person has actually been held liable to the victim by a court or arbitrator. In practice, however, the insurer will normally be brought into the picture as soon as a legal action is started against the client; if the action is thought to be worth defending, the insurer will then take over the actual conduct of the case.

The fact that liability insurance is seen as something which affects only the insurer and the client places severe restrictions upon the protection which it offers to victims. An important limitation was exposed by the case of *Normid* v. *Ralphs*,[1] in which the defendant architect was faced by a professional negligence claim from the plaintiffs which was clearly enough to bankrupt him. The wording of the defendant's professional indemnity insurance policy was not entirely clear as to the maximum which the insurers could be made to pay, and the defendant agreed with the insurers to accept £250 000 in full settlement of all claims on the policy. The plaintiffs, who felt that the insurers could have been made to pay more, attempted to have this settlement agreement overturned, but their attempt failed. The Court of Appeal held that, since the defendants were under no legal duty to have liability insurance at all, any genuine settlement was purely between the defendants and their insurers. The plaintiffs had no rights whatever to intervene, unless they could establish bad faith.

Ironically, had the defendant in this case actually been made bankrupt before settling with the insurers, the plaintiffs might have been in a stronger position. Section 1(1) of the *Third Parties (Right against Insurers) Act 1930* provides that, where a person or company with liability insurance becomes insolvent, any claim which the insured person could have been made against the insurers is automatically transferred to the victim. As a result, the plaintiffs here could have refused to settle with the insurers as the defendant had done and could have instead sued the insurers for the higher amount which they claimed was due under the policy.

Although the 1930 Act improves the position of victims, it is still subject to strict limits, as was demonstrated in the case of *Bradley* v. *Eagle Star*.[2] The House of Lords ruled in that case that the 1930 Act only transfers to a plaintiff those rights which the insured person already had against the insurers, and pointed out that these do not arise until the insured person has been held liable to the plaintiff. As a result, unless a successful claim is made against a company while it still exists (or at least while it can still be restored to the Companies' Register), the victim cannot take action against the company's liability insurers.

Although the point did not arise in the *Bradley* case, the decision carries an important implication. Any defence which an insurer would have against the client is equally available against a victim who takes over the client's rights by virtue of the 1930 Act. Thus, for example, where a person who has become bankrupt has failed to comply with some condition of a liability insurance policy (e.g. by failing to give notice of claims within a specified time), the insurers will be entitled to refuse payment to a victim.

Loss insurance

As we have mentioned, a loss insurance policy provides cover not for a person's legal liability to others, but for losses which fall directly upon that person. In the construction field, such cover is required by a client on whom the contract places the risk of damage to the contract works (as does JCT 80 clause 22C).

There is an important general principle of the law governing loss insurance, known as **subrogation**. Under this principle, where a loss insurer pays the client in respect of a loss which has been caused by someone else's default, such as a breach of contract or a tort, the insurer is then entitled to take over any legal rights which the insured person could have exercised against the third party responsible. In such a way, the insurer will seek by suing in the client's name to recover from that third party the amount which has been paid out to the client.

However, it must be stressed that there is *no* right of subrogation against any person who is also insured under the same 'loss insurance' policy. This in fact is why many building contracts provide that any loss insurance policies which the contract requires are taken out in the joint names of the client and the contractor, and sometimes also of any sub-contractors. The legal effect of such a practice is shown by the case of *Petrofina* v. *Magnaload*,[3] in which a **contractors' all-risks policy** taken out in respect of an extension to an oil refinery defined the insured persons as including the employer, contractors and/or sub-contractors. The contract works were extensively damaged due to the negligence of sub-contractors engaged to lift heavy equipment, whereupon the insurers duly paid the owners. It was held that the insurers were not then entitled to recover their loss from the sub-contractors under the doctrine of subrogation.

15.1.2 Construction insurance under JCT 80

Personal injury and damage to property

The general scheme of the insurance provisions of JCT 80 operates in two stages. First, it allocates as between client and contractor the risk of various kinds of loss or damage which may arise in the course of building work. It then imposes responsibility for insuring against those risks.

The crucial clause in this process is clause 20, under which the contractor undertakes to indemnify the employer against certain kinds of liability 'arising out of or in the course of or by reason of the carrying out of the works'. In particular, this includes under clause 20.1 any liability of the employer (e.g. as occupier of the premises) for *injury* to or *death* of any person, except to the extent that this is due to any act or neglect of the employer or of any person for whom the employer is responsible. This wording, which was introduced by an amendment in 1986, makes it clear that such liability may be *shared* between the employer and the contractor; the previous position was that *any* negligence on the part of the employers left them entirely responsible.[4]

As to the persons whose 'act or neglect' can be attributed to the employer for this purpose, these clearly include members of the employer's staff, any direct contractors on the site and in all probability the contract administrator. However, they do *not* include any sub-contractor, whether domestic or nominated. This means that where a person is injured or killed through a sub-contractor's negligence, any resulting legal liability for the employer may be passed on to the main contractor.

The contractor's duty to indemnify the employer also covers under clause 20.2 *damage to property*, but in this instance only to the extent that it is due to 'negligence, breach of statutory duty, omission or default' by the contractor or by someone for whom the contractor is responsible. Again, the 1986 amendment enables responsibility to be shared, where previously a defaulting employer lost all rights against the contractor.[5] In this context, the contractor bears responsibility for the conduct of anyone properly on the site in connection with the works, except for those persons who are the employer's responsibility (presumably the same as those falling under clause 20.1).

The original wording of clause 20.2 did not make clear whether the contractor's obligation was merely to indemnify the employer against any claims made by third parties whose property was damaged, or whether it also covered damage to the employer's own property (including the contract works). However, the 1986 amended version expressly provides that the only parts of the *contract works* which are included in clause 20.2 are those in respect of which a certificate of practical completion has been issued or which have been taken over by the employer. The remaining parts fall instead under clause 22C, which is discussed below. As for other property of the employer such as *existing buildings*, it appears that the contractor will not be liable for causing this to be damaged by a 'Specified Peril' (defined in clause 1.3 to include such things as fire, explosion, flood, burst pipes, etc.). However, the contractor *will* be liable for negligently causing or permitting such property to be damaged in other ways such as by impact, subsidence, theft or vandalism.

Duty to insure

Clause 20 of JCT 80 thus defines the scope of the contractor's responsibility to the employer for causing personal injury or damage to property. Clause 21 then provides that the contractor shall 'take out and maintain' certain insurance policies which will for the most part cover these forms of liability. In the case of damage to property, cover is to be to a financial level imposed by the employer by means of an entry in the Appendix to the contract. In practice, this obligation will normally be satisfied by a combination of the contractor's 'public liability' and 'employer's liability' policies, although the 'third-party' section of the contractor's motor insurance policy may also be relevant in appropriate cases.

To protect the employer's position in respect of these insurances, clause 21 requires the contractor on demand to provide evidence that the policies are in force and that they provide the necessary cover. If this is discovered *not* to be the case, then the employer is empowered to take out personal insurance against any liability or expense which may be incurred and to charge the premiums to the contractor.

A loophole in the insurance protection effected by these clauses was discovered in the case of *Gold* v. *Patman & Fotheringham*.[6] The employer was there held *strictly* liable in nuisance for damage to neighbouring property due to subsidence caused by the works. However, the contractor, who had not been guilty of any negligence, was not bound to provide an indemnity. To deal with the result of this case, JCT 80 clause

21.2 now states that the contractor can be instructed by the contract administrator to take out and maintain a **joint names policy**, which will indemnify the employer against both strict liability to third parties and any damage to his or her own property (other than the contract works and materials on site) arising out of collapse, subsidence, heave, vibration, withdrawal of support, lowering of ground water and similar causes. It should be noted that this provision only applies where the Appendix to the contract so states; further, although it is the contractor's responsibility to take out and maintain the policy, it is to be done at the employer's expense.

Damage to contract works in new buildings

If there were no specific contractual provisions on the matter, and assuming that there had been no negligence by either employer or contractor, the risk of damage to the contract works would lie on the contractor. This is because it is the contractor's basic obligation to complete the job. On this basis, it was held in *Charon* v. *Singer*[7] that, where the works were damaged by vandalism, the contractor's duty of substantial performance of the contract meant that he must do everything necessary to restore the works to the contractual standard.

This basic legal position is substantially affected by JCT 80 clauses 22 to 22C, as redrafted in the 1986 amendment. These clauses are extremely complicated, but an important key to understanding them lies in the distinction which they maintain between two classes of insurable risk. On the one hand, there are the 'Specified Perils', a list of catastrophes which includes damage from fire, lightning, explosion, storm, tempest, flood, burst water pipes, earthquake, aircraft and riot. On the other hand, there is 'All Risks Insurance', which covers 'any physical loss or damage to work executed and site materials', subject to some specific exceptions such as wear and tear, design defects, radioactivity or other nuclear-linked damage, sonic booms or terrorist action. This is not the place for a detailed comparison of the two lists, but 'All Risks' is clearly much wider than 'Specified Perils', including for example such causes of damage as impact, subsidence, theft and vandalism.

Where the contract in question is concerned with the erection of a new building, JCT 80 offers a choice of two alternative clauses. These place the responsibility for taking out 'All Risks Insurance' in joint names on either the contractor (clause 22A) or the employer (clause 22B). Whichever of these choices is adopted, it is provided by clauses 22.3 that the party taking out the insurance must see to it that all sub-contractors (both nominated and domestic) are protected from any 'comeback' action by the insurers. However, it is important to note that this protection for sub-contractors relates only to damage resulting from the 'Specified Perils'.

Under the Private editions of JCT 80, any failure by either party to maintain the required insurance cover will entitle the other party to insure and charge the cost to the defaulter. In the Local Authorities editions, this remedy is available only to the employer. It is, however, specifically provided that the contractor may fulfil this obligation by maintaining a suitable annual policy to which the names of the employer and the sub-contractors can be added.

A significant difference between clauses 22A and 22B lies in their treatment of any repair or restoration work which may be necessary and which it is the contractor's obligation to carry out. Where the *contractor* has insured, payment by the employer for this work will not exceed what is received from the insurer; by contrast, where the *employer* has insured, the contractor's work will be valued as if it were brought about by a variation under clause 13.

Damage to contract works in existing buildings

Where the contract works consist of alterations to or the extension of existing structures, neither of the above clauses should be used; the appropriate provision is clause 22C. In so far as it applies to the *contract works*, this clause is broadly similar to clause 22B; it is for the employer to insure in joint names, and to see that all sub-contractors are protected. However, in relation to the *existing structures*, clause 22C differs from clause 22B in two important respects: first, the employer need insure only against the 'Specified Perils', rather than against 'All Risks'; and second, there is no obligation to protect *domestic* sub-contractors against any 'comeback' claims by the insurers.

A further innovation in clause 22C is the provision that, where damage is caused to the contract works by an insured risk, either party may determine the contractor's employment if it would be 'just and equitable' so to do. This provision, which is only intended to be used in cases of very serious damage or destruction, is discussed in Chapter 23.

Insurance for loss of liquidated damages

Assuming that the insurance cover specified in clause 22A, 22B or 22C is taken out and maintained at an adequate level, the costs of repair and restoration following damage to the contract works from the vast majority of causes should be recoverable. However, these costs are not the only ones which may result from damage to the contract works. In particular, where the cause of the relevant damage is one or more of the 'Specified Perils', the contractor may be entitled to an extension of time for completion under clause 25.4.3, in which case the employer will of course lose the right to claim liquidated damages for the period of delay. This aspect of the employer's loss is clearly *not* covered by the insurance required by the clauses mentioned above.

In order to close this loophole, JCT 80 has since 1986 given the option for the employer's loss of liquidated damages to be separately insured. Clause 22D provides that where the Appendix to the contract makes it clear that such insurance *may* be required, the contract administrator shall immediately the contract is entered into either instruct the contractor to arrange it or state that it is not needed. In the former case, the policy is to be kept in force until the date of practical completion, and the sum insured is to be based on the contract rate for liquidated damages.

Clause 22D is a rather odd provision. Since the insurance with which it deals is designed entirely to protect the employer, and since it is the employer who pays for it through an addition to the contract sum, it is not at all clear why the contractor is called upon to arrange it. No doubt many employers will prefer to make arrangements directly with their own insurers.

Professional indemnity insurance

The various professional members of a design and construction team, such as the architect, structural engineer and quantity surveyor, will each have their own insurance policy to indemnify them against liability for professional negligence. Such policies, which are often taken out as part of a scheme run by the relevant professional body, will of course vary greatly, but a few general points are none the less worth bearing in mind:

- A *contractor*, at least one who does not specialize in 'design and build' work, may well not have insurance cover of this kind; indeed, a limited company may well find such insurance difficult or impossible to obtain. As a result, the client may have less insurance protection in respect of a contractor's design input than under a conventional set-up in which design is carried out by an architect.
- The cover provided by most professional indemnity insurance policies is subject to financial limits, and once those limits are exceeded, the professional's own money is at stake. And of course once *that* money is exhausted, the loss inevitably falls on the client!
- Few of the standard terms under which professionals are engaged in the construction industry contain any requirement to take out or maintain professional indemnity insurance. Indeed, even where they do, the client's only remedy for failure to insure would presumably be to claim damages which, one assumes, the uninsured professional would be unable to pay! In any event, as we have noted at the

beginning of this chapter, such insurance is a matter between the insured and the insurer – the client has only very limited *direct* protection.

- Standard professional indemnity policies cover the insured against liability for *professional negligence*, but there are considerable doubts as to whether they extend to other forms of liability. Thus, if an architect is held to have *guaranteed* the suitability of a design, rather than merely undertaking that reasonable skill and care has been used, any resulting liability might well not be covered. Indeed, many policies specifically *exclude* liabilities which the professional voluntarily assumes by way of such guarantees. This, as we have seen in Chapter 2, has caused major problems in the context of 'collateral warranties'.

- It is worth noting that most professional indemnity policies are written on a 'claims made' basis. This means that they cover claims actually made against the professional person during the period of insurance, regardless of when the negligent act took place. As a result, it is essential that insurance cover is maintained, even after the retirement or death of the professional concerned, and this can usually be arranged on a single-premium 'run off' basis.

    One might assume that the benefit of cover on a 'claims made' basis is that one is protected in respect of acts of negligence committed before the policy is taken out. However, while this is broadly speaking true, what should not be overlooked is that a person who seeks insurance has a legal duty to disclose all 'material facts' to the insurer. As a result, a professional who takes out a new policy or who renews an old one, without revealing to the insurers that a claim is pending, will probably find that the policy is voidable and that the insurers need not pay.

15.2 BONDS AND GUARANTEES

A **bond** or **guarantee** is an arrangement under which the performance of contractual obligations by a person is backed up by a third party. This third party, which is commonly a bank or insurance company, promises to pay a sum of money if the other person defaults. In this context, the person whose obligation is being guaranteed is the **principal debtor**, or simply 'principal'; the person to whom that obligation is owed is the **beneficiary**; and the person giving the bond is the **bondsman, surety** or **guarantor**.

15.2.1 Nature and types of bond

It is quite possible for almost any contractual obligation to be the subject of a bond but, in practice, they are normally found in certain commercial fields where their use is well established. In the construction context, the obligations most commonly guaranteed in this way are the following:

- *Payment.* This may be either the employer's duty to pay the contractor or the contractor's duty to pay a sub-contractor.
- *A specific limited obligation,* such as a promise by a sub-contractor not to withdraw a tender. This is of great practical importance where, say, a main contractor tenders on the basis of bids received from domestic sub-contractors. If the main contractor is awarded the job, but then finds that a sub-contractor's bid is no longer open for acceptance, the main contractor may have to pay a significantly higher price to another sub-contractor for that part of the work.
- *Performance of the contract in general.* This is the most common type of bond, in which every aspect of the contractor's performance is guaranteed. An optional requirement for the contractor to provide such a bond is found in both ICE 6 and in the FIDIC Conditions of Contract, 4th edn. JCT 80 contains no such requirement; however, the contract is frequently amended to ensure that it does, normally to a level of 10% of the contract sum. Where there *is* such a requirement, failure by the contractor will probably justify the employer in terminating the contract; furthermore, a contract administrator who fails to check that the bond is in place may be liable to the client for professional negligence.

It is important to appreciate that what these bonds *really* guarantee is the solvency of the principal debtor, either the employer or the contractor. This is because, a party who remains solvent, can of course be sued directly. Further, even if the beneficiary chooses to sue the surety instead, the surety has an automatic right of recourse against the principal. Indeed, the risk carried by the surety is further reduced by the fact that, where another person is also to blame (such as where a defect in the building is partly the contractor's fault and partly due to negligent design by the architect), the surety can claim a contribution from that other party under the *Civil Liability (Contribution) Act 1978.*

A recent development which should be mentioned is the increased use of **unconditional** or **on-demand bonds**, which have spread from international commercial contracts into the construction field. Such bonds enable the person for whose benefit they are expressed to call upon the surety to pay *whether or not there has been default under the main contract.* Their use in construction contracts is on the whole undesirable since, while the employer may not intend to call on such bonds irresponsibly, the contractor cannot rely on this; the contractor must therefore increase the tender price to cover the cost of something which is not really necessary. A preferable alternative, if the employer feels extra security is warranted, is to increase the size of the retention under the contract.

15.2.2 Creation of bonds

A contract of guarantee must either be made in writing or at least evidenced by writing, in order to satisfy section 4 of the *Statute of Frauds 1677*. In practice, it will frequently be made in the form of a deed, and it should certainly take this form wherever the bond is given *after* the main contract is entered into. This is because the beneficiary in such a case will not have given any consideration in return for the surety's promise and thus, if the bond is not made by deed, it will be unenforceable.

The *duration* of a guarantee depends upon the terms in which it is given. If no specific time limit is mentioned, then a surety for the contractor's performance is not released by completion or even by the final certificate but remains liable, as does the contractor, for any breach of contract which comes to light within the relevant limitation period. Perhaps because of the potential length of this period, some guarantors now make express provision for release when the final certificate is issued.

The *financial limits* of liability are invariably expressed in the contract of guarantee and it should be made clear in order to avoid disputes whether interest on money due, and legal costs, are included in the overall limit. It is also worth noting that some bonds provide for the entire sum guaranteed to become payable on any breach by the principal, regardless of how serious or trivial that may be. If this is the case, the provision is likely to be struck down as a 'penalty', so that the beneficiary will be entitled only to so much of the sum as will compensate for the actual loss which has been suffered.

15.2.3 Release of surety

General principles

Today the giving of bonds and guarantees is a lucrative commercial enterprise for financial institutions. In Victorian times, however, bonds were more commonly given by benevolent uncles to guarantee the debts of extravagant nephews! Perhaps because of this, the law is rather quick to find a reason for releasing the surety from the guarantee.

It has even been held on occasion, by analogy with the law which governs insurance contracts, that the surety cannot be held responsible unless all material facts (such as unusually difficult construction conditions) are disclosed when the guarantee is entered into. However, it was confirmed by the House of Lords in the leading case of *Trade Indemnity* v. *Workington Harbour & Docks Board*[8] that there is no general rule to this effect. In that case a firm of contractors submitted the lowest tender (£284 000) for a civil engineering contract which, as usual, provided that the contractors must satisfy themselves as to site conditions. The engineers warned the contractors that their excavation prices were far too low for ground with high-water levels and gave them an opportunity to withdraw. When the contractors maintained their tender figure, the employers (advised by the engineers) insisted on a bond of £50 000. The bondsman later sought to be released, claiming that these matters should all have been disclosed. However, it was held that, since the contract clearly showed that adverse ground conditions were solely at the contractor's risk, the employers owed no duty of disclosure.

It should also be borne in mind that, while the general law does not require the beneficiary to sue the principal before claiming against the surety, nor even to give notice to the surety that the principal is in breach of contract, either of these requirements may well be imposed by the contract of guarantee. If this is so, then non-compliance by the beneficiary may well entitle the surety to be released from the guarantee. In *Clydebank* v. *Fidelity Deposit*,[9] for example, an employer's failure to give written notice of a contractor's delay, which might lead to a claim for liquidated damages, proved fatal to his claim against a surety. This was despite the fact that the claim against the surety did not relate to liquidated damages at all, but instead was for the cost of having the work completed when the original contractor became insolvent.

Alteration of contract terms

Any material variation in the terms of the main contract will release the surety from his or her obligation since it alters the nature of what is guaranteed. Oddly, perhaps, this applies even to alterations which appear to be for the benefit of the principal such as where the beneficiary waives or compromises a claim against the principal. The reason why this releases the surety is said to be that the removal of pressure from the contractor may make it more likely that the contractor will breach the contract and so render the surety liable.

In accordance with this approach, guarantors of payment obligations have been held to be released where the creditor agrees to accept a late payment from the principal, though not where the creditor merely acquiesces in a payment which is late. As for performance obligations, complete discharge of a surety has followed a knowing overpayment by the employer, the payment of an instalment before it was due and agreement by the employer to give the contractor extra time to complete. However, an employer who *unintentionally* overpays the contractor will not thereby lose the right to claim against the surety, nor will one who fails to discover or even acquiesces in the contractor's breaches of contract.

REFERENCES

1. *Normid Housing Association Ltd* v. *Ralphs* (1988) 43 B.L.R. 18.
2. *Bradley* v. *Eagle Star Insurance Co. Ltd* [1989] 1 All E.R. 961.
3. *Petrofina (UK) Ltd* v. *Magnaload Ltd* [1984] Q.B. 127.
4. *Walters* v. *Whessoe Ltd* (1960) 6 B.L.R. 23.
5. *AMF International Ltd* v. *Magnet Bowling Ltd* [1968] 2 All E.R. 789.
6. *Gold* v. *Patman & Fotheringham Ltd* [1958] 2 All E.R. 497.
7. *Charon (Finchley) Ltd* v. *Singer Sewing Machine Ltd* (1968) 207 E.G. 140.
8. *Trade Indemnity* v. *Workington Harbour & Docks Board* [1937] A.C. 1.
9. *Clydebank District Water Trustees* v. *Fidelity Deposit of Maryland* 1916 S.C. (H.L.) 69.

PART SIX

Sub-Contracts

16

General principles of sub-contracting

One of the most noticeable features of the construction industry in the UK is the extent to which the actual work of construction is carried out not by the 'contractor' firm which undertakes to do it, but by other firms which specialize in particular aspects of the work. It is normal to find at least 50% of the work carried out in this way. And, of course, where a project is set up under a **management contracting** method, the main contractor may do no physical work at all.

This fragmentation of the work is not very surprising in itself because increasingly sophisticated methods of building require a high degree of specialization. What *is* striking is the fact that, for the most part, these specialists do their work under contracts made not with the employer, but with the main contractor.

There is no compelling *logical* reason for this – it would be quite easy to remove such work from the ambit of the contract altogether, and to give it to the specialist under a direct contract with the employer. This indeed is precisely what happens under the system of procurement known as **construction management**. The reason is the *practical* one that such a move would impose upon the employer certain direct liabilities to the specialist not only as regards payment, but also in respect of delay or disruption caused by other contractors. In effect, the employer would be carrying the co-ordinating responsibilities for the main contractor. It would also expose the employer to claims by the main contractor if defaults of the specialist caused delay or disruption. It is in order to avoid the burdens and risks connected with project co-ordination that the sub-contract structure is normally adopted.

Later in this chapter, and in Chapters 17 and 18, we consider in detail the complex set of legal rules which operate when sub-contracts are used. First, however, it is necessary to explain how sub-contracts fit in with the general legal principles which govern the scope of contractual liabilities.

16.1   NOVATION, ASSIGNMENT AND VICARIOUS PERFORMANCE

It is an important principle of contract law that, where there is a contract between A and B, A may not simply decide to be replaced by C. If A wishes to hand over all rights and obligations to C, and then simply drop out of the picture, there must be a **novation**. In effect, this is a new contract to replace the old one, and it must be agreed on by all three parties. The law's view is that B has made this contract on the basis of holding A responsible on it, and the right to do so is not to be unilaterally taken away.

A novation, then, is a contract which transfers both rights and obligations from one of the original parties to a new party. An **assignment**, on the other hand, occurs where an original party transfers only contractual *rights*. For example, employers who are property developers might wish to assign to the first purchaser of a building their rights to claim against the contractor for breach of contract if any defects appear. Similarly, a contractor might seek to raise money from a bank by assigning to the bank the future rights to be paid under a particular building contract.

The law of contract permits assignments in principle, but this is subject to any terms in the particular contract. It should be noted that both JCT 80 and ICE 6 contain restrictions. Under JCT 80 clause 19.1.1, neither party may assign the contract (or any rights under the contract)[1] without the other's written consent. However, clause 19.1.2 provides an optional exception. If it is stated in the Appendix to the contract that this clause is to apply, then the employer can after practical completion assign the right to sue for defects to a purchaser or tenant of the building. As for the ICE conditions, it is interesting to note that the 5th edition placed no restriction at all upon the employer's right to assign. However, ICE 6 provides that neither the employer nor the contractor can assign without the other's written consent (which is not to be unreasonably withheld).

Leaving aside the issues of novation and assignment, there is the possibility that a party may wish to remain legally responsible for the performance of contractual obligations, but to have those obligations actually carried out by someone else. This is known as **vicarious performance** and, in principle, it is quite acceptable. However, it will *not* be permitted where the other contracting party has been specifically selected for some personal qualification, skill or competence. After all, if you hire a particular rock group for a concert, you do not expect to find the job carried out by a substitute! In the building contract field, vicarious performance will be impliedly ruled out in respect of those jobs which call for highly specialized skills, such as geological investigation of the site. Furthermore, it seems likely that although, on a large project, it is legitimate to sub-contract the physical work of construction, the builder's 'managerial' functions (i.e. the co-ordination and control of the entire project) will be treated as personal and therefore as non-delegable.

In any event, most modern standard form contracts place express limits on the extent to which the main contractor may satisfy contractual obligations through the medium of sub-contractors. For example, JCT 80 clause 19.2 provides that 'the Contractor shall not without the written consent of the Contract Administrator (which consent shall not be unreasonably withheld) sub-let any portion of the Works'. This is reinforced by clause 19.4, which provides further that any sub-contract must contain certain conditions which are designed to protect the employer's position. The importance attached to this clause is shown by the fact that unauthorized sub-letting is a ground for the employer to determine the contractor's employment under clause 27.1.4.

Where a dispute arises over a refusal by the contract administrator to consent to a proposed sub-letting, this can only be resolved by arbitration. However, JCT 80 contains no explicit sanction at all for mere *delay* by the contract administrator in giving such consent. A contractor who is not prepared to take the risk of merely going ahead without such consent, but who decides instead to wait for the contract administrator's decision, will not be entitled to an extension of time, nor for compensation for any loss and expense incurred. However, it is at least possible that such delay might consitute a breach of the employer's implied duty of co-operation, in which case the contractor would be entitled to claim damages.

Not surprisingly, the other contracts in the JCT range (e.g. CD 81, IFC 84 and MW 80) deal with the basic question of sub-contracting in much the same way as does JCT 80. That is to say, they require the contractor to obtain the consent of either the employer or the contract administrator, and provide that such consent is not to be unreasonably withheld. By contrast, ICE 6 provides in clause 4 that 'the Contractor shall not sub-contract the whole of the Works without the prior written consent of the Employer. Except where otherwise provided the Contractor may sub-contract any part of the Works or their design.' This represents a marked relaxation of the position under the 5th edition, which required the Engineer's written consent to any sub-contracting. That form of contract also provided that, if the contractor *did* sub-let any part 'to the detriment of good workmanship or in defiance of the Engineer's instruction to the contrary', then the employer could expel the contractor from the Works.

There is one further aspect of the employer's right to control sub-contracting which should be mentioned here. It concerns the common practice, when specifying a particular supplier of material, of following this with some such phrase as 'or other approved firm'. It has been held by the Court of Appeal[2] that this does *not* mean that the contractor is entitled to choose a substitute of equivalent quality. The employer, through the contract administrator, has an absolute discretion to refuse any alternative, and need not even give reasons for such a refusal.

16.2   THE CONTRACTUAL CHAIN

The basic position in law, as we have noted in Chapter 1, is that the main contract and the sub-contract (and the sub-sub-contract, if there is one) are regarded as the links in a chain. Each contract is of direct legal concern only to those who are its parties. Thus the main contract affects only the employer and the main contractor; the sub-contract affects only the main contractor and the sub-contractor; and so on. There may be other types of legal action (e.g. in tort) between parties who are not linked by a contract, but there can be no claim arising out of the contracts themselves.

This idea of **chain liability** works perfectly well so long as all the links are intact. For example, where there are defects in the sub-contractor's work, the employer will have a contractual remedy against the main contractor who will, in turn, take action against the sub-contractor. Similarly, the sub-contractor's right to payment will be exercised against the main contractor who will be reimbursed by what is received from the employer. However, a chain is only as strong as its weakest link, and considerable problems arise as soon as one of the links breaks. What, for instance, is the position where the terms of the two contracts are significantly different, so that a liability may arise which cannot simply be passed down the chain? Or (a distressingly frequent occurrence in the construction industry) where one of the parties is insolvent and therefore unable to meet any liabilities?

In the next two chapters we consider the extent to which one party may be held legally responsible for the defaults of another in circumstances where that responsibility cannot be passed on. Also considered is the extent to which a 'missing link' may be bypassed by finding some alternative form of legal liability. Those chapters concentrate mainly on sub-contractors' defaults and on sub-contractors' rights to payment; for the moment, however, the dangers of a broken chain may be illustrated by a Canadian case of a different kind. *Smith and Montgomery* v. *Johnson Bros*[3] concerned a sub-contract for tunnelling work, which was to be carried out 'according to the dimensions and specifications as set forth in the main contract'. A clause of that main contract empowered the engineer to order any work to be stopped, in which case the main contractor would be entitled to an extension of time but not to compensation for loss and expense. Acting under this clause, the engineer ordered the tunnelling work to be stopped, and the main contractor passed on this instruction to the sub-contractors. This, it was held, entitled the sub-contractors to recover damages from the main contractor for breach of contract. The sub-contract had no term equivalent to that in the main contract, nor had the main contract term been incorporated by reference into the sub-contract.

16.3 TYPES OF SUB-CONTRACT

A simple classification of sub-contracts is by reference to the kind of work which they involve. At one end of the spectrum are those contracts for the supply of materials only (i.e. where the sub-contractor carries out no work other than that of delivery). At the other end are 'labour only' sub-contracts, in which no material of any kind is supplied. Between these two extremes lie many contracts involving the supply of both work and materials (which of these aspects dominates will of course vary from one contract to another). It is also worth remembering that the *work* element in such a hybrid contract may take place either on site (as with a standard 'supply and fix' arrangement) or off site (as with the supply of pre-cast units).

This factual classification of sub-contracts has a certain legal significance, in that it governs the question of which set of statutory terms should be implied into the contract in question. A pure supply or 'materials only' contract, assuming that no hire purchase or similar arrangement is involved, will be subject to the *Sale of Goods Act 1979*. A 'labour only' contract will fall instead under Part II (the 'services' provisions) of the *Supply of Goods and Services Act 1982*. As for contracts which contain both elements, these are again caught by the 1982 Act – the transfer of materials is subject to Part I and the provision of services to Part II.

A further point which should be made is that, with the greatly increased specialization of the modern construction industry, much sub-contract work now includes significant elements of *design*. This raises special problems of legal responsibility in case of defects, and these are dealt with in Chapter 18.

A second and more significant way of classifying sub-contracts is by reference to the question of whether the sub-contractor is selected by the main contractor or the employer. For the remainder of this chapter we examine a range of possibilities which exist under the most important standard forms.

16.3.1   Domestic sub-contractors

A 'domestic' sub-contractor is one in whose selection and appointment the employer plays no part, other than simply giving consent where this is required under the terms of the main contract. In theory at least, the appointment of the sub-contractor is entirely for the benefit of the main contractor, a purely 'domestic' matter. If the main contract concerns itself at all with such sub-contracting, it will usually merely insist that any sub-contract should contain certain clauses, which are designed to protect the interests of the employer. These will cover such matters as determination (it is important that, if the main contract is brought to an end, the sub-contract should also fall) and the ownership of materials brought on to the site.

As to the terms of domestic sub-contracts themselves, there is no doubt that these are far less 'standardized' than those of main contracts. Many sub-contractors, especially those who simply supply materials, have their own 'standard form' of sub-contract, as do many main contractors. However, there have been complaints that the latter are often harsh and onerous, and that they are imposed upon sub-contractors by means of superior bargaining strength. Partly because of this, some efforts have been made to provide sub-contract forms which are designed to be used with the standard forms of main contract. For instance, the Joint Contracts Tribunal has produced a form of domestic sub-contract (IN/SC) for use with IFC 84 and, of course, there is the Works Contract which forms part of the JCT 87 Management Contract. Furthermore, while JCT itself provides no domestic sub-contract for use with JCT 80, some of the constituent bodies of the JCT have drafted such a form, which is known as DOM/1. The three organizations concerned are the National Federation of Building Trades Employers (now the Building Employers' Confederation), the Federation of Associations of Specialists and Sub-contractors and the Confederation of Associations of Specialist Engineering Contractors. Again, there is no official ICE sub-contract, but the form published by the Federation of Civil Engineering Contractors is widely accepted.

Space does not permit detailed consideration of the provisions of domestic sub-contracts. However, it is worth noting that while their terms may generally follow those applicable to 'nominated' or 'named' sub-contractors, there are certain essential differences. In particular, domestic sub-contracts will seldom involve the contract administrator or quantity surveyor in their administration. Such matters as extensions of time, compensation for loss and expense and entitlement to interim payments are usually left to be decided by the contractor and sub-contractor alone.

Before leaving the subject of 'domestic' sub-contracts, mention should be made of the procedure found in JCT 80 clause 19.3. This enables an employer to gain at least some control over the identity of a sub-contractor, without accepting the risks which attach to 'naming' or 'nomination'. Clause 19.3 permits the contract bills to specify that certain work, although priced by the main contractor, is to be carried out by a person selected by the contractor from a list annexed to the bills. The list must contain at least three names, and if the number falls below three, either more names may be added by agreement of the parties or the main contractor may take on the work. Further, either party may in any event add names to the list, subject to the consent of the other, which is not to be unreasonably withheld. As a result, a contractor may deprive the employer of control in this situation by simply adding a favourite sub-contractor to the list and then insisting on selecting that one!

If this 'clause 19.3' procedure is adopted, the person selected then becomes a domestic sub-contractor. Unfortunately, JCT 80 fails completely to indicate what shall happen if such a sub-contractor fails to complete the work. Must there be a 're-listing', or can the main contractor simply take over the work? In either event, who is responsible for any extra costs involved? It seems highly probable that such questions (which, as we shall see in Chapter 18, have caused enormous problems in relation to nominated sub-contractors) will sooner or later also surface under clause 19.

16.3.2   Nominated sub-contractors

Benefits of nomination

Nomination is the practice by which an employer, through the contract administrator, selects persons who then enter into sub-contracts with the main contractor. This procedure is found mainly in the UK and in those countries whose standard building contracts are based on the major UK forms. It is often said to have developed in order to give the employer control over the *quality* of sub-contract work, but it also has an important bearing on *time* and *price*. As to time, it is often necessary for specialist work to be ordered well in advance, possibly long before the main contract is let. In such circumstances, the employer will order the work and will inform the main contractor at tender stage as to who the sub-contractor is to be.

The effect of nomination on price comes about in two ways. First, where certain work is made the subject of nomination, the process of tendering by the relevant specialists for the work in question is carried out only once. Further, this process may take place before, after or at the same time as the tendering process for the main contract. If this system were not used, every main contractor would need, before submitting a tender, to obtain tenders for specialist work from each potential sub-contractor. This would be an obvious duplication of effort and a lengthy procedure. Nomination therefore reduces the time and the cost of tendering.

Secondly, where a **prime cost** or **provisional sum** is inserted in the main contract, the main contractor prices only for attendances and profit. This means that the final decision on the price of this work is made by the employer, rather than by the main contractor. This may be of particular importance in cases (perhaps involving design) where it is necessary to balance price against quality or long-term performance.

The foregoing explains how the nomination system benefits employers, but it may also be worth noting that the system offers some important advantages to contractors. Apart from the fact that a main contractor's responsibility for the defaults of a nominated sub-contractor is drastically limited under JCT 80, that form of contract contains a remarkable hidden bonus for the main contractor. This lies in the fact that interim certificates issued by the contract administrator govern payment not only under the main contract, but under all nominated sub-contracts as well. And when the provisions of the relevant sub-contracts are closely examined, it becomes clear that the main contractor can earn a 'cash discount' of 2½% for prompt payment of the sub-contractor, without actually disrupting project cash flow at all. This is because, while the contractor must pay within 17 days of certification to qualify for the discount, the employer must have paid the money to the contractor within 14 days. Given the high percentage of a project that is usually the subject of nomination, this apparently small profit on *turnover* may represent a very substantial profit in terms of *capital employed*, and is in fact an important element in contract profitability.

An employer who has decided to adopt the 'nominated sub-contractor' approach to any particular aspect of the work is, it appears, committed to it. Since the employer's power under clause 13.1 of JCT 80 cannot be used to omit work from the contract simply to give it to another contractor,[4] it seems likewise that it cannot be used to omit work which has been given to a nominated sub-contractor. What is more, it has been held that the main contractor has neither the right nor the obligation to carry out work which is allocated to a nominated sub-contractor, either by identification in the contract documents or by a subsequent instruction in respect of a prime cost sum.[5]

A main contractor, then, may not simply take over work designated as sub-contract work. However, it is provided in clause 35.2 that the main contractor may, in certain circumstances, be permitted to tender for such work in competition with other 'genuine' sub-contractors. For this to take place, the work in question must be of a kind which the contractor carries out directly in the normal course of business; the main contractor must have indicated in the Appendix an intention to tender for it; and the contract administrator must be willing to receive such a tender. If these conditions are satisfied, the contractor may submit a tender, but there is no obligation on the employer to accept this tender, even if it is the lowest. If the tender *is* accepted, clause 35.2 provides that the contractor may not sublet the work without the contract administrator's consent (and there is no requirement that this consent shall not be unreasonably withheld).

Nomination of sub-contractors under JCT 80

The mere fact that a sub-contractor is effectively selected by the employer does not in itself make this a 'nominated sub-contract' under JCT 80. That will only be so if the employer's selection comes about in one of the ways specified in clause 35.1; these are as follows:

- Where the sub-contractor is named in the bills.
- Where the bills contain a prime cost sum.
- Where the contract administrator issues an instruction on the expenditure of a provisional sum in the bills.
- Where certain variations are ordered.
- Where an agreement is made between the contract administrator and the contractor.

Where any of these is applicable, the person chosen must be nominated in accordance with the procedures laid down in clause 35. This means that, depending on which of two permitted methods is adopted, the contractor and sub-contractor will enter into a specified form of sub-contract. In most cases, the sub-contractor will also be required to enter into a collateral agreement with the employer. The main purpose of this agreement is to provide protection for the employer against certain sub-contractor defaults, thus making it possible to free the main contractor from responsibility for those defaults. The resulting triangular relationship is extremely complex and has apparently proved very unpopular with the construction industry. In practice, clause 35 is frequently deleted from contracts, and a simpler nomination system substituted.

Assuming that clause 35 does apply, the first point to note is that it provides two procedures for nomination, described by JCT Practice Note 10 as the 'basic method' and the 'alternative method'. The basic method is thought to be preferable where the sub-contract works are of major significance in terms of their cost or because of their importance in the programme, and is suitable where sub-contract tenders can be considered before the main contract is let. This procedure involves the sub-contractor in tendering on NSC/1, which will contain as much information as possible about the main contract. Once the employer decides on the sub-contractor (who must also have completed the relevant part of the collateral agreement NSC/2), the employer completes the remainder of NSC/2 and the tender is passed to the main contractor with a preliminary notice of nomination. It is then up to the main contractor and sub-contractor to settle any outstanding terms within 10 days, failing which the contract administrator may renominate under clause 35.23. Once the main contractor and the sub-contractor are agreed, the contract administrator formally nominates the sub-contractor on NSC/3. When this document is issued, the main contractor and sub-contractor are automatically bound by the terms of sub-contract NSC/4.

The alternative method of nomination, which is likely to be quicker, is suggested as appropriate in cases where the sub-contract work is both straightforward and of less significance to the remainder of the project. The contract administrator may obtain tenders from prospective sub-contractors by any appropriate means, and it is for the employer to decide whether or not collateral agreement is required. If it is, then NSC/2a will be used. Once the employer decides on the sub-contractor, the contract administrator issues a nomination instruction (*not* on form NSC/3) and the main contractor and sub-contractor are intended to enter into a sub-contract (NSC/4a) within 14 days. Again, failure to agree may lead to renomination by the contract administrator under clause 35.23.

Whichever method of nomination is adopted, the result is a complex set of rights and obligations which link employer, main contractor and sub-contractor in a triangular relationship. Further complications arise from the fact that the contract administrator, who has no part to play where domestic sub-contractors are concerned, assumes a much more important position in relation to nominated sub-contractors. Apart from the important part played in the nomination process itself, the contract administrator is directly concerned with various financial provisions of the sub-contract. These include payment, variations and practical completion. The contract administrator is also responsible *indirectly* through the contractor for making decisions on applications by the sub-contractor for extensions of time, claims for loss and/or expense, and disputes between the contractor and sub-contractor over possible determination of the sub-contract.

Nomination of suppliers under JCT 80

JCT 80 clause 36 contains a complex definition of a 'nominated supplier'. The overall result is that a person is only a **nominated supplier** within the meaning of this clause where the goods or materials to be supplied are the subject of a prime cost sum. This prime cost sum may be contained in the original bills, it may arise from the conversion of a provisional sum in the original bills or it may be included in a contract administrator's instruction on a variation. Without it, however, there is no 'nomination' under this clause, even where the intended source of supply is expressly identified or where there is only one source of supply for the specified item.

Where a prime cost sum *is* specified in one of these ways, clause 36.3 provides that the amount payable by the employer to the contractor shall be the net cost to the contractor under the supply contract. This cost includes any charges for packing, transport and delivery, and also any expense properly incurred by the contractor which would not otherwise be reimbursed under the contract. This formulation means in effect that, apart from a 5% 'discount for cash' which the nominated supplier must allow the contractor for payment within 30 days of the end of the month following delivery, a contractor who is able to negotiate the benefit of a 'trade discount' will not be able to keep it.

Although there is no compulsory form of supply contract for use with JCT 80, clause 36.4 attempts to control to some extent at least the terms on which a contractor and a nominated supplier do business. Indeed, the Joint Contracts Tribunal publishes a form of tender TNS/1 and strongly recommends its use by nominated suppliers. This document contains all the terms specified in clause 36.4 and also provides an optional warranty agreement TNS/2. When TNS/2 is used, the supplier guarantees that design, selection of materials and satisfaction of performance specifications have been and will be carried out with care and skill. The supplier also undertakes to indemnify the employer if any default entitles the contractor to an extension of time or loss and/or expense under the main contract.

Whether or not the recommended form of tender is used, clause 36.4 of JCT 80 provides that the contractor cannot be forced by the contract administrator to enter into a contract with a nominated supplier unless that contract contains certain terms. By and large, these terms merely confirm the supplier's obligations such as to deliver in accordance with any agreed programme and to bear responsibility for defects. However, there is also mention of the contractor's 5% 'discount for cash' and, more controversially, a statement that ownership of all materials shall pass to the contractor upon *delivery*, irrespective of payment. The supply contract must also contain a term to the effect that none of its other terms shall override or modify those terms which are included to give effect to clause 36.4.

Nomination under ICE 6

The ICE 6 approach to nomination is different in a number of respects from that of JCT 80, presumably in the hope of avoiding some of the problems encountered under the JCT forms. Clauses 58 and 59 of ICE 6 provide a code of rules which apply equally to both nominated sub-contractors and nominated suppliers. First (and this is similar to JCT 80) is the contractor's right of objection to any proposed nomination. In addition to a general right to 'raise reasonable objection', clause 59(1) specifically entitles the contractor to refuse any sub-contractor who will not contract on terms which protect the contractor in various ways.

If the contractor exercises this right of objection, the situation may be dealt with in a variety of ways. Under clause 59(2) the engineer may:

- make an alternative nomination;
- vary the works;
- omit the item in question and have it carried out by a direct contractor;
- instruct the contractor to find a potential domestic sub-contractor and submit a quotation;
- invite the contractor to carry out the work.

16.3.3   Named sub-contractors

IFC 84 introduced, for the first time in JCT contracts, a system under which the employer could 'name' a sub-contractor for specific work without adopting the full and complex 'nomination' procedure of JCT 80. The form of sub-contract which is to be used (NAM/SC) is in fact based upon that intended for *domestic* sub-contractors under JCT 80 (DOM/1), although a person named under IFC 84 is rather more than a domestic sub-contractor.

The IFC 84 system provides two alternative methods by which sub-contractors can be named, although both of these require the sub-contractor to tender on JCT Form NAM/T and to enter into a sub-contract using JCT Form NAM/SC. The first method, which is dealt with in clause 3.3.1, will be to the employer's advantage to use where both the work involved and the sub-contractor can be sufficiently identified at an early stage. Under this method, the main contract tender document names the intended sub-contractor and provides a detailed description of the work which is to be performed. It is then up to the main contractor to price this work when tendering. There is no need for the main contractor to be bound by the tender submitted by the proposed sub-contractor.

Once the main contract tender is accepted, the sub-contract must be entered into within 21 days. Should this prove impossible, because the contractor and sub-contractor cannot reach agreement, there is no power under clause 3.3.1 for the contract administrator simply to name an alternative sub-contractor. The situation must be dealt with in one of the three following ways:

1. Where the problem arises out of some 'particulars given in the contract documents' (i.e. matters contained in NAM/T), the contract administrator may change those particulars so as to remove the impediment.
2. Again, where the problem arises out of some 'particulars given in the contract documents', the contract administrator may choose to omit the work altogether.
3. Whatever the cause of the problem, the contract administrator may omit the work in question from the contract documents and substitute a provisional sum.

If either the first or the second option is chosen, the contract administrator's instruction is to be treated as a variation and valued accordingly. This means that, in respect of any subsequent delay, the contractor will be entitled to claim both an extension of time and for any direct loss and/or expense incurred. However, all three of these options place the risk of the *initial* delay on the contractor. Except in so far as the contract administrator is guilty of unreasonable delay in giving the instruction, the contractor can make no claim against the employer for an extension of time or for loss and/or expense.

The second method of naming a sub-contractor under IFC 84 is dealt with by clause 3.3.2. This consists of the insertion of a provisional sum in the main contract documents, and a subsequent contract administrator's instruction as to the expenditure of that sum. Such an instruction must incorporate a full description of the work and the chosen sub-contractor's tender for it. The contractor must then, unless exercising the right of objection on reasonable grounds, enter into a sub-contract with that person within 14 days. In these circumstances, while the sub-contractor is entitled to payment in accordance with the tender, what the main contractor in turn receives from the employer is based on a fair valuation of the work (clause 3.7).

Where this method is adopted, any delay or disruption caused to the contractor may be the subject of a claim for an extension of time or for loss and/or expense. Furthermore, if it proves impossible to conclude the relevant sub-contract, then it seems that the contract administrator must issue further instructions as to the provisional sum, again at the employer's expense.

REFERENCES

1. *Linden Gardens* v. *Lenesta Sludge Disposals Ltd* (1991) CSW, 24 January.
2. *Leedsford Ltd* v. *Bradford Corporation* (1956) 24 B.L.R. 49.
3. *Smith and Montgomery* v. *Johnson Bros* [1954] 1 D.L.R. 392.
4. *Carr* v. *J.A. Berriman Pty Ltd* (1953) 89 C.L.R. 327.
5. *North West Regional Hospital Board* v. *T.A. Bickerton & Son Ltd* [1970] 1 All E.R. 1039.

17

Rights of sub-contractors

In this chapter we consider the main rights which a sub-contractor can exercise against the main contractor, and the more limited rights against the employer. The reason why the second group is more limited is that whereas the sub-contract which links the main contractor and the sub-contractor will usually be very detailed, and will contain numerous clauses creating mutual rights and obligations, any direct contractual link between the sub-contractor and the employer is likely to be of a much simpler kind. In either case, however, the sub-contractor's main interest lies in getting paid; all other rights are subordinate to this.

17.1 RIGHTS AGAINST THE MAIN CONTRACTOR

17.1.1 Payment

General principles

A straightforward application of contract law leads to the conclusion that the payment rights of a sub-contractor are to be found exclusively within the terms of the relevant sub-contract. With one exception, the main contract has no bearing on this issue. Even if the main contract expressly prohibits sub-contracting, a main contractor who disobeys that prohibition will be liable to pay the sub-contractor for work done.[1]

The exception to this general principle lies in the fact that it is, of course, quite possible for the sub-contract itself to incorporate, expressly or impliedly, some of the main contract terms. In one case,[2] for example, an order form sent by a main contractor to a nominated sub-contractor stated that the sub-contractor was to observe the conditions contained in the main contract, and that payment was to be made in accordance with the certificates and terms of the main contract. The main contract there provided expressly that payment in respect of any work comprised in a nominated sub-contract should not fall due until the main contractor received an architect's certificate. It was held by the Court of Appeal that the second provision in the order form (though not the first) had the effect of incorporating the main contract clause. As a result, the sub-contractor was not entitled to be paid until a certificate was issued.

The payment provisions found in standard form sub-contracts usually draw an important distinction between nominated and domestic sub-contractors. It is common to provide (as is done, for example, in NSC/4 clause 21.3) that payments to a *nominated* sub-contractor do not become due from the main contractor unless and until the contract administrator issues a certificate to this effect. However, it would be most unusual for the contract administrator to play any part in the entitlement to payment of a *domestic* sub-contractor; this is a matter for agreement between the main contractor and the sub-contractor.

Contractor's right of set off

As we have noted in Chapter 11, a sub-contractor's demand to be paid is frequently challenged by the main contractor, who claims to be entitled to reduce or even eliminate altogether the amount due on the ground that the sub-contractor is guilty of delay, defective work or other breach of contract. Readers should refer to that chapter, in view of the critical importance of this topic in practical contract administration. In the current context, we need only repeat the main points made earlier:

- An **express contractual right** to set off in this way must be exercised in strict accordance with any conditions laid down such as a contract administrator's certificate of delay or the service of a notice in an appropriate form.
- The **common law right** of set-off which is normally implied, and which is not subject to any conditions of this kind, will only be excluded by clear words in the contract.

'Pay when paid' provisions

A feature of many sub-contracts is some provision to the effect that the main contractor will pay the sub-contractor not when the sum is *certified* by the contract administrator, but only when the main contractor *actually receives the money* from the employer. As yet, the UK standard forms do not contain any such terms. They are, however, in a everyday use in standard form contracts used in Hong Kong and Singapore, which are largely modelled on JCT forms. They are also to be found in many of the non-standard forms of sub-contract which are drafted by UK main contractors and imposed on their sub-contractors by virtue of superior bargaining power.

Perhaps the most important purpose of a **pay when paid provision** is to protect the main contractor's cash flow. A contractor who merely acts as a channel of payment between the employer and the sub-contractor will be in no danger of having to finance the sub-contractor's work. However, such a clause also has a second and less obvious effect, in that it makes the sub-contractor carry the risk of the employer becoming insolvent. This will happen in circumstances where the employer's insolvency occurs after sub-contract work has been certified, but before the main contractor has been paid for it. Under a JCT form of contract, it is the main contractor who will bear the resulting loss, in the sense of having to pay the sub-contractor and then recoup whatever can be salvaged in the employer's liquidation. Under a 'pay when paid' clause, by contrast, the main contractor need only pass on to the sub-contractor what can be recovered in the employer's liquidation, and even this will naturally be put first to meeting the main contractor's own claims!

The way in which 'pay when paid' clauses shift risks on to sub-contractors strikes some people as unfair.[3] Such clauses have seldom been considered by the English courts, but when they have, the judges have appeared somewhat suspicious of them and interpreted them strictly against the main contractor. Indeed, there is even a tentative suggestion that, where a 'pay when paid' clause is imposed as part of the main contractor's standard terms, it may be subject to a test of 'reasonableness' under section 3 of the *Unfair Contract Terms Act 1977*.

This is not the place to speculate at length on the future of 'pay when paid' clauses, but attention must be drawn to one problem which the UK courts will sooner or later certainly have to face. This is the question of what exactly constitutes 'receipt' by the main contractor of the sum claimed by the sub-contractor. The main contractor will argue that payment in cash or its equivalent is what is required, but what is the position where the employer exercises a right of set-off or deduction, for instance, on the ground of delay? In some situations, the law clearly treats such a set-off as 'payment', but the courts in countries where such clauses are in common use seem to suggest that the main contractor need not pay in this situation.[4]

The problem is this: if 'receipt' really does signify 'physical receipt of the money', this would mean that a main contractor can refuse to pay a sub-contractor, even where the reason for the employer's non-payment is the main contractor's own breach! Such a conclusion would permit contractors to benefit from their own wrongdoing, something which the law normally strives to avoid as being totally unfair. On the other hand, if 'receipt' includes cases where the employer exercises a right of set-off, this would mean that the main contractor must pay sub-contractor A, even when the reason for the employer's non-payment is a breach of contract by sub-contractor B. Such a result would also seem unfair, this time on the main contractor! Quite how the courts can resolve this matter remains to be seen.

17.1.2   Other rights

The rights of a sub-contractor against the main contractor are, of course, dependent upon the terms of their sub-contract, so that no precise list can be compiled. It is of course possible for terms to be implied into the sub-contract, but an implied term will not be allowed to override clear express terms. For example, where a sub-contract stipulated that the work was to be carried out 'at such time or times as the contractor shall direct or require', it was held by the Court of Appeal that there could be no implied term that the main contractors would make sufficient work available to the sub-contractors to enable them to work in an efficient and economic manner.[5]

One term which *is* likely to be implied into any sub-contract, if the matter is not covered expressly, is that the main contractor will not deprive the sub-contractor of the opportunity of carrying out the work and thus earning money. If the main contractor is guilty of a breach of the main contract which leads to the employer ejecting both the main contractor and the sub-contractor from the site, the sub-contractor will be entitled to recover damages from the main contractor.

This is what happened in *Dyer* v. *Simon Build*[6] where, under a previous version of the ICE form of contract, the main contractors were expelled from the site after the engineer had certified that they had failed to proceed with due diligence. The main contractors argued that this entitled them to terminate their sub-contract with the plaintiffs (made on the FCEC conditions), and to pay the plaintiffs only what was due under those conditions. This would not include anything for the plaintiffs' lost profits. However, it was held that since the main contract had not been 'determined' by the employer's action the FCEC clause did not apply. Accordingly, the plaintiffs were entitled to recover as damages an amount which included their lost profits.

The result which was achieved in this case might well be different under JCT contracts. Both NSC/4 and DOM/1 provide for the automatic determination of the relevant sub-contract if the main contract is determined, and they make provision for the amount which the sub-contractor is to be paid where this occurs. Quite remarkably, however, as we shall see in Chapter 23, a domestic sub-contractor is given no right to claim for loss and expense in this situation, even where it is some default of the main contractor which has triggered the process. It therefore remains to be seen whether the courts would permit the sub-contractor in such circumstances to maintain an action for breach of an implied term in the sub-contract, and thus to recover damages from the main contractor.

17.2 RIGHTS AGAINST THE EMPLOYER

17.2.1 Payment

General

As a basic principle, the lack of a direct contractual link between an employer and a sub-contractor or supplier means that the employer is not liable to pay the sub-contractor directly for work done or materials supplied. This point, which applies to both domestic and nominated sub-contractors, was settled by the House of Lords in 1917. In *Hampton* v. *Glamorgan CC*,[7] a lump sum contract to build a school in accordance with the specifications of the defendants' architect included a provisional sum for heating apparatus. The plaintiff submitted a scheme to provide this, and the architect told the builder to accept it. When the builder failed to pay the full amount, and the plaintiff sued the defendants for the balance, it was held that the builder's overall obligation included providing the heating apparatus within the provisional sum. In employing the plaintiff for this purpose, the builder was contracting personally and not as agent for the defendants; the latter were therefore not liable to the plaintiff for the balance of the price.

Although the terms of the main contract may lead to the conclusion that the employer *is* personally responsible for payments to sub-contractors,[8] such an interpretation is extremely unusual. Most of the cases in which liability has been imposed have been ones in which the employer has entered into direct negotiations or dealings with a sub-contractor or supplier.[9] Even here, however, the courts are slow to reach the conclusion that any direct obligation has been assumed. In one case,[10] for example, where a main contractor was on the brink of liquidation, certain sub-contractors threatened to stop work. The employer then promised to 'ensure payment of all amounts outstanding' to the sub-contractors. However, it was held that even this did not create any legal obligation on the employer's part.

A particular aspect of the courts' attitude in this situation is their reluctance to permit a contract administrator, as agent for the employer, to bring the latter into a direct contractual relationship with a sub-contractor. This reluctance is exemplified by the case of *Vigers* v. *Swindell*[11] where, under a contract which permitted direct payment of sub-contractors on the main contractor's default, the main contractor

liquidation and the contract was taken over by one of its
The architect instructed sub-contractors to lay flooring and
promised that the employer would pay for this. It was none the less held
that the architect had no authority to commit the employer in this way
and that since the employer had not ratified his action the plaintiff
sub-contractors could not recover payment from her.

Direct payment provisions

Notwithstanding this clear lack of any obligation to see that a sub-
contractor is paid, there is nothing to prevent an employer from taking
on some responsibility in this matter. This in fact often happens in
respect of nominated sub-contractors (as, for example, under ICE 6
clause 59). The detail of such arrangements naturally varies from one
form of contract to another, but JCT 80 provides a good illustration.

While JCT 80 is careful to preserve the basic position that the employer
is not directly liable to a nominated sub-contractor (clause 35.20), it goes
on to set out a scheme under which, if the main contractor fails to
discharge an obligation to pay the sub-contractor, the employer may pay
directly. This power is in principle to be exercised at the employer's sole
discretion, but where there is a collateral agreement (NSC/2 or NSC/2a)
with the relevant sub-contractor, it becomes a binding obligation on the
employer. It is, in effect, the 'price' which the employer pays in return for
the sub-contractor's direct warranty.

These direct payment provisions of JCT 80 require the contractor to
show proof to the contract administrator that payments to nominated
sub-contractors have been duly discharged. If such proof cannot be provided, then any future payment certified as due to the contractor shall be
reduced by the amount owing to sub-contractors, and this amount shall
be paid directly by the employer. It is important to note that the employer is not bound to pay any more than can be obtained in this way – it
is not the employer's own money which is at risk, but only that which
would otherwise be due to the main contractor. Clause 35.13 further
provides that, where more than one nominated sub-contractor has been
left unpaid, the employer shall apply the sums available pro-rata or may
adopt any other method of apportionment which appears to the employer
to be fair and reasonable.

Direct payment provisions of this kind are said to be for the benefit of
employers since they encourage sub-contractors to tender for work by
giving them an extra assurance of payment. However, the added security
should not be too heavily relied on since it is of doubtful value in
precisely those circumstances where it is most important, namely the
main contractor's insolvency. The reasons for this lie in the general law of

bankruptcy (liquidation in the case of a company) which seeks to ensure that all creditors of the bankrupt are treated on an equal footing and that none receives unfairly preferential treatment. If, when a main contractor defaults, one sub-contractor receives payment in full (under a direct payment scheme), it is at least arguable that this is unfair preference over other creditors, and also over other sub-contractors who do not have the benefit of such an arrangement.

The main principles by which the law of insolvency seeks to achieve its ends are worth noting. The first point to be made is that, where the main contract does *not* contain an express provision permitting direct payment of sub-contractors, an employer who makes such a payment will be at risk if the contractor then goes into liquidation. Thus, where an employer paid a supplier of materials directly after the contractor had gone bankrupt owing money to the supplier, it was held that the employer must pay the money again to the contractor's trustee in bankruptcy, so that it would be available to *all* the contractor's creditors.[12]

Where there is an express power to make direct payments to sub-contractors, it has been held[13] that such payments are valid against a liquidator or trustee in bankruptcy. This is apparently on the ground that since the contractor's right to be paid is dependent upon the issue of a certificate, the contract administrator's decision not to certify parts of the work does not amount to a dealing with the insolvent person's property. It is instead something which prevents that person from acquiring any rights to property in the first place. This seems a reasonable suggestion, and certainly there are strong arguments of policy in favour of these clauses in the construction context. None the less, doubts as to their effectiveness have been raised by a majority decision of the House of Lords in a quite different context.[14] It has been held that when an airline company went into liquidation agreements which it had made with other airlines for setting off mutual debts were invalid since they contravened insolvency law. This decision was reached despite the court's acknowledgement that what were being overridden were perfectly sensible business arrangements, and so it may well be that a court would similarly override a direct payment provision in a construction case.

Whatever the true position may be, the uncertainties outlined above have led to the insertion of a provision in clause 35.13.5.4 of JCT 80 to the effect that the 'direct payment' procedure shall automatically cease as soon as the contractor is subject to liquidation proceedings. Further, it is provided in clause 7.2 of NSC/2 that, if the employer pays a sub-contractor directly and then discovers that such proceedings had already been commenced, the money must be repaid on demand. The practical lesson for a sub-contractor is therefore clear; on becoming aware that the main contractor is in financial difficulties, the sub-contractor should inform the employer immediately. In this way, money which is ultimately intended for the sub-contractor can be prevented from reaching the main contractor, and from forming part of the main contractor's general assets on insolvency.

17.2.2   Rights over materials

The general principles governing the transfer of ownership in building materials from the contractor to the employer (which we have considered in Chapter 10) gain an extra dimension where a sub-contractor or supplier is involved. However, the basic position in such cases is relatively straightforward: once ownership of the materials has passed from the sub-contractor to the main contractor, any lien or similar right on the sub-contractor's part comes to an end.[15] The sub-contractor accordingly loses any leverage which might otherwise have been used against the employer to ensure payment.

In an effort to improve their position, many sub-contractors and suppliers have in recent years sought to contract upon terms which incorporate a **retention of title** clause. Such clauses vary in scope, but they are generally designed to ensure that title to materials does not pass to the main contractor (and thence to the employer) unless and until the sub-contractor has been paid for them. Provided that a clause of this kind is validly incorporated in the relevant contract it seems in principle that it will be effective.

In the leading case on this subject, *Dawber Williamson* v. *Humberside CC*,[16] a sub-contractor who had contracted to supply and fix a roof delivered a quantity of slates to the site. The main contractor was paid by the employer for these slates, but then went into liquidation before paying the sub-contractor. It was held that a retention of title clause in the sub-contract was effective, so that the slates remained the property of the sub-contractor. Terms in the *main* contract which purported to pass ownership of unfixed materials to the employer, once their value had been included in an interim certificate, were irrelevant since they applied only to goods which the main contractor already owned. As a result, the employer was liable in damages for refusing to allow the sub-contractor to remove the slates.

It is important to appreciate that the sub-contract in the *Dawber Williamson* case was of the 'supply and fix' variety, which means that it was classified in law as a contract for 'work and materials'. Had it been a contract merely to *supply*, which would have been classified as a contract for 'sale of goods', the position might well have been different. The reason for this is section 25 of the *Sale of Goods Act 1979*, under which a person who has 'bought or agreed to buy goods' and who is allowed by the seller to have possession of those goods, may, by delivering them under any 'sale, pledge or other disposition', pass title to a bona fide third party.

In the Scottish case of *Archivent Ltd* v. *Strathclyde*,[17] section 25 was applied in the context of a construction contract. The plaintiffs in that case supplied ventilators to a firm of contractors who were working under JCT 63 on a project for the defendants. The ventilators were delivered directly to the site, their value was duly certifed, and the defendants paid the contractors. However, the contractors then went into liquidation without having paid the plaintiffs. The plaintiffs' action to recover 'their' ventilators from the defendants failed since it was held that the defendants had received title from the contractors by virtue of section 25.

Although the *Archivent* case thus creates a crucial distinction between a contract to supply and install and one merely to supply, the limits of that decision should be noted. In a more recent case,[18] where timber was supplied under a contract with a title retention clause, the main contract (unlike that in *Archivent*) contained no express terms relating to interim payments and the passing of property in materials. It was held that although interim payments were in fact made, these did not have the effect of the employer 'buying' any particular materials from the contractor. As a result, section 25 of the *Sale of Goods Act 1979* did not apply and the timber remained the property of the supplier.

This discussion clearly shows that while the precise effect of title retention clauses may be uncertain, their presence in a sub-contract may represent a danger to the employer. In recognition of this, the currently amended versions of JCT 80 and its associated sub-contracts contain various provisions which are designed to protect the employer's position. These, briefly, are as follows:

- A *nominated sub-contractor* can only be appointed under NSC/4 or NSC/4a, neither of which contains a title retention clause.
- While there is no compulsory form of contract for use with a *nominated supplier*, clause 36 of JCT 80 prescribes certain provisions which any such contract must contain. These, naturally, are incompatible with any attempt at title retention on the part of the supplier.
- In the case of a *domestic sub-contractor*, DOM/1 (where it is used) will adequately protect the employer. As for other forms, clause 19.4 of JCT 80 makes the contractor responsible for ensuring that the sub-contract contains equivalent terms.
- The position of a *domestic supplier* constitutes an interesting loophole, in that JCT 80 makes no attempt to control the terms on which such a person contracts to supply materials to the main contractor. In this situation therefore the employer remains at risk from any title retention clause which the supply contract may contain.

17.2.3   Retention money

We have discussed in Chapter 11 the general rules governing the retention by an employer of a small percentage of interim payments made to the contractor so as to create a fund from which the employer can rectify defects in the building if the contractor fails to do so. It was there noted that:

- The employer is regarded as a trustee in respect of that fund, which enables the main contractor or any nominated sub-contractor to insist that the money be held in a separate bank account so as to protect it in the event of the employer's insolvency.
- Notwithstanding this status as trustee, the employer is entitled to use retention money in satisfaction of any claim against the contractor which would give rise to a right of deduction or set-off.

These general principles gain an extra dimension where nominated sub-contractors are concerned, at least under JCT 80. Clauses 30.4.2 and 30.5.2.1 require the contract administrator to identify separately the 'Contractor's retention' and the 'Nominated Sub-contract retention' for each such sub-contractor. The crucial question which arises is whether these provisions effectively operate to create *separate* trusts in favour of the main contractor and each nominated sub-contractor. If they do, then the employer's right to have recourse to retention money to satisfy a claim will extend only to the part which relates to the party in default (i.e. in respect of whom the set-off was exercised).

In one English case[19] it was held that this was indeed the position. The making of a sub-contract was treated as an assignment to the sub-contractor of the main contractor's interest in the relevant part of the retention so as to protect it from the employer's right of set-off. However, this reasoning was convincingly criticized in a Hong Kong case,[20] where it was pointed out that *all* retention money in the employer's hands must ultimately pass to the main contractor, and that the main contractor might then be entitled to exercise rights of deduction or set-off over it against the sub-contractor. As a result, it was held, the *whole* retention fund has to be treated as money 'due to' the main contractor, and thus as vulnerable to any right of recourse of the employer.

REFERENCES

1. *O'Toole* v. *Ferguson* (1912) 5 D.L.R. 868.
2. *Dunlop and Ranken Ltd* v. *Hendall Steel Structures Ltd* [1957] 3 All E.R. 344.
3. Huxtable, P.J.C. (1988) *Remedying Contractual Abuse in the Building Industry.* Technical Infomation Service 99, Chartered Institute of Building, Ascot.

4. *Schindler Lifts (Hong Kong) Ltd* v. *Shui On Construction Co. Ltd* (1984) 29 B.L.R. 95; *Nin Hing Electronic Engineering Ltd* v. *Aoki Corporation* (1987) 40 B.L.R 107; *Brightside Mechanical & Electrical Services Group Ltd* v. *Hyundai Engineering & Construction Co. Ltd* (1988) 41 B.L.R. 110.
5. *Martin Grant & Co. Ltd* v. *Sir Lindsay Parkinson & Co. Ltd* (1984) 29 B.L.R. 31.
6. *E.R. Dyer Ltd* v. *Simon Build/Peter Lind Partnership* (1982) 23 BLR 23.
7. *Hampton* v. *Glamorgan CC* [1917] A.C. 13.
8. E.g. in *Hobbs* v. *Turner* (1902) 18 T.L.R. 235.
9. E.g. *Smith* v. *Rudhall* (1862) 3 F. & F. 143.
10. *Victorian Railway Commissioners* v. *Lames L. Williams Pty Ltd* (1969) 44 A.L.J.R. 32.
11. *Vigers Sons & Co. Ltd* v. *Swindell* [1939] 3 All E.R. 590.
12. *Re Holt, ex parte Gray* (1888) 58 L.J.Q.B. 5.
13. *Re Wilkinson, ex parte Fowler* [1905] 2 K.B. 713; *Re Tout and Finch Ltd* [1954] 1 All E.R. 127.
14. *British Eagle International Airlines Ltd* v. *Compagnie Nationale Air France* [1975] 2 All E.R. 390.
15. *Pritchett and Gold and Electrical Power Storage Co. Ltd* v. *Currie* [1916] 2 Ch. 515.
16. *Dawber Williamson Roofing Ltd* v. *Humberside CC* (1979) 14 B.L.R. 70.
17. *Archivent Sales and Developments Ltd* v. *Strathclyde Regional Council* (1984) 27 B.L.R. 98.
18. *W. Hanson (Harrow) Ltd* v. *Rapid Civil Engineering Ltd & Usborne Developments Ltd* (1987) 38 B.L.R. 106.
19. *Re Arthur Sanders Ltd* (1981) 17 B.L.R. 125.
20. *Hsin Chong Construction Co. Ltd* v. *Yaton Realty Co. Ltd* (1986) 40 B.L.R. 119.

18

Defaults of sub-contractors

The obligations taken on by a sub-contractor or supplier are primarily defined in the relevant sub-contract. In this chapter we are concerned with the effects of a breach by the sub-contractor of those obligations. Naturally, the immediate effect is that the sub-contractor is liable to the main contractor for breach of contract, but other implications are also relevant. Most important among these is the extent to which the employer can hold the main contractor responsible for the sub-contractor's defaults, but we shall also consider the limited scope for the employer to take action directly against the sub-contractor.

18.1 LIABILITY OF THE SUB-CONTRACTOR TO THE EMPLOYER

About this not very much needs to be said. A sub-contractor who is in breach of any term of the sub-contract is liable to the main contractor, as the other party to that contract. And, of course, it should not be forgotten that the sub-contract may contain *implied* terms (e.g. as to workmanship, quality of materials, and so on) equivalent to those in the main contract.

One additional point is perhaps worth making since it is sometimes overlooked. A sub-contractor who is in breach can expect to pay damages to the main contractor, and these damages will reflect the losses which the main contractor has suffered. As a result, if the terms of the main contract do not make the main contractor liable to the employer for what has happened, then the sub-contractor in turn will not be liable to the main contractor. To take a simple example, where delay caused by a nominated sub-contractor entitles the main contractor to an extension of time, this means that the main contractor is not liable to pay liquidated damages to the employer during the relevant period. It follows that the main contractor has no reason to claim the amount of the liquidated damages from the sub-contractor, who therefore escapes responsibility for causing the delay! It is for this very reason that direct contractual links between an employer and a sub-contractor (such as NSC/2 under JCT 80) provide that a nominated sub-contractor who causes delay in such circumstances will become personally liable to the employer for the liquidated damages which are lost.

18.2   LIABILITY OF THE MAIN CONTRACTOR FOR SUB-CONTRACTOR DEFAULTS

On any construction project in which sub-contractors are involved (which effectively means virtually every project of any significant size), the possibility of default by a sub-contractor is an inherent risk. The allocation of that risk, as between the employer and the main contractor, is a matter for the main contract. The question which must be answered is this: 'if the sub-contractor executes defective work, causes delay, repudiates the sub-contract or becomes insolvent, is the resulting loss to fall on the employer or on the main contractor?'

Before turning to the way in which main contracts allocate, as between employer and main contractor, the risk of default by different categories of sub-contractor, it is worth reminding ourselves of the position under the law of tort. In *D. & F. Estates* v. *Church Commissioners*,[1] the tenant of a flat sued the main contractors who built the block in the tort of negligence for defective plastering work carried out by a firm of sub-contractors. This claim failed on the ground that the tenant's loss was a purely financial one and that it was therefore not recoverable in tort. However, the House of Lords also ruled that, even if physical damage had occurred, the main contractors could not have been held responsible for it. This was because not only were they not *vicariously* liable for the negligence of their sub-contractors, they did not even owe the plaintiffs a duty of care in tort to supervise those sub-contractors. The somewhat surprising result is that, even if the main contractor is 'negligent' in failing to check the work of sub-contractors (and even if this failure amounts to a breach of the main contract), there can be no liability for this *in tort*.

We may now consider the extent to which a main contractor can be held liable by the employer for the defaults of sub-contractors.

18.2.1   Domestic sub-contractors

In theory, at least, the appointment of a domestic sub-contractor is entirely for the main contractor's benefit. It is hardly surprising therefore that, as a general rule, any risks involved in such a sub-letting are to be borne by that main contractor. The *contractual* duty of performance rests entirely on the main contractor, and if this is broken by the actions of a chosen sub-contractor, either in breaching the contract or in dropping out altogether, there can be no excuse. Thus, for example, where a contractor who installed an up-and-over garage door for a client selected a lintel from a supplier's brochure, and this proved to be defective (it deflected two years later), the contractor was held liable.[2] The contractor's duty to the employer was to supply suitable materials, not merely to exercise reasonable care in selecting them.

Of course, it is important not to lose sight of what the main contractor's obligations actually *are*. If, as will normally be the case under a conventional procurement method, the contractor has no responsibility in respect of design, then there can be no liability for any loss or damage which results from a 'design fault' in the work of a domestic sub-contractor.

18.2.2 Nominated sub-contractors

The question: 'who is responsible for a nominated sub-contractor?' is not one to which a simple or straightforward answer can be given. It depends upon the type of default which is in issue, the kind of loss caused, the person who suffers the loss, the subsequent actions of the parties and, most important, the precise terms of the contract. With these qualifications in mind, we may turn to consider some of the more important situations which arise.

Defective work and materials

A main contractor's responsibility for a nominated sub-contractor's work is most likely to arise in respect of failure to comply with required standards of workmanship, or the quality and fitness for their purpose of any materials supplied. It has already been noted that, quite apart from any express terms in a building contract, it is the contractor's implied obligation to build in a workmanlike manner with materials which are of good quality and fit for their intended purpose. Further, while the obligation as to the *fitness* of materials only arises where the employer has relied on the 'skill and judgement' of the contractor, and will therefore be excluded where a sub-contractor is nominated, the obligation as to *quality* is strict and will therefore normally remain intact.[3] However, there may be special circumstances which are sufficient to displace even the implied warranty as to the quality of materials. This would occur, for example, where the main contractor has no right to object to a nomination, or where the contract administrator selects a supplier who, as the employer knows, will only contract on terms which exclude or limit the supplier's liability.[4]

Whatever the position may be in respect of workmanship and materials, it appears very unlikely that a main contractor can be held responsible for errors of *design* by a nominated sub-contractor in those cases where design is delegated in this way. This is on the basis that the contractor's obligation is merely to build in accordance with the design which is supplied. While this is logical, it should not be overlooked that all defects in *materials* are the contractor's responsibility, even those which arise from design errors. Thus the contractor's position will differ crucially according to whether a 'nominated sub-contractor' or a 'nominated supplier' is involved.

The 'implied term' position outlined above is by and large repeated by the express provisions of JCT 80 and its supporting sub-contract documents. Under clause 2.1 of NSC/2, the nominated sub-contractor warrants to the employer that all reasonable skill and care has been and will be exercised in design of the works, selection of materials and satisfaction of any relevant performance specification or requirement, so far as such matters are left to the sub-contractor. Clause 35.21 of JCT 80 then provides that, *whether or not such a collateral agreement has been entered into*, the main contractor shall not be liable to the employer for anything which it would cover. However, it is made clear at all times that the basic contractual obligations of both main contractor and sub-contractor as to workmanship and materials are not affected (i.e. the chain of liability remains intact).

Two further provisions of JCT 80 (and NSC/4) are worth noting in this context. First, when a nominated sub-contractor is required to enter into a sub-sub-contract or a contract of supply, it may be found that the other party seeks to exclude or restrict liability. In such circumstances, the nominated sub-contractor can refuse to make the contract unless the contract administrator gives specific written approval to the exclusion or restriction. If this approval is given, then the liability of the sub-contractor to the main contractor is likewise excluded or restricted (NSC/4 clause 2.3), as is that of the main contractor to the employer (JCT 80 clause 35.22).

The second point is that the contract administrator is obliged to make provision for final payment of the nominated sub-contractor within 12 months of practical completion of the sub-contract works. This obligation, which arises under NSC/2 clause 5 and NSC/2a clause 4, applies even though this may be some time before the issue of the final certificate under the main contract. Where this is done, and the sub-contractor subsequently fails to rectify any defect, shrinkage or fault in the work, it is provided by JCT 80 clause 35.18 that the employer shall nominate a substitute sub-contractor to carry out the necessary remedial work. The employer must obtain the main contractor's consent (which is not to be unreasonably withheld) to this nomination, and to the price which the substitute will charge. If the employer is then unable, despite taking all reasonable steps, to recover the cost from the original sub-contractor, the main contractor must indemnify the employer against any shortfall in what is recovered.

The foregoing discussion has concentrated entirely upon those consequences of defective work by a sub-contractor, such as the cost of rectification, which fall first upon the employer and which the employer will then seek to pass along the chain of contracts to the contractor, the sub-contractor, and so on. However, there may be other losses arising out of such work which do not concern the employer at all. In particular, while delay arising out of a nominated sub-contractor's default may entitle the main contractor to an extension of time for completion (JCT 80 clause 25.4.7), it is most certainly not something for which claim for loss and/or expense can be made under clause 26.2. Thus, if the main contractor's work is disrupted for this reason, there can be no claim against the employer; the contractor's sole remedy lies against the sub-contractor under NSC/4 clause 13.3.

A similar principle applies where the default of one nominated sub-contractor disrupts and causes loss and/or expense to another. The innocent sub-contractor is entitled to claim against the main contractor under NSC/4 clause 13.2, which specifically makes the main contractor responsible. The main contractor may then pursue the culprit under clause 13.3 of the relevant sub-contract, and the employer is not involved at all.

Delay

A particularly controversial area of risk allocation in respect of nominated sub-contractors and suppliers is that of delay. All JCT contracts have for some time treated this as an area where the employer should bear responsibility for those who have been chosen, by providing for the main contractor to be granted an extension of time. The reason why this is controversial is that, where such an extension of time is granted, the employer is deprived of the right to claim liquidated damages *which the main contractor would otherwise have passed on to the delaying sub-contractor*. As a result, unless the employer can make a direct claim against the sub-contractor under a collateral warranty agreement, the main incentive for the sub-contractor to keep to time will simply disappear.

The underlying reasoning of such provisions was critically examined by the House of Lords in the case of *Westminster* v. *Jarvis*,[5] which concerned the erection of a multi-storey car park. There a piling sub-contractor had apparently completed on time, but serious defects were subsequently discovered in the work. The sub-contractor duly returned to the site and rectified these defects, but this whole process caused considerable delay to the project. The main contractor thereupon claimed an extension of time under JCT 63 clause 23(g) for 'delay on the part of nominated sub-contractors which the contractor has taken all reasonable steps to avoid or reduce'. The House of Lords, overruling the Court of Appeal, held that no extension should be granted since these words referred only to cases in which a nominated sub-contractor patently failed to achieve practical completion of the sub-contract work by the correct time. They did *not* cover cases where, as here, the apparent state of the sub-contract works was such as to justify the architect in accepting them, and where defects were only discovered at a later date.

Clause 23(g) was probably *intended* to cover 'any delay *caused by* a nominated sub-contractor'. The House of Lords' interpretation was therefore a very narrow one, and this is clearly because the judges regarded the clause as highly undesirable and one which ought to be restricted as far as possible. None the less, despite such critical comments from the House of Lords as 'unjust and absurd', 'illogical and defective' and 'a provision under which a sub-contractor can benefit from its own default', the clause appears in the same form in JCT 80.

The present position therefore is that, where a nominated sub-contractor is late in achieving practical completion and this causes delay to the main contractor, the latter will be entitled to an extension of time. The employer may then take action directly against the sub-contractor under NSC/2 clause 3.4 to recover the liquidated damages which have been lost. As for any losses suffered directly by the contractor (including any liability which the contractor incurs to other sub-contractors), these can be recouped from the guilty sub-contractor under NSC/4 clause 13.3. The employer is not at all involved in this aspect of the loss since delay by a nominated sub-contractor or supplier is not one of the 'relevant matters' giving rise to a claim for loss and/or expense under clause 26.2. Nor can the contractor claim extra payment for a 'variation' if, in order to help out when a supplier is guilty of late delivery, the contract administrator authorizes changes to the order of the work.[6]

One final point which may be worth noting is that, even where sub-contract works lie on a project's critical path, the fact that a nominated sub-contractor receives an extension of time does not automatically entitle the main contractor to a similar extension. However, most of the 'relevant events' listed in NSC/4 are identically worded to those in JCT 80, so that parallel applications may be made. Naturally, however, the main contractor will be left unprotected in cases where the true cause of the delay is the main contractor's own default.

Repudiation

The most difficult area of nominated sub-contractor default is that which arises when the sub-contractor, without any justification, repudiates the sub-contract. Where this occurs, it obviously leaves the parties with the question of responsibility for completing the unfinished work, the cost of which may have increased considerably due to inflation. Less obviously, it leaves them with an additional trail of financial damage, including, for instance, the cost of rectifying defects (which may in effect mean paying twice for the same work), the consequent disruption of the main contractor's programme, disturbance to other sub-contractors and overall delay.

Once again, the question is whether responsibility for these losses is to lie with the main contractor, or whether the employer must bear the cost of nominating a substitute and pursue the guilty sub-contractor under any collateral agreement which exists. The answer given by English law has come about as a result of a series of cases dealing with JCT 63, the decisions in which have, in turn, led to drafting amendments in JCT 80.

The starting-point is the notorious decision of the House of Lords in the *Bickerton* case,[7] which arose when the plaintiffs engaged the defendants under JCT 63 to erect certain additional units at a hospital. A firm by the name of Speediwarm Ltd was nominated as sub-contractor for the installation of a heating system. The sub-contract was duly entered into, but Speediwarm soon went into liquidation. When the main contractor, who then agreed to do the relevant work on a 'without prejudice' basis, claimed that this had cost more than the original sub-contract price, the question which arose was whether the employers were liable for the increase. The House of Lords held that the employers *were* liable, on the basis that it was their responsibility, when a nominated sub-contractor dropped out, to renominate. This was because, on the wording of JCT 63, the main contractor had neither the right nor any obligation to carry out work which the contract assigned to a nominated sub-contractor. As a result, it was the duty of the employer to renominate and to pay the substitute sub-contractor's account, even if this was more than the original.

The effect of the decision in *Bickerton* was clearly that many of the costs arising out of a nominated sub-contractor repudiation would fall on the employer. However, the House of Lords did *not* treat the sub-contractor's default as if it were a breach of contract by the employer. There was thus no reason to suppose that losses suffered by the main contractor (due to disruption, etc.) were recoverable from the employer.

The next case, *Percy Bilton* v. *GLC*,[8] arose when the defendants engaged the plaintiffs under JCT 63 to build a housing estate in South London, and nominated a firm named Lowdells as sub-contractors for mechanical services. Lowdells went into liquidation when the work was partly completed. There was then a lengthy delay (partly inevitable, and partly due to the fault of the architect) in nominating a replacement, and completion of the main contract works was seriously delayed. The architect granted an extension of time to cover this delay, and the employer deducted liquidated damages for other unconnected delays which were entirely due to the contractor. The contractor then raised a technical argument to the effect that JCT 63 in fact gave no power to extend time merely because a replacement sub-contractor could not meet the original deadline for completion, but that this delay must be regarded as the employer's responsibility under *Bickerton*. As a result, said the contractor, the time for completion was now at large and the liquidated damages clause therefore fell.

This argument was rejected by the House of Lords, on the ground that the employer's 'responsibility' required only a renomination within a reasonable time. The contractor would be entitled to an extension of time for any *unreasonable* delay in renominating. However, any delays arising *inevitably* were at the contractor's risk, and the employer's right to claim liquidated damages for this period (and for any other period resulting from contractor-caused delays) remained intact.

The ruling in *Bilton* (which is now expressly covered by JCT 80 clause 35.24.9) appeared, at first sight, to swing the legal position back in favour of the employer. However, the whole decision was effectively undermined by a dictum of Lord Fraser, who gave the only judgment in the case. In an effort to show that the decision was not unduly harsh towards contractors, Lord Fraser stated that the contractor 'could have exercised its right of 'reasonable objection' under clause 27(a) to prevent the nomination of any new sub-contractor who did not offer to complete his part of the work within the overall completion period for the contract as a whole'. If correct, this means that where, as will often be the case, a renomination will inevitably involve delay, the main contractor can create a total impasse by refusing to accept any replacement sub-contractor unless the employer undertakes to provide compensation for the effects of the first sub-contractor's default. In such circumstances, the employer who is not prepared to omit the relevant work altogether, will be forced to submit to the main contractor's demands, thereby effectively taking on virtually the whole risk.

In *Fairclough* v. *Rhuddlan*,[9] the Court of Appeal confirmed that this was indeed the position. The defendants in that case engaged the plaintiffs under JCT 63 to construct a leisure complex, and nominated a firm named Gunite as sub-contractors for certain specialist work on a swimming-pool. When the work was partly completed, Gunite, who had received some £60000 for work subsequently found to be worthless, repudiated the sub-contract and withdrew from the site. There was then a delay, which was held to be inevitable, of some five months before a renomination instruction was issued. At that point, the date for completion of the main contract was only 13 weeks away, while the proposed sub-contract would give the replacement sub-contractors 27 weeks. The plaintiffs, relying on this incompatibility of time and also on the fact that the replacement sub-contract did not include the £240 000 worth of work necessary to remedy defects in Gunite's work, refused to accept the renomination.

In ruling upon various preliminary issues, the Court of Appeal held as follows:

1. The contractors were entitled to refuse any nomination of a sub-contractor who would not undertake to complete by the date for completion of the main contract, even if the effect of delays already accumulated would mean that *actual* completion would not be delayed. It was also suggested by the Court of Appeal that a contractor who *did* accept such a nomination would be entitled to an extension of time until the date fixed for completion of the sub-contract work.
2. According to *Bickerton*, a main contractor cannot be called upon to carry out work which is assigned to a nominated sub-contractor. It follows that the main contractor cannot be called upon to rectify any defects in such work, whether these relate to design, workmanship or materials. The contractors in this case were therefore entitled to reject any proposed renomination which did not include whatever work was necessary to remedy defects in the original sub-contractor's work. This is now expressly covered by JCT 80 clauses 35.24.5 and 35.24.6.
3. Where the defaulting sub-contractor has already been paid for work which is then shown not to be in accordance with the sub-contract, the employer is entitled as against the main contractor to be credited with the amount of the overpayment (JCT 80 clause 30.6.2.1). However, the employer must otherwise bear the full cost of renomination, including any remedial work which is necessary, except where the sub-contractor's withdrawal is itself due to the main contractor's breach (JCT 80 clause 35.24.8).

As a result of *Fairclough*, it seems that the position of the employer will, in practice, depend upon the relative size of the various losses caused by the withdrawal of a nominated sub-contractor. If the main contractor is already substantially in delay, the employer may find it worthwhile to omit the sub-contract work in order to preserve the right to liquidated damages. However, this may not be possible without disrupting the entire works and risking claims for loss and/or expense. In such cases, the employer may be forced to compensate the main contractor for all losses suffered, in order to induce the main contractor to accept a renomination.

The position arrived at by this series of cases has been heavily criticized[10] on the following grounds:

1. In cases where there is no direct agreement between employer and nominated sub-contractor, it positively *encourages* sub-contractors to repudiate a contract which has become disadvantageous or burdensome to them.
2. It gives no incentive to main contractors to keep a sinking sub-contractor afloat, although JCT 80 clause 35.25 does at least prohibit the main contractor from determining the sub-contractor's employment under the sub-contract without first obtaining a contract administrator's instruction to this effect.
3. It involves the utter absurdity that the legal responsibility for defective work which may be borne by the main contractor and sub-contractor (on the chain liability principle) may be eliminated by the simple expedient of repudiating the sub-contract.

Other defaults

Apart from the three categories of nominated sub-contractor default considered above, the question whether 'responsibility' for nominated sub-contractors lies with the employer or the main contractor is occasionally brought into focus by other specific contractual provisions. In this context, two recent decisions are of particular importance.

In the first of these, *Jarvis* v. *Rockdale*,[11] the defendants engaged the plaintiffs under JCT 80 to construct 50 flats for the elderly, together with some ancillary accommodation. The firm which was nominated as piling sub-contractors started late, produced defective work and then wrongfully withdrew from the site, whereupon the architect instructed the plaintiffs to stop work. After this suspension had lasted for more than one month, the plaintiffs gave notice purporting to determine their employment.

It was held by the Court of Appeal that, although such a notice could not validly be given if the instruction to suspend work was brought about 'by reason of some negligence or default of the contractor', this did not include negligence or default of a *nominated* sub-contractor. The contractor could not be held responsible for such a person, and could accordingly determine his employment in such circumstances. The distinction thus drawn between nominated and domestic sub-contractors is now made explicit by JCT 80 clause 28.1.3.1.

The second important decision in this field was made by the House of Lords in a Scottish case[12] which arose out of a contract to build two naval submarines. Under the terms of this contract, the main contractor was entitled to claim for loss and/or expense arising out of disruption caused by any matters 'beyond the contractor's control'. The House of Lords held that this phrase included defects in cables which were obtained from a nominated supplier. What is especially surprising is that the House of Lords' reasoning was expressed in terms wide enough to apply equally to *domestic* sub-contractors and suppliers. If this is correct, it seems to undermine entirely any remaining idea that the main contractor must bear responsibility for a sub-contractor's defaults!

Other forms of nomination

The drafting of JCT 80 appears to suggest that an employer who reserves the right to nominate a sub-contractor inevitably takes on responsibility for the risks involved. Any such suggestion is simply not true; risk allocation is always a matter of choice for whoever is responsible for drafting the contract in question. This is strikingly illustrated when one considers the previous (2nd) edition of GC/Works/1. Clause 31 of that contract gave the contractor the right to object on reasonable grounds to any nomination. However, it then provided that the contractor should be responsible for any sub-contractor or supplier, whether domestic or nominated, and should accordingly make good any loss suffered by the employer through a sub-contractor's default. It was further spelled out by clause 38(5) that, in the event of the termination of a nominated sub-contract, it was entirely the contractor's responsibility either to find a substitute or to carry out the work personally. In either case, payment would only be what was due on the original sub-contract.

Interestingly, the third edition of GC/Works/1 appears to have accepted the modern notion that the risk of a nominated sub-contractor's insolvency should be borne by the employer. Accordingly, the contract provisions about nomination follow those of the 2nd edition but with one crucial exception. It is stated in clause 63(9) that, if a nominated sub-contractor becomes insolvent, the employer must reimburse the contractor for the difference between the extra costs incurred in getting the work completed and the amount which can be extracted from the defaulting sub-contractor.

The way in which ICE 6 deals (in clauses 58 and 59) with nominated sub-contractors is also of considerable interest, because provisions which appear very different from those of JCT 80 in fact produce a rather similar result. ICE 6 begins by providing that, as a general principle, the contractor is fully responsible for any breach of contract by a nominated sub-contractor. This liability is not limited (as it was under the 5th edn) to the amount which the contractor succeeds in recovering from the sub-contractor. However, it is qualified to the extent that the contractor cannot be held responsible for matters of *design*, unless this is expressly stated both in the main contract and the sub-contract.

Although the contractor is therefore fully responsible for the defaults of a nominated sub-contractor *while the sub-contract remains in operation*, things change once the sub-contract is brought to an end. Provided that termination of the sub-contract takes place with the engineer's written consent, the contractor's only obligation thereafter is to 'take all necessary steps and proceedings as are available to him' to recover both personal losses and those of the employer from the defaulting sub-contractor. To the extent that this proves impossible, it is the employer's obligation to reimburse the contractor.

Nominated suppliers under JCT 80

With one exception, the general principle under JCT 80 is that the employer is not concerned with a nominated supplier's defaults. If materials are defective, in the sense that they do not comply with whatever express or implied standards are contained in the main contract, then the contractor is in breach. This will involve liability to the employer for any loss such as the cost of replacement. The main contractor must then seek to recover this loss, plus any personal losses, from the supplier in question. The only exception to this is that delay on the part of a nominated supplier is a ground on which the main contractor may be entitled to an extension of time.

The policy of JCT 80 in this situation is clearly that a chain of liability shall be established and, as we have already noted, clause 36.4 requires the supply contract to contain certain terms which are designed to secure this. However, clause 36.4 is subject to contrary agreement between the contract administrator and the contractor and, moreover, there may be situations in which, although all the prescribed terms are present, the supply contract restricts the liability of the nominated supplier in other ways. Clause 36.5 deals with these possibilities by stating that, provided the contract administrator's written approval is obtained for any restriction of the supplier's liability, the liability of the contractor to the employer shall be restricted to exactly the same extent. As a result, the contractor cannot be saddled with a liability to the employer which cannot be passed on to the supplier who is responsible.

18.2.3   Named sub-contractors under IFC 84

As we have seen in Chapter 16, the prescribed form of contract for named sub-contractors under IFC 84 is NAM/SC. Once a sub-contract is made in this form, and while it remains in operation, responsibility for any default by the named sub-contractor rests to a large extent upon the main contractor. The main contractor will be responsible to the employer (and the sub-contractor will, in turn, be responsible to the main contractor) for keeping to time and for rectifying defects in workmanship or materials in the sub-contract work. Further, should such defaults on the part of the sub-contractor cause problems of delay or disruption to the contractor personally, this will be of no concern to the employer since it is not a matter for which the contractor can claim either an extension of time or compensation for loss and/or expense.

To this general principle there is one important qualification. Where the sub-contract contains any element of design, the sub-contractor may undertake direct responsibility to the employer for design, selection of materials or satisfaction of any performance specifications (e.g. under the RIBA/CASEC Form of Employer/Specialist Agreement ESA/1). However, whether or not such direct responsibility is undertaken, clause 3.3.7 of IFC 84 makes it clear that the *main* contractor is not be liable to the employer for any of these matters.

While the sub-contract remains operative, the position in respect of sub-contractor defaults is relatively straightforward. However, when it is brought to an end, there are no fewer than five possible legal situations which may result, depending on *how* the sub-contract is determined and what instructions the contract administrator gives. To take the second point first, clause 3.3.3 empowers the contract administrator to name another person to execute the sub-contract work (or what is left of it); to instruct the contractor to make other arrangements for the work, in which case the contractor has the option of sub-letting to a domestic sub-contractor; or to omit the work altogether.

As to the first point, clause 27.1 of NAM/SC provides power for the main contractor to determine the employment of the sub-contractor for various breaches of the sub-contract relating to such matters as suspension of the work, delay, defects and unauthorized sub-letting. Clause 27.2 gives a similar power on the occurrence of certain events connected with the sub-contractor's insolvency. Under each of these clauses, there are specified procedures which must be followed if the determination is to be valid.

The consequences which may arise on determination of the sub-contract are as follows:

- Where the first sub-contractor was named in the contract documents, and the contract administrator names a replacement to complete the work, the contract sum is varied (upwards or downwards) to reflect the difference between the two sub-contract prices for that work (clause 3.3.4(a)). The employer need *not* pay the contractor for the cost of rectification, nor compensate for loss and/or expense, though the contractor will be entitled to an extension of time if the main contract work is delayed.

• Where the first sub-contractor was named in the contract documents, and the contract administrator instructs the contractor to make other arrangements for the work, this is to be valued as a variation (clause 3.3.4(b)). Furthermore, the contractor may claim where appropriate for an extension of time and for loss and/or expense.

• Where the first sub-contractor was named in the contract documents, and the contract administrator orders that the work shall be omitted, this is again to be valued as a variation (clause 3.3.4(b)), and the contractor may again be entitled to an extension of time and compensation for loss and/or expense.

• Where the original sub-contractor is named in an instruction as to the expenditure of a provisional sum, whatever the contract administrator decides is regarded as a further instruction as to this sum (clause 3.3.5). As a result, the work will be valued under clause 3.7 and, where appropriate, the contractor will be entitled to claim for an extension of time and for loss and/or expense.

In all the above cases, the employer is likely to suffer loss as a result of the determination of the sub-contract. If this does happen, it is provided by clauses 3.3.6(b) that the main contractor shall take all reasonable steps to recover such losses from the original sub-contractor, and shall then account to the employer for the amounts recovered. ('Reasonable steps' for this purpose do not include arbitration or litigation, unless the employer undertakes to cover the main contractor's legal costs.) In this connection, clause 27.3.3 of NAM/SC imposes an obligation on the sub-contractor not to argue in proceedings brought on this basis that the contractor has not personally suffered the loss in respect of which the claim is brought.

The four categories described above all assume that the sub-contract has been determined in accordance with clauses 27.1 or 27.2 of NAM/SC. Indeed, clause 3.3.3 of IFC 84 specifically provides that the contractor shall not determine the sub-contract in any other way, nor allow the sub-contractor to determine it. Where determination *does* take place in some other way, the consequences for the contractor may be disastrous. The contract administrator may once again deal with the situation in any of the ways outlined above, but clause 3.3.6(a) makes it clear that this can only result in a reduction of the contract sum. Further, there can in such a case be no entitlement to any extension of time or to loss and/or expense.

18.3 LIABILITY OF SUB-CONTRACTOR TO EMPLOYER

18.3.1 Contractual liability

The doctrine of privity of contract means that it is not possible for a sub-contractor to be made directly liable to the employer for a breach of the *main* contract. Equally, the employer, who is not a party to the *sub-contract*, cannot in principle claim damages for breach of it. In practical terms, this means that unless the main contractor is liable to reimburse the employer for the loss caused by the sub-contractor, neither of them can sue the sub-contractor for that loss! The only possible exception to this would be where the sub-contractor has specifically undertaken not to raise this defence. Whether or not such an undertaking is legally effective has not yet been tested in the courts.

Although the ordinary contractual structure does not provide for any direct claim by an employer against a sub-contractor, there is nothing to prevent the parties from creating an additional contractual link. This indeed is precisely what is done under those standard forms which require a nominated sub-contractor to enter into a collateral agreement with the employer. In addition, there is the possibility that a court may construct (which means 'invent') a collateral contract between the employer and a sub-contractor or supplier. This has been done in cases where an employer has been persuaded by certain assurances to nominate a particular sub-contractor or supplier, and the effect is to make those assurances legally binding. For example, in the case of *Shanklin Pier* v. *Detel Products*,[13] the plaintiffs were about to have their pier repainted. They were assured by the defendants, who were paint manufacturers, that their paint would be suitable for the job, would be impervious to rust and would last for between 7 and 10 years. On the basis of these assurances, the plaintiffs instructed their contractors to use the paint in question. When the defendants' claims proved to be wildly optimistic, it was held by the Court of Appeal that they formed the basis of a 'collateral contract' between the plaintiffs and the defendants, and that the defendants were accordingly liable in damages for its breach.

In the *Shanklin Pier* case the suppliers gave express assurances directly to the plaintiffs, but it seems that a collateral contract may arise without this. In a later case[14] it was accepted, in principle (though the claim failed on the facts), that suppliers might be made liable on this basis for making extravagant claims about their products in advertising brochures, if these were relied on by an employer or architect in deciding what materials should be specified.

18.3.2 Liability in tort

Whether or not there is any direct contractual link between the employer and a sub-contractor, there exists, at least in principle, a potential claim in the tort of negligence. The possibility of such a claim arising, and the legal difficulties standing in its way, we have dealt with in some detail in Chapter 4, and it is accordingly not necessary to give more than a very brief summary at this point.

In the light of certain remarks passed by members of the House of Lords in the case of *Murphy* v. *Brentwood DC*,[15] it is at least possible that a sub-contractor might incur tortious liability to the employer in the following situations:

- Where the defective work causes physical damage to other parts of the structure.
- Where the work of a *nominated* sub-contractor is simply defective but there is a relationship of sufficient 'proximity' between the parties.

REFERENCES

1. *D. & F. Estates Ltd* v. *Church Commissioners for England* [1988] 2 All E.R. 992.
2. *Lee* v. *West* [1989] E.G.C.S. 160.
3. *Young & Marten Ltd* v. *McManus Childs Ltd* [1969] 1 A.C. 454.
4. *Gloucestershire CC* v. *Richardson* [1969] 1 A.C. 480.
5. *Westminster CC* v. *Jarvis & Sons Ltd* [1970] 1 All E.R. 942.
6. *Kirk and Kirk Ltd* v. *Croydon Corp* [1956] J.P.L. 585.
7. *North West Regional Hospital Board* v. *T.A. Bickerton & Son Ltd* [1970] 1 All E.R. 1039.
8. *Percy Bilton Ltd* v. *GLC* [1982] 2 All E.R. 623.
9. *Fairclough Building Ltd* v. *Rhuddlan BC* (1985) 30 B.L.R. 26.
10. Wallace, I.N.D. *Construction Contracts: Principles and Policies in Tort and Contract*, Sweet and Maxwell, London, p. 336, 1986.
11. *John Jarvis* v. *Rockdale Housing Association Ltd* (1986) 36 B.L.R. 48.
12. *Scott Lithgow Ltd* v. *Secretary of State for Defence* (1989) S.L.T. 236.
13. *Shanklin Pier Co. Ltd* v. *Detel Products Ltd* [1951] 2 K.B. 854.
14. *GLC* v. *Ryarsh Brick Co. Ltd* [1985] C.I.L.L. 200.
15. *Murphy* v. *Brentwood DC* [1990] 2 All E.R. 908.

PART SEVEN

Alternative Procurement Methods

19

Design and build contracts

Design and Build is a procurement method which has been in use for
a long time. The process is found in many industries. When some-
body buys something, the 'usual' process seems to be to ask someone for a product, and the thing produced will probably have been
designed by its producer. Examples of this are found in fields as
diverse as ship building and micro-electronics. Indeed, before the
emergence of architecture as a profession distinct from fabrication,
pre-industrial society used to procure buildings by a process of
design and build. It was the separation of responsibility for fabrication from responsibility for design that led to the emergence of
so-called 'traditional' general contracting in the nineteenth century.
This separation of design from construction in the building industry
has for a long time been the source of many problems,[1] and remains
so.

19.1 BACKGROUND TO DESIGN AND BUILD

It would seem, then, that design and build is what would happen if the
construction industry were to suddenly come into being, without the
evolution of professional institutions which pre-define certain roles in
the process. It could be seen as the most logical way to procure a
building, given a clean slate to start with. Unfortunately, such a 'clean
slate' does not exist, and over the last 150 years the construction professions have carved out their respective niches.

The roles of the professional consultants continue to develop and
change. Consequently, the methods of procuring buildings also change.
Because the contractual relationships in the construction process are
difficult and complex, most people who participate in the process prefer
to standardize the contracts. Although the wisdom of this is questionable,
it is a phenomenon which seems inevitable. The emergence of a standard

form of contract for design and build took a long time. One milestone on the way was the publication by the NFBTE (now BEC) in 1970 of a standard form of contract for 'design and construct' packages.[2] This form was not generally well received, and it rapidly faded into obscurity.

The publication in 1981 of the JCT Standard Form of Contract With Contractor's Design (CD 81) coincided with the publication of the Contractor's Designed Portion Supplement to JCT 80. The CD 81 form is for use where the contractor's design *responsibility* extends over the whole of the works, even though significant parts of the design may have already been done before the contract is executed, being embodied within the employer's requirements. The contractor's designed portion supplement is a set of modifications to be made to JCT 80 when the contractor's design responsibility is for only a portion of the works, the remainder of which will have been designed by consultants in the usual way. There is therefore a significant difference between the two. This chapter is about the JCT With Contractor's Design form.

Examples of successfully completed design and build projects are too numerous to mention. They range from housing, through industrial and commercial projects to major complexes. It is clear that this procurement method has a very wide applicability.

Design and build is one type of a variety of 'package deals' in construction. This phrase can often be found referring to a range of different types of procurement, from **turnkey** to **system building**. At one extreme is the type of package deal where the client selects the contractor before any consultants have been approached. In this respect, a package deal may include acquisition of the site, as well as procuring the finance and leasing the building to the occupier. These arrangements are beyond the scope of this analysis. At the other end of the scale of types of package deal is the procurement of a standard building, or system building. While this may appear to match the essential features of design and build, the actual design work in such an arrangement can be minimal, and may have been carried out at some time in the past by someone other than the contractor. In this case, the contractor is simply providing a pre-designed building to the client's specification.

While on this topic, it is worth mentioning that there are different applications of system building. When an experienced designer uses this process as if it provided a kit of parts, system building lends itself very well to design and build procurement. An architect who knows the system well, and understands its limitations, can manipulate ideas very rapidly. This can help to overcome problems caused by poor or inadequate briefing, which is a particularly important aspect in design and build. It is most important that the brief is concise and unambiguous at an early stage. By using system building, the pressure is taken away from the early stages. This does not mean that design and build is exclusively for system building; its applicability is extremely wide. System building has been responsible for the supply of some dreadful failures of the construction industry. The alliance of system building with design and build has produced an unfortunate association of ideas. The problems and disadvantages of bad system building are not problems that are caused by utilizing design and build.

The British Property Federation (BPF), an influential group of private sector property developers, have committed themselves to supporting design and build to such an extent that they have developed their own system for procuring buildings which contains many of the elements of design and build as its basis.[3] However, the biggest impact of the BPF system has been on the way in which we think about the procurement of buildings and meeting client's requirements. The BPF system itself, while extremely influential, has not had the wide use that was expected of it. Perhaps this is what has prompted the BPF to request the JCT to produce its supplementary conditions? These can be found at the end of CD 81 and are included so that the BPF system can be used with a standard form of contract that has been produced by JCT.

19.2   FEATURES OF DESIGN AND BUILD CONTRACTS

The essential features of design and build contracts can best be dealt with in terms of how the employer describes the requirements for the job; how the contractor proposes to achieve them; the pricing mechanism; and the roles and responsibilities within the process.

19.2.1   Employer's requirements and contractor's proposals

The first of the essential features of a design and build contract is that the employer approaches a contractor with a set of requirements defining what it is that the employer wants. The contractor responds with proposals which will include fabrication, as well as design work. The scale of design work included depends on the extent to which the employer has already commissioned such work from others. The contractor's design input varies from one contract to another, ranging from the mere detailing of a fairly comprehensive design to a full design process including proposals, sketch schemes and production information. There will usually be some negotiation between the employer and the contractor, with the aim being to settle on an agreed set of contractor's proposals. These proposals will include the contract price, as well as the manner in which it has been calculated.

Once the employer's requirements and the contractor's proposals match, the contract can be executed and the contractor can implement the work. The contractor will be totally responsible for undertaking the design work outlined in the contractor's proposals, for fabricating the building and for co-ordinating and integrating the entire process. This includes the appointment of consultants if the contractor does not have the necessary skills 'in house'. The employer may also choose to appoint consultants in order to monitor the various aspects of the work, but this is not necessarily the case.

19.2.2   Price

A feature that is sometimes present in design and build deals is a **guaranteed maximum price** (GMP). This helps clients to feel reassured that they are not signing a blank cheque! As an incentive to the contractor, any savings made by completing the project for a price below the GMP may sometimes be shared between the client and the contractor.

The price in CD 81 is governed by means of a **contract sum analysis** (CSA). There are no bills of quantity needed in CD 81. The nature of a CSA is very different from that of a bill of quantity, its form not being prescribed by the contract. A CSA can be presented in any form appropriate to the circumstances of the project, but some of the purposes of a CSA have their parallels in bills of quantity. These are calculation of stage payments (in some circumstances), valuation of employer's change instructions and exercising the fluctuations clauses (where applicable). The CSA should enable the design content of the work to be reflected in any estimation of the value of variations.[4]

19.2.3   Roles and responsibilities

One of the most significant features of design and build arrangements is the lack of an independent certification role in the contract. There is no architect or contract administrator to settle differences between the parties, and there is no independent quantity surveyor responsible for preparing the basis upon which contractors tender. This changes some of the basic assumptions about the roles which are required on construction projects, and the consequences of this are discussed later.

Figure 19.1 shows the contractual relationships encountered in design and build contracts. The role of the quantity surveyor is shown in parentheses because, although cost information and economic advice are essential, there is not the need for traditional quantity surveying in this form of procurement. There is no standard method of measurement, no

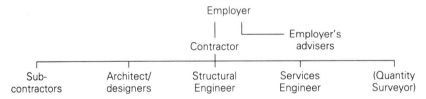

Fig. 19.1 Contractual relationships in design and build.

bills of quantity and no *contractual* role for the quantity surveyor. However, a contractor may choose to employ the skills of the quantity surveyor. Alternatively, or in addition, the employer may choose to employ architects, quantity surveyors, engineers, and so on.

Many quantity surveyors have welcomed the departure from traditional bills of quantity and the British approach to cost control which may be seen as counter-productive in serving the best interests of the client. Such quantity surveyors have seized the opportunity of becoming specialist client advisers in all aspects of the economics of building and the procurement process. There are large numbers of consultants who are qualified to advise the client during the whole of the process. These consultants come into the category of employer's advisers and would be used by the employer when dealing with the contractor. It is often the case that employers who are more experienced in traditional general contracting will set up their own project team, with a counterpart for each of the professional advisers in the contractor's project team. The contractor's team may or may not be in-house.

The contractual relationships in design and build offer some advantages over other methods of construction procurement. The most important advantage, as clearly shown in Fig. 19.1, is that the contractor is responsible for everything. This 'single-point' responsibility is very attractive to clients, particularly those who may not be interested in trying to distinguish the difference between a design fault and a workmanship fault. This single-point responsibility also means that the contractor is not relying on external firms for the execution of design or for the supply of information. By removing these blocks to effective communication, experience has shown that programmes and budgets are more likely to be adhered to, and the speed of building is likely to be quicker.[5]

The design and build process increases the opportunities for harnessing the benefit of the contractor's experience during the design stages of the project. Many of the developments in procurement processes, and much of the work in the field of study known as 'buildability', have been undertaken with this purpose in mind. The benefits of the integration of designers and builders are more economic buildings, as well as a more economic and effective fabrication process.

One reported disadvantage of design and build is that where there is a conflict between aesthetic quality and ease of fabrication, the requirements for fabrication will dominate. A further criticism has been that a design and build contractor will put in the minimum design effort required to win the contract. These two criticisms suggest strongly that quality, particularly architectural quality, will suffer under this procurement process. However, this is not a valid criticism of the process itself, but rather of some of the people who may be exercising it. As such, it is a criticism which can be made about any process. Further, like much of the criticism of design and build, it is based upon institutionalized ideas about roles and responsibilities, and thus suffers from the same weakness as all stereotyping. It should be noted that the RIBA Code of Conduct allows architects to take part in construction as company directors. As a result, architects may be found practising design and build.

The relationships between the consultants can be of several types. For example, the employer may employ an architect (or designer) to work up some initial proposals. These would form the basis of the employer's requirements, and the employer could subsequently assign the architect's contract to the builder. Alternatively, the client may approach directly a design and build contractor who employs in-house consultants. It is this inherent flexibility which is one of the strengths of design and build as a method of procurement. This flexibility happens not just between projects, but also within projects. For example, a commercial client with a prestigious office building may have some very detailed requirements, comprehensively designed by an architectural team, concerning the façade and the entrance lobby of the building. Other less prestigious parts, such as the corridors, staircases, toilets and lifts, may then be left to the contractor to design.

19.3 USE OF JCT DESIGN BUILD FORM (CD 81)

The 'head note' to the contract appears above the Articles of Agreement, which indicates that the Joint Contracts Tribunal view it as extremely important. It states that this contract is **not** for use where the employer has appointed an architect/contract administrator. This is all the advice given in the contract about the circumstances under which it should be used.

Considering the range of uses to which the form has been put, and its inherent flexibility, it would not be sensible to define circumstances for using it in terms of specific types of building project. Rather, the overriding features should be to do with the nature of the client's requirements regarding risk apportionment, the nature of the client's experience and the availability of suitable contractors to undertake the work.

The characteristics of projects where design and build would be suitable can be considered under the following headings:

1. the client's familiarity with construction;
2. the relative importance of client priorities (time, cost, function, quality, value for money, etc.);
3. the technical complexity of the project;
4. the need to make variations to requirements as work proceeds;
5. the patterns of responsibility and communication;
6. the need for an early start on site.

Each of these is discussed below.

19.3.1   The client's experience

Unlike some of the novel forms of procurement, it is not necessary for the design and build client to be an 'expert' client. However, the so-called 'traditional' method of procurement, **general contracting,** has evolved as a response in many ways to the lack of trust endemic in the construction industry. The clients of general contracting like the feeling of control that the high degree of documentation gives them. However, if the price of this control is the difference between hitting cost targets and over-running cost targets, then perhaps it has become too expensive.

Novice clients who know nothing of the construction industry, particularly clients requiring small works, will often stumble into design and build without realizing it! For example, an uninsured householder whose chimney blows down in a storm may invite one or more local small contractors to come and look at the damage and to provide an estimate for remedying it. In such a case, a builder might ask the householder whether the replacement chimney needs to match the old one, or even if it can be dispensed with and capped off in the absence of an open fire. This process may take place with a few builders, each of whom will have their own ideas about how best to achieve an economical solution. The client considers the options and eventually appoints one of the builders to do the work. This shows how a complete novice can inform a series of contractors about the 'employer's requirements' and enter into negotiations with each of them about the 'contractor's proposals'. Modifications are made to requirements and proposals until they match, and prices are discussed until the client feels that the most economical and effective job will be done. Therefore, while design and build clients may be very sophisticated, it is equally likely that they may not be. Because of this, unlike some other forms of procurement, the choice about whether or not to use design and build does not depend upon the client's familiarity with construction.

19.3.2   Relative importance of client priorities

Clients who require their buildings quickly, cheaply and of high quality, achieving all the required functions and avoiding any claims or other conflicts are probably asking too much of the construction industry! Clearly, there are ideals, but they have to be compromised if a working relationship is to be formed. Whatever system of procurement is used, the client ought to make clear to the tendering contractors what the objectives of the project are, and how they relate to one another. It is generally felt in the construction industry that quality is the first thing to suffer in design and build contracts. However, the evidence does not support this.[5] There are some good quality buildings which have resulted from design and build, and there are low quality buildings which have resulted from general contracting and other procurement methods. There is no correlation between procurement method and perceived quality of the product.

Cost certainty for the employer is one of the advantages of design and build. It is a fixed price contract (though not necessarily a firm price one!), so the risk associated with pricing is entirely the contractor's, except to the extent that fluctuations clauses apply. However, notwithstanding the cost certainty, design and build is not necessarily cheap. Single-point responsibility, and fixed price contracts, mean that the contractor carries more of the risk than a general contractor would. Risk attracts a premium, so it is to be expected that a design and build contractor would add an element on to a tender to allow for this extra risk. Similarly, design and build encourages economical solutions, and enables value to be considered as well as price. A truly economical approach to the employer's problem may not produce the cheapest building in terms of capital outlay. In this respect, design and build may be more expensive than traditional general contracting. On a high risk project it may be inappropriate to pass too much risk over to the contractor, and other forms of procurement should be considered.

As a procurement method, design and build offers different possibilities in combinations of priorities. A client whose highest priority is aesthetic quality can appoint a design and build contractor with a reputation for architectural merit, perhaps a specialist design and build firm which includes architects as directors. A client whose highest priority is speed or money should appoint a design and build contractor with a record of success in hitting such targets. Clearly, there are numerous ways of configuring the priorities for a project, and the client should make explicit decisions about these before inviting contractors to respond with their proposals. It is essential that the client takes an opportunity to look at previous work by, and speaks to previous clients of, the contractor. Different contractors have different skills, and the selection process should take some account of this in choosing the most appropriate contractor.

An element of competition is usually seen as advantageous when appointing a contractor. Traditionally, contractors submit tenders based upon a description of the works. In this situation, they are competing on price alone, since they are all pricing the same description of the works. One of the strengths of design and build is that the contractor's proposals will include design solutions to problems posed in the employer's requirements. Here contractors are competing not only on price, but also on any other criteria which the client thinks important. This presents opportunities for making the level of accommodation the selection criterion, where a client can put forward a budget and ask the bidders to demonstrate how much building they can supply for the money. Clearly, the element of competition is far more flexible in design and build than in traditional arrangements.

One of the biggest disadvantages of design and build is that the brief (in terms of the employer's requirements) must be very clear and unambiguous. Also it should not be subject to change during the project. This is not such a problem in general contracting because the brief can be developed alongside feasibility studies and sketch schemes.[6]

19.3.3 Technical complexity of the project

When dealing with technically complex projects, the solution adopted by the construction industry, like any other, is to specialize. The range of specialists in construction is extensive and comprehensive. Design and build is one of the few procurement processes which is not conducive to the employer's selection of the specialists. In general contracting the process of nomination has emerged, so that the employer may reserve the right to select particular specialists which the contractor must employ. In construction management the employer appoints all of the trade and specialist contractors directly. This cannot be done under a design and build contract. The employer who wishes to specify particular contractors to undertake particular parts of the work must do this in parallel with the design and build agreement, but beyond the terms of the design and build contract. This means that if technical complexity is to be confronted by the use of specified (nominated) specialists, design and build is unsuitable. Even though most design and build contractors will accommodate such specialists if they are named within the employer's requirements, there will be no direct relationship between the employer and the named sub-contractors.

The technical complexity of the client's process may lead to solutions which are more akin to engineering than to building. While this does not mean that design and build is unsuitable, it is likely that in such circumstances the use of other forms of procurement will be favoured. This is because of the more comprehensive pre-contractual documentation which may be required by the client with a technically complex project.

19.3.4 Variations to requirements as work proceeds

Variations to client requirements are a constant source of problems in the construction industry. They are one of the most frequent causes of claims and often lead to litigious disputes. A client who wishes to reserve the right to alter requirements during the fabrication process should *not* use design and build. It is a process which demands early agreement between employer's requirements and contractor's proposals. A change in either of these documents makes the agreements awkward. The valuation of variations can be difficult without a comprehensive contract sum analysis, and the employer's insistence on time and cost targets becomes less convincing if the requirements are altered. Therefore, a client who needs to retain the right to make variations should either consider an alternative procurement method, or should consider allowing the design and build contract to be completed on its original basis, making variations the subject of additional contracts after the conclusion of the project.

The limited scope for variations and changes is thus a weakness of the design and build process.

19.3.5 Patterns of responsibility and communication

Single-point responsibility is the most obvious advantage offered by design and build. There is no division of responsibility between design and fabrication, so the finished building should reflect the trade-offs made between the design exigencies and the fabrication exigencies. This question of quality has been addressed above, and will be returned to later. In terms of choosing the procurement method, it is essential to appreciate that design and build does *not* mean poor quality. It is a method to be used where the project is one for which it makes sense to combine responsibility for design with responsibility for fabrication. The types of project for which design and build contracts are suitable are those where the contractor's responsibility for design extends over the whole project, whether the design is partially completed by others or not. This is as distinct from the situation where the contractor's responsibility for design only covers a particular portion of the works.

The communication patterns observed in design and build projects are among the most effective found in any form of procurement. Since the institutionalized roles are reduced in their importance, there is less likelihood of there being institutional axes to grind. No separate firms will be vying for ascendancy, and consequently all of the pre-litigious guarded responses within letters, memos and minutes of meeting tend to disappear.

19.3.6   Early start on site

Since the contractor is undertaking the design work, there are opportunities to overlap the design and construction processes and thus to make an early start on site. This may be attractive to those clients, particularly in the public sector, who need to start spending their budget within a short time of the money being allocated. For such clients the appeal of an early start on site is that they can spend some of the budget before the money is withdrawn in favour of departments with more urgent needs.

In this sense, design and build will give the benefits that any form of fast-track construction will give, but at the cost of the same penalties. The benefit of fast-tracking is that the overall construction process can be speeded up by not having the fabrication process delayed while the whole of the design is completed. However, the use of overlapping too much will result in penalties arising from the need to revise early design decisions as the design is refined. If the project has already started on site by the time that these revisions are made, it is often the case that work has to be undone before further progress can be made. In extreme cases, this can lead to fast-tracking taking even longer to complete than a traditional method.

19.4   CHARACTERISTICS OF CD 81

The contract itself is divided into 39 clauses, and is therefore of approximately the same complexity as JCT 80. It is in fact a modified version of JCT 80 rather than a different contract, with about 75% of the text being identical. Rather than describe all of the clauses, it is better to pick out those areas where the contract differs from JCT 80. Briefly, these are as follows.

19.4.1   Articles of Agreement

The Articles of Agreement contain a significant difference in the first recital. The employer specifies the scope and location of the works in a few lines in the normal way, and as usual this is defined as 'the works'. This is followed by the statement that the client has issued to the contractor the 'employer's requirements'. The second recital records the fact that the contractor has submitted contractor's proposals and a tender figure. The figure is presented in the form of an analysis, and this analysis is referred to as the 'contract sum analysis'. The third recital makes it clear that the employer has examined the contractor's proposals and contract sum analysis and is satisfied that they *appear* to meet the employer's requirements. There is a footnote to the effect that where there is any divergence between the employer's requirements and the contractor's proposals, the former shall be revised to ensure that there is no divergence.

This is a procedural method for ensuring that the employer's requirements and the contractor's proposals both say the same thing. It is typical of the JCT to arrive at this point with such a procedure because it spells out the steps which must be gone through. In non-JCT design and build forms of contract, such as the BPF/ACA agreement, there may be an absence of contractor's proposals at the tendering stage. This means that the onus is on the contractor to ensure that what is built meets the requirements of the employer. The JCT position, however, is that the employer takes responsibility for ensuring (albeit superfically) that the employer's requirements are met by the contractor's proposals. The difference seems to be that, in CD 81, the contractor is obliged to produce whatever is described in the proposals, whereas under other contracts the contractor is obliged to build whatever is described in the requirements.

The contractor's obligations are clarified in clause 2, which states that the contractor must carry out and complete the works as referred to in the employer's requirements, the contractor's proposals and the other contract documents. In consequence, the employer's duty to check that the contractor's proposals seem to meet the employer's requirements does not absolve the contractor of liability for any of the work to be done.

In terms of discrepancy, the articles of agreement, conditions and appendices will prevail over other documents. There are provisions about how to deal with discrepancies *within* either the employer's requirements or the contractor's proposals, but no mention is made of how to deal with discrepancies between them. This falls back to the third recital, which makes it incumbent on the employer to deal with discrepancies between these two documents before the contract is executed.

The first article of agreement specifically states that the contractor's obligations are to complete the design and fabricate the building. The second article defines the amount of the contract sum, and the third article names the employer's agent for the purposes of acting in the employer's interest in interpreting contract documents, monitoring progress of the work, receiving or issuing information requests or instructions and generally acting for the employer in exercising any of the employer's rights or duties under the contract. Clearly, this person is a key player in helping the employer to discharge the contract effectively. The employer's agent may be an architect, building surveyor, quantity surveyor, engineer, or other professional. Indeed, it is not necessary to appoint an employer's agent from one of the construction professions; however, it is advisable to ensure that whoever is appointed is thoroughly conversant with the construction process and its products. The agent should also have a deep understanding of the employer's requirements. The absence of such a person will greatly reduce the reliability of the process.

The fourth article states that the employer's requirements, the contractor's proposals and the contract sum analysis have been signed by the parties and identified in the third Appendix to the conditions. This removes any possible misunderstanding about the basis of the contract. The need for agreement between the employer's requirements and the contractor's proposals will often produce a series of pre-contract negotiations over their content. This will lead to revisions and refinements to the documents as each is adjusted until they reflect the same ideas. The contract documents must be consistent with one another. By identifying the precise documents from within the contract, severe misunderstandings can be avoided. The fifth article is the arbitration agreement.

19.4.2   Conditions of Contract

The Conditions of Contract show some very interesting differences from those of JCT 80. The similarities are also interesting, but space precludes their discussion here.

There is no architect specified in CD 81, but there is instead an 'employer's agent'. However, the status of the employer's agent is not the same as that of a JCT 80 contract administrator since all responsibilities for 'contract administration' are ascribed to the employer and not to the agent.

Any discrepancies within the contractor's proposals must be pointed out to the employer by the contractor, and the contractor must make some sort of proposal about how to remedy the problem. The employer can choose the course of action which is to be taken, but there is no extra expense incurred because of this.

Clause 4 deals with employer's instructions. These are analogous to architect's instructions under JCT 80, but the employer's power to issue instructions is not as wide under CD 81. For example, the employer cannot issue instructions which affect the design of the works, without the consent of the contractor. A feature of clause 5 is that the contractor must supply to the employer drawings of the works as-built, as well as information about the maintenance and operation of the works, in effect a maintenance manual. This provision is clearly necessary because the contractor is responsible for the consultants' detailed design work. As a result, any information that would have been supplied by the consultants to the employer under the general contracting system needs to be catered for under the design and build system.

Clause 6 covers statutory obligations and includes arrangements for planning permission. Clearly, planning permission and Building Regulations approval need to be covered by this contract, to allow for the circumstances where the contractor is appointed at a very early stage in the process. However, there may also be circumstances where the contractor is appointed after these approvals have been sought. This clause applies except to the extent that the employer's requirements explicitly state that the project complies already with statutory requirements. In other words, if the employer's requirements are silent on this point, the contractor is responsible for obtaining all necessary approvals and permissions.

Variations are referred to as changes in this contract, at clause 12. This clause is very similar to clause 13 of JCT 80.

The situation regarding sub-contractors is very much simpler than that under JCT 80, and has more in common with JCT 63. There are supplementary conditions which allow for the use of named sub-contractors, somewhat in the manner of IFC 84. The employer has a right to object to the sub-letting of any work, including the sub-letting of design work.

The provisions for extensions of time, and those for loss and expense, follow very closely the provisions in JCT 80, with the addition of planning permission or changes in statutory requirements as being both a relevant event and an item in the list of matters leading to a money claim.

Despite criticisms voiced since the publication of CD 81, the determination clauses still do not treat the insolvency of the employer as a ground for the contractor to determine its own employment. Apart from this, the determination clauses are substantially the same as their counterparts in JCT 80.

The payment clause is an interesting departure from traditional practice. Clause 30 contains alternatives, in that interim payments may be by means of stage payments (option A) or by periodic payments (option B); the Appendix must state which alternative applies. Stage payments are made not at timed intervals, but upon completion of particular items of work. These are entered at Appendix 2 by means of brief descriptions, with cumulative values assigned to them. By this means, the contractor is paid as each identifiable part of the work is completed. The alternative is more like JCT 80's provisions, in that the work is valued at timed intervals, usually of one month. There are familiar arrangements covering retention, changes (variations) and fluctuations. Under the option for stage payments, there are no provisions for the contractor to be paid for unfixed materials, unlike the periodic payment option, which is more familiar. Since there is no architect or quantity surveyor, the contractor makes application for the money to be paid. The contractor decides how much is due, depending upon whether option A or option B applies, and tells the employer who is then obliged to pay it, subject to the right to object in writing with reasons. If there is disagreement about the amount to be paid, the conditions very carefully set out provisions which entitle the contractor to the employer's estimate of what is due, without prejudice to the contractor's right to any money which has been withheld improperly. Immediate arbitration is available as a method of resolving disputes over payment.

The final account details are a little more straightforward than under JCT 80, and the time limits seem shorter. The effect of the final certificate is as limited in terms of its conclusiveness as it would be under JCT 80.

Most of the other provisions hold few surprises; indeed, the main surprise is that such a large amount of text is directly transferred from JCT 80!

19.5 RISK IN DESIGN AND BUILD

The apportionment of risks in design and build contracts is unique among procurement methods. This uniqueness is brought about by the single-point responsibility and by the nature of the relationship between employer's requirements and contractor's proposals.

19.5.1 Money

Whether the contract sum is derived by negotiation or by competition, it is a price for the whole of the contractor's responsibilities, including design, fabrication and any necessary statutory approvals, such as planning permission, unless expressly mentioned in the employer's requirements. The contractor must do whatever is necessary to achieve the employer's requirements, whether or not particular items of work or materials have been included in those requirements. This means that the client's financial commitment is quite clear, and there is not much risk associated with this for the client. The risk of the cost exceeding the price lies entirely with the contractor. Of course, any changes in the employer's requirements, or any hindrance by the employer, will result in the employer being liable for extra money. However, of all of the procurement procedures, design and build offers the highest confidence in the contract sum.

19.5.2 Completion of the project

The contractor is committed to complete the project, and the employer is committed to allow the contractor to complete. None the less, the design and build contract may be determined prematurely in some circumstances. These events, which are listed in clause 28, are the same as those in JCT 80.

19.5.3 Default by employer or contractor

Any fault in the finished building will be the liability of the contractor. It is not necessary for the employer to attempt to distinguish whether a particular problem is a design fault, a manufacturing fault or an assembly fault. The contractor is liable for the performance of the building. This single-point responsibility is tremendously appealing to clients of construction, and is often cited as the greatest strength of design and build.

19.5.4 Time

Again, single-point responsibility means that the contractor is responsible for ensuring that the project is completed on time. Any delays beyond the control of the employer will be at the risk of the contractor. However, as in JCT 80, there is a list of relevant events at clause 25 of CD 81, dealing with extensions of time. These provisions are substantially the same as those for JCT 80, the difference being that in CD 81 it is the employer who decides what extension is to be granted, there being no contract administrator or architect to exercise this function. As with all JCT forms, many of the provisions relating to extensions of time are there to protect the employer's right to deduct liquidated damages. Extensions of time are *not* just in the contractor's interest.

19.5.5 Quality

Quality is not compromised simply by using the design and build form of procurement. There are design and build contractors who do not understand aesthetics or architecture, just as there are clients who do not understand these things. The fact that design and build allows such people to join together and produce buildings may be seen by some as a disadvantage, or by others as an advantage! However, if the client requires a high quality building, in the subjective sense of the word, there are no features of this procurement method which would necessarily compromise that requirement. In fact, the nature of the tendering documentation, and the inherent flexibility of the system, may well encourage better architecture. The current emphasis on quality in the construction industry is based upon the British Standard definition of quality as being 'conformance to requirements'. This deals with objective criteria which can be measured, and again, there is nothing in design and build which compromises this. Since the contract is based upon a comprehensive statement of employer's requirements, there is theoretically a better chance of producing a high quality building, in the British Standard sense, than there would be by writing a bill of quantities and putting that out to competitive tender.

The reputation of design and build has suffered from criticisms by some construction professionals of projects which involve system building and standardization. This type of project often leads to very poor buildings. It is unfortunate that, in the minds of some people, design and build has become synonymous with system building. This is not the case in practice, and criticism of system building should be distinguished from criticism of design and build. In any event, most buildings procured under general contracting are not of substantial architectural merit. It is not the procurement process itself that causes good quality, but rather the people used within that process. The process selected may certainly help, or it may hinder, but it is of secondary importance.

The only reliable way to encourage quality in a building is to obtain a clear statement about what constitutes high quality for a particular client, and to have that statement embodied within the employer's requirements.

₅19.6 CONCLUSIONS

Design and build is a logical, clear and sensible method for procuring a wide range of buildings. Its increase in popularity has been steady, and there are very few reports of clients who are dissatisfied with it. As a procurement method, it is a realistic and worthwhile alternative to general contracting or construction management. There is no real limit on the type or scale of project for which it can be used, but it is inadvisable to use it for high risk projects, or for adventurous schemes. It offers a high degree of cost certainty.

As with any procurement method, it is the selection of the personnel for the project team which is the most important thing. Having selected the team, the choice of design and build as a procurement method is unlikely to compromise good practice. It has been used for centuries and its use seems likely to continue.

REFERENCES

1. Banwell, G.H. *The Placing and Management of Contracts for Building and Civil Engineering Work.* HMSO, London, 1964.

2. Evans, R.W. Hallmark of real change. *Building*, 20 January 1978, 71.
3. British Property Federation. *Manual of the BPF System*. British Property Federation, London, 1983.
4. Joint Contracts Tribunal. *Practice Note CD/1A*. RIBA Publications, London, 1989.
5. Pain, J. and Bennett, J. JCT with contractor's design form of contract: study in use. *Construction Management and Economics*, **6**, 1988, 307–37.
6. Robinson, P. Design and builders. *Architects' Journal*, 23 August 1989.

20

Management contracts

Judging by some of the literature on **management contracting**, it would seem that it is a new direction and a solution to all of the problems inherent in construction projects. Sadly, it is neither of these! Management contracting has actually been in use for a considerable time, although it is only since 1987 that there has been a standard form of contract for this type of procurement. Prior to 1987, there were many instances of management contracts, but they were let using either modified standard forms or contracts drafted by one of the parties (usually the contractor). For example, the project which led to the case of *IBA* v. *EMI & BICC*[1] used the IEE/IMechE Model Conditions. These conditions were used for both the contract between employer and management contractor and that between contractor and sub-contractor, even though they were entirely inappropriate to cover the main contract.[2] Another project which was run as a management contract was the construction of the British Library in London. This was entered into before the Joint Contracts Tribunal issued its Standard Form of Management Contract MC 87, and was let on the Property Services Agency's own terms. All in all, management contracting is not as new as it seems.

20.1 BACKGROUND OF MANAGEMENT CONTRACTS

The characteristics of a management contract are that the client engages the management contractor to participate in the project at an early stage, contribute construction expertise to the design and manage the construction.[3] Because of these requirements, it is normal for the management contractor to be an experienced builder or construction company, but this is not necessarily a prerequisite. The management contractor is *not* employed for the purposes of undertaking any of the works, but solely for managing the process. In effect, management contracting is a

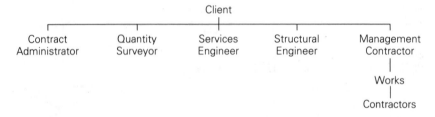

Fig. 20.1   Contractual relationships in management contracts.

procurement method consisting of 100% sub-contracting. Every item of building work is sub-contracted to 'Works Contractors'.

This 'sub-contracting' feature is what distinguishes management contracting from the 'construction management' approach, discussed in Chapter 21, under which the separate works contracts are all made directly between the employer and the works contractors.

The contractual relationships in management contracting are summarized in Fig. 20.1.

As the figure clearly shows, the relationships provide an opportunity for the contractor to become part of the design team, at a level which can be equated with that of the professionals involved. It is important to recognize this feature, as it is one of the main reasons why management contracting is favoured by the contracting side of the construction industry, and it has indeed achieved a dominant position. As a form of procurement it offers contractors the opportunity to become professionals, to dispense with their labourforce, plant and equipment, and reduces their operating costs to a previously unheard of level. Furthermore, as befits this status as one of the consultants, the management contractor's *risk* in connection with the project is reduced to a level that is similar to that of the other design consultants. In effect, the contractual risk associated with the construction of the building is distributed entirely between the client and works contractors. This leaves the management contractor with very little contractual risk, as we shall see.

As we have mentioned, an important purpose of the management contracting approach is to provide the project team with access to the experience of a contractor at an early stage. It is for this reason that the standard form of management contract distinguishes the pre-construction stage from that of construction. Because of this distinction, there is in fact an opportunity for the employer to terminate the relationship after the design stage, but before construction work actually commences.

Although they are projects which involve 100% sub-contracting of the works, management contracts are typified by an array of linked documents. This linking creates some special relationships that do not exist in other forms of contract, and it also makes management contracts seem bewildering and confusing. We shall be examining the range of documentation that constitutes a management contract, and considering the types of legal relationships set up by this documentation. While we will concentrate on the JCT standard form of management contract, it must always be borne in mind that it is relatively straightforward to set up a management contract under other forms of documentation since it is analogous to 100% sub-contracting.

In the remainder of this chapter we shall look at the conditions which favour the use of management contracts, before considering the way in which risks are apportioned under this type of contract.

20.2 THE JCT MANAGEMENT CONTRACT

20.2.1 When to use MC 87

The guidance note issued with the JCT MC 87 contract indicates suitable circumstances in which to use this form of contract.[4] Several of the suggested criteria are not new; indeed, they are individually important on a variety of different types of standard form contracts. Further, since the guidance note specifically states that not all these conditions are necessary for a successful management contract, it is perhaps only when the majority of these factors act in combination that the management contract should be used.

The conditions mentioned are as follows:

1. The employer wishes the design to be carried out by an independent architect and design team.
2. There is a need for early completion.
3. The project is fairly large.
4. The project requirements are complex.
5. The project entails, or might entail, changing the employer's requirements during the building period.
6. The employer requiring early completion wants the maximum possible competition in respect of the price for the building works.

Each of these aspects is dealt with below.

Independent architect and design team

This means that the employer wants the architect and design team to be independent of the contractor. There is nothing new about wishing to have an independent architect and design team; indeed, independence is a normal characteristic of design consultants. The reason for specifically mentioning it, in this context, is that management contracting is clearly being offered as an alternative to, and perhaps in competition with, 'design and build' packages, where independence of the designers from the builders is not assured. The use of this form of words may indicate a certain disenchantment with, or suspicion of, design and build and other package deal contracts.

Early completion

There is also nothing new about wanting early completion, and there are various approaches available to the client who seeks it. Chief among these is what is called **'fast-track' construction**, under which the contract is let as soon as sufficient work is documented and ready to start on site. Although this *encourages* faster overall times, due to the overlapping of design with construction, it causes severe problems of communication. Information must be very carefully co-ordinated if site problems are to be avoided. Indeed, there are many people who claim, with good reason, that this overlapping of design with construction actually slows down the process of construction because of the increase which it brings in variations, disputes and the escalation of disputes. It is these extra problems of fast-tracking that management contracting is possibly designed to avoid, not just general lack of speed for which traditional contracting is notorious!

Size of the project

It might be thought that the difference between a 'large' project and a 'small' one would be fairly self-evident, but this is a very subjective criterion. It is not at all clear whether size is meant to refer to cost, area, height or level of accommodation. Perhaps it is hoped that clients will simply make a value judgement that their project is 'fairly large'!

Complexity of the project

Complexity is perhaps more easily recognized than size alone. In any event, complexity should be weighed up with size. It is the combination of size and complexity that results in the need for management contracts. Take, for example, a project such as a prestigious modern office development in the heart of London, with a restricted site and high levels of building services required, together with extremely high-level finishes. The risks for the contractor on such a project are so high as to lead to an inflated price, as the tendering contractors try to cover the risks. It may well be in such circumstances that the client is in a stronger position to be able to bear the risks, especially if the client is a property developer who builds frequently. As we have seen in Chapter 2, where a client with large resources builds frequently, the level of uncertainty associated with contractual risk is reduced in that client's building projects. If this occurs, it is in the interests of the client to choose a contractual form which reduces or even eliminates contractual risk for the contractor, and a management contract is a prime candidate.

Changes to the employer's requirements during construction

This is another feature which is not particularly novel. We have looked in Chapter 11 at the provisions in various standard forms of contract enabling the employer to change the requirements for the project; we noted there how exercising these provisions for variations can involve the client in enormous cost and delay, and how essential it is that variations are kept to a minimum if claims, prolongation and disruption are to be avoided. It is strange, then, that the guidance notes for the management contract seem to suggest that the contract is going to facilitate, or somehow make it easier for the client to alter, the requirements for the project. These notes ought really to emphasize that changes should *be avoided at all costs*! That said, however, it would seem that the structure of this procurement path, in which the work is let in packages, means that the freezing of design decisions can be left to a later stage than is possible under the traditional process. For example, the earthworks and substructures packages can actually be let and started on site before much of the detail of the superstructure has been finalized.

Competition on price

Although seeking early completion, the employer may still want a keen price for the works. These two priorities are usually in direct opposition, and consequently have to be traded against each other. However, proponents of management contracting suggest that, because the works packages can be let separately, the lowest price for each package can always be chosen. This will result in a keener price because each package of work will be undertaken by a specialist who will be more competitive for that part of the works. Had that same works contractor tendered for the whole of the works, then they would not have been as competitive.

This argument seems somewhat mis-directed, if not wholly spurious. When the practice of front and back loading of bill rates is considered, some parts of the works will naturally show wide variations in pricing if they are tendered for as a whole but analysed as separate packages. However, once the works contractors are only invited to tender for packages of work, their start-up costs will be multiplied, their rate loadings will not be able to spread over so many items and the differences and advantages in specific groups of rates may well disappear.

More important, the depression of prices hoped for by applying this tendering mechanism, if it is successful, will result in a far greater likelihood of cost overruns for each package. Ultimately, there is even the risk that works contractors will screw down their prices so far that they become insolvent, at great expense to the client.

20.2.2   Contents of MC 87

Although the management contract conditions contain many familiar clauses and phrases, the principles underlying this form of procurement are very different from those of other more traditional contracts. One particular feature not found in other JCT forms is the use of **Schedules**, which are attached to the back of the contract. These Schedules, which are referred to in the Recitals, define the scope of the work, as well as certain of the responsibilities under the contract. The fact that they are appended as Schedules enables them to be easily tailored to suit individual projects. They also provide a succinct summary of what it is the parties are actually agreeing to do.

Schedules

- **1st Schedule – description of project**. This is simply a blank page to be filled in. There seem to be no constraints on how the project is to be described. Presumably, this allows a certain amount of flexibility in the use of a mixture of text, diagrams sketches and calculations; but considerable care is necessary. This description is referred to in the 1st Recital, and it is thus fundamental in defining the purpose of the contract.
- **2nd Schedule – definition of 'prime cost'**. Unlike JCT 80 and other similar forms, MC 87 is not a lump sum contract. The amount to be paid to the management contractor is the prime cost of all work done under the contract, plus the management contractor's fee. Excluded from payment are any costs incurred as a result of the negligence of the management contractor in discharging its obligations, as well as any costs already recovered as part of the pre-construction management fee.

  Although there is no Contract Sum in this form, there is a Contract Cost Plan. This will have been prepared by the quantity surveyor, based upon the project drawings and the project specification. However, the management contractor has *no* contractual responsibility if the prime cost of the project exceeds the contract cost plan.

  An alternative approach is available within the JCT documentation. There are certain parts of the 2nd Schedule that may be dealt with by a lump sum: items such as site staff, sundry costs, labour and/or materials provided by the management contractor, etc. If these items are listed at the end of the 2nd Schedule, and an amount of money is entered in the Appendix, then they can be dealt with on a lump sum basis instead of being direct-cost reimbursement items.

- **3rd Schedule – services provided by management contractor**. It is interesting to note that the roles of the contract administrator and the quantity surveyor are not defined in the form. The management contractor simply interacts with 'the professional team'. The roles of the professional team remain to be co-ordinated via their own professional terms of engagement. This is a task for the professional institutions, not for the Joint Contracts Tribunal.[5]

  The services to be provided by the management contractor are divided between the pre-construction period and the construction period. During the pre-construction period, alterations can be made to the services intended to be provided at the subsequent construction stage, provided they are initialled by both parties. The pre-construction stage consists mainly of the advisory role to be played by the management contractor, for example, in advising on the breakdown of work packages or assisting with negotiations. After the pre-construction stage, there are services such as programming and planning, monitoring off-site preparation work, instituting effective cost control techniques, labour relations and site management.

- **4th Schedule – list of project drawings**. This Schedule exists for the purposes of the 1st Recital, Article 6.1 and clause 1.3 (definitions), which cross-refer to it. There is also a reminder here that all drawings must be signed by or on behalf of the employer and the management contractor.

- **5th Schedule – site facilities and services**. This Schedule, which is again cross-referred to by the main contract, lists the site facilities and services which are to be provided by the management contractor. A footnote refers to the JCT practice note, for model of the type of things to be included here.

Recitals

The 1st Recital states that the employer 'wishes to have constructed the building works described in the *first schedule*', and these are referred to from then on as 'the project'. So, for the first time in standard form building contracts, the phrase 'the project' has a legal and *contractual* meaning. This must not be confused with the 'works', which is a word reserved for describing the building work and/or service installations to be carried out by works contractors.[6] Similarly, the 'professional team' is defined as those professional advisers whom the employer has appointed for the design of the project and for other services in connection with the project. The Recital states that the professional team have prepared, or are preparing, drawings and a specification for the project. These are known as the 'project drawings' and the 'project specification'.

The 2nd Recital makes it clear that the works are to be carried out under Works Contracts by persons other than the management contractor, and that the management contractor will provide sufficient services and facilities on site to enable this to happen.

The 3rd Recital states that the management contractor will co-operate with the professional team during the design stages and in planning, programming and cost estimating for the project and, further, that the management contractor will secure the carrying out and completion of the project.

Conditions of Contract

The contract itself is divided into nine sections. Briefly, these are as follows:

- **Section 1 – intentions of the parties**. This section contains an interpretation clause, a general statement of the management contractor's obligations and provisions about the contract documents and certification. The definitions are, for the most part, similar to those found in JCT 80. However, some items are new and exclusive to the management contract. In particular, there is a pre-construction period, as well as a construction period, and the management contractor's fee is expressed as a separate fee for each of these periods. Variations to the *Works Contracts* are allowed under the contract, in a very similar manner to JCT 80. However, the contract also defines a 'Project Change', which gives the employer the opportunity to change the scope of the project. This is much wider than the type of change allowed under the JCT 80 form, and presumably represents part of the extra flexibility claimed by the authors of the contract. As in JCT 80, there are detailed provisions for the valuation of works contract variations, but there are no rules or provisions for valuing the effects of a 'project change'. This may indicate that such changes are not envisaged after works contracts have been let. It would seem that the need for 'project change' provisions is because the contractor is appointed so early in the process. It would be disastrous for the client if the appointment of the management contractor meant that major changes could no longer be made to the client's plans or intentions!
- **Section 2 – possession and completion**. There is a requirement here that the employer must give notice for the management contractor to

proceed. This means at the point between pre-construction and construction. If the notice is not forthcoming within one month, then the contractor's employment will be deemed to have been determined. However, if the failure to give notice is an error, it can be recognized as such and treated as a project extension item.

- **Section 3 – control of the project**. This section contains the 'acceleration clause', which we discuss later. There are also provisions about materials, goods, workmanship, assignment, fair wages, etc.
- **Section 4 – payment**. The significant features of this section are discussed later under the heading of 'Money'. There is no provision for altering the management fee payable to the management contractor in respect of extensions, delays, etc. Final certification is similar to JCT 80.
- **Section 5 – statutory obligations**. The contents of this section follow closely the analogous provisions of JCT 80, and contain no surprises.
- **Section 6 – injury, damage and insurance**. Again, these provisions are similar to those of JCT 80.
- **Section 7 – determination**. The provisions for determination are based on their JCT 80 counterparts, but there are a few very significant differences. Most important, the employer can determine the contract at will, at any time! There are provisions for dealing with this eventuality, so that the site can be made safe if necessary and the works contractors can be paid.
- **Section 8 – works contractors**. The main contract makes it an obligation for the management contractor to use the standard Works Contract Conditions, unless otherwise agreed by the contract administrator and management contractor. The Works Contract consists of Works Contract/1 (Tender Enquiry), Works Contract/2 (Contract Conditions) and Works Contract/3 (Employer/Works Contractor Agreement). The last of these is a direct warranty agreement, similar to NSC/2, which is to be used only as required.
- **Section 9 – settlement of disputes**. These provisions are in line with JCT 80.

20.3 RISK IN MANAGEMENT CONTRACTING

To state that one of the main purposes of a management contract is to limit the main contractor's exposure to risk is not quite as cynical as it sounds! Many of the kinds of project which are regarded as most suitable for a management contract approach involve a high degree of commercial risk. And as we suggested in Chapter 2, one of the fundamental principles underlying the apportionment of risk should be that, where a risk is transferred from one party to another, a financial adjustment must be made to balance it. Consequently, if an experienced and competent contractor were asked to tender under a traditional system for such a project, there would have to be a significant premium on the price to absorb the excessive risk. It is accordingly not only in the contractor's interest to have a low risk contract, but may well be in the client's interest as well.

Many of the employers who used management contracts are developers. Not only are they used to building, they also build frequently. As Chapter 2 demonstrated, constant exposure to hazards reduces the level of uncertainty and its attendant risk. Clients who regularly engage in the process of building procurement are well placed to absorb some of the risks attached to the process. It ought to be expected therefore that the risk that has been removed from the contractor, now the management contractor, has been transferred to the employer.

In the early days of management contracting, the intention was indeed to create a 'no-risk' contract for the contractor. This was seen as the best way to encourage the contractor to act as professional consultant. However, as management contracting increased in popularity, some clients sought to draft contracts in such a way as to shift many of the risks back to the management contractor. The main risks involved in this way were risks associated with responsibility for works contractors, time overruns, defects maintenance, preliminaries and design. Effectively, this process resulted in the management contractor carrying as much risk as the main contractor under a normal JCT 80 contract, and created a situation equivalent to a traditional contract under which 100% of the work had been sub-let.[7] This shifting of the burden of risk led, in turn, to one of two results: either the management contractor would absorb the risk and put up the price, whereupon relations between the management contractor and the employer became strained as they tended towards the adversarial; or the management contractor would let the works contracts under more onerous conditions, thus passing the risks down to sub-contractors who were less able to bear them.

In theory, the emergence of a standard form for management contracting should remove this problem of constantly 'moving the goalposts'. We may now examine the way in which risks are apportioned under MC 87, to see if this has indeed been achieved.

20.3.1 Allocation of risks under MC 87

Money

The most significant difference in risk allocation between MC 87 and traditional forms of contract lies in the price to be paid by the employer for the works. The employer has to pay whatever the management contractor spends, plus an amount for the management fee, which may be either a lump sum or a percentage of the prime cost. This means that the contract between the employer and the management contractor is a cost reimbursement contract. The quantity surveyor prepares an outline cost plan, and this becomes the Contract Cost Plan when the contract is executed. The cost has to be certified by the contract administrator, and payment is made on interim certificates which state which parts of the works are covered, so that the money can be apportioned correctly between works contractors. The management fee is also apportioned and included in the interim certificates, so that the management contractor is paid in instalments.

Apart from questions of price, MC 87 provides that, if a works contractor claims from the management contractor as a result of the default of another works contractor, the management contractor is committed to pursuing recovery from the defaulting works contractor. If this is not possible, for example, because the works contractor is insolvent, then the employer has to make up the shortfall. This is, of course, a vital transfer of risk from the management contractor to the employer.

Commitment to complete the project

MC 87 confers considerable protection upon a client by providing in effect that there is at no stage a legal commitment to proceed either with the project or with the particular management contractor. The Fourth Recital and clause 2.1 effectively provide a 'break clause'. The Fourth Recital states that the employer intends to give the management contractor written notice as referred to in clause 2.1. This written notice requires the management contractor to continue to co-operate and to proceed to set out and secure the carrying out and completion of the project in accordance with Article 1. The recital also states that the management contractor is willing to receive this notice and to act upon it.

Clause 2.1 states that when the contract administrator notifies the employer that it will be practicable to commence the construction of the project, and the relevant parties have signed and initialled certain parts of the documentation, the employer shall notify the management contractor within 14 days whether it is to continue in this role. Within the text of this clause there are multiple references to signing and initialling various schedules and documents. All in all, these seem to turn the provisions into an extremely long and tortuous way of saying a fairly straightforward thing: that, subject to the approval of the employer, and the correct completion of the Appendices and Schedules, the management contractor will commence construction operations!

Default by employer or management contractor

Most of the contractual provisions governing termination of the contract, determination of the contractor's employment, insolvency, corruption, and so on, are similar to those found in JCT 80. However, as we have mentioned, there is the important additional right for the employer to determine the contract at will. This is called the 'Employer's Option' and states that, without prejudice to any other rights or remedies that the employer or management contractor may possess, the employer may at any time determine the employment of the management contractor under the contract. In order to do this, notice must be given in writing.

Where the employer exercises this option, the benefit of any outstanding contracts for works or supply is automatically assigned to the employer. This is subject only to the rights of the relevant works contractors to make reasonable objection to any further assignment by the employer.

Time

Management contracting arrangements are designed to encourage a large amount of overlap between the processes of design and construction. For this reason, the chances are that a building will progress from conception to completion more quickly than under a traditional arrangement.

MC 87 contains some special provisions relating to time, most notably an 'acceleration clause' which is new to UK building contracts. This is an optional clause that only applies if the Appendix to the contract states that it is to apply. At common law, it is not permitted for one party unilaterally to change the terms of a contract once the contract has come into existence, although a variations clause does of course give such a power in respect of what is to be built. Perhaps because a clause giving the employer power to change the *time* for the works contractor to do the work is so unusual that the works contractor may make reasonable objection, although it is not clear what could constitute 'reasonable' or 'unreasonable' in such circumstances.[8]

The acceleration provision is found in clause 3.6, and there is a corresponding provision in clause 3.4.3 of the works contract. The clause is carefully set out to avoid the worst excesses of unreasonable employers. It operates through a process consisting of a preliminary instruction by the contract administrator, an opportunity for the management contractor to object, and then withdrawal or modification of preliminary instruction. After the acceptance by the contractor of a preliminary instruction, the contractor has to inform the contract administrator in writing, in respect of each works contract, the amount of money as a lump sum required by the works contractor in order to achieve the new completion date. Alternatively, if an appropriate lump sum cannot be ascertained, then there is provision for an amount to be ascertained under the relevant works contract. The contract administrator, after receiving this information, has to see if the employer is willing to pay the price for acceleration. If the employer *is* so willing, then the contract administrator can issue the instruction to accelerate.

This highly procedural clause is an attempt to compromise between the needs of the employer for flexibility, and the needs of the works contractors to be paid for incurring expenditure. The clause can be brought into effect to cancel or reduce a previously granted extension of time.

In dealing with the extension of time provisions under the JCT Management Contract, an important distinction has to be drawn between 'Relevant Events', which entitle a *works contractor* to an extension, and 'Project Extension Items', which entitle the *management contractor* to an extension of time for completion of the entire project. The former group closely resemble those found in JCT 80, but the management contractor's position is very different. The project time may be extended if there are any causes which impede the proper discharge by the management contractor of its obligations under the contract (including omissions or defaults by the employer). However, the management contractor is most definitely *not* entitled to any extension where the delay has been caused or contributed to by any default of the management contractor *or of a works contractor* (including in each case their servants, agents or subcontractors). As a result, while a works contractor may have an extension of time when delayed by another works contractor or by the management contractor, this will not constitute grounds for a Project Extension Item.

These extension of time rules, coupled with the management contractor's liability to pay liquidated damages to the employer if the whole project is not completed by the completion date, appear to impose a very heavy burden of risk on the management contractor. Nothing could be further from the truth! Clause 3.21 of MC 87 effectively means that, where delay is caused by a works contractor, the employer can only recover liquidated damages from the management contractor to the extent that the management contractor is, in turn, able to recover them from the works contractor concerned. Clause 3.21 makes it a duty of the management contractor to take all necessary steps to ensure that the works contractors meet their obligations, and it is also a duty of the management contractor to pursue claims for breach of contract by a works contractor, even to the extent of arbitration and litigation. However, even this does not ultimately impose any serious risk on the management contractor, since the employer is bound to reimburse the management contractor for any money spent in pursuing these obligations.

Quality

Quality of both materials and workmanship is governed by clause 1.7 of the management contract, which states that the management contractor shall be fully liable to the employer for any breach of the terms of this contract, *including any breach by any of the works contractors* under the terms of their works contracts. Once again, this apparent allocation of a considerable risk to the management contractor is turned on its head by clause 3.21, which limits the management contractor's liability to whatever can be recovered, in turn, from the defaulting works contractor. The philosophy underlying this provision has been expressed saying that 'no independent liability can be attached to the management contractor for any defects in workmanship and materials, on the basis that it is the works contractors who are the parties responsible for the completion of the works'.[9]

In conclusion, it is clear that there are many differences between this and other forms of contract, and the complex interlinking documentation is, at first sight, bewildering. However, a familiarity with JCT 80 is an enormous benefit in this respect, as a large number of clauses are either identical or at least very similar. What must always be remembered is that management contracting does not aim to be an automatic solution to the problems inherent in procuring buildings. It is no more than a mechanism whereby the employer can harness the experience and knowledge of a co-operative and highly motivated building contractor/expert. It will not by itself alter awkward people, nor re-orientate contractors who are habitual claimers. The employer needs to be very careful in identifying priorities, and even more careful than usual in selecting personnel to appoint to the project team. And, of course, this team includes the management contractor!

REFERENCES

1. *Independent Broadcasting Authority* v. *EMI Electronics Ltd & BICC Construction Ltd* (1978) 14 B.L.R. 1.
2. Parris, J. *Default by Sub-contractors and Suppliers.* Collins, London, 1985.
3. CIRIA. *A Client's Guide to Management Contracts in Building.* Special Publication No. 33. Construction Industry Research and Information Association, London, 1984.

4. JCT. *Practice Note MC/1: Management Contracts Under the JCT Documentation*. RIBA, London, 1987.
5. Wakefield, R. A welcome addition. *Building*, 29 January 1988, 31.
6. JCT. *Practice Note MC/2: Commentaries on JCT Management Contract Documentation*. RIBA, London, 1987.
7. Hayes, R. Who carries the risk? Management contracting – yesterday, today and tomorrow. *Building Technology and Management*, June 1986, 42–45.
8. Brown, J.C. Will the JCT's new management contract stand the test of time? (pt 2). *Building Technology & Management*, April/May 1988, 10–11.
9. *Ibid.*

21

Construction management

The single most important distinguishing feature of **construction management**, and the one which distinguishes it most clearly from **management contracting**, is that the client places a direct contract with each of the specialist and trade contractors. In order to co-ordinate these contracts, the client buys in the expertise of a 'Construction Manager' who acts in the role of consultant. This technique overcomes many of the problems of the management contracting method because there is no direct contractual link between the construction manager and the trade contractors.

21.1 BACKGROUND OF CONSTRUCTION MANAGEMENT

Construction management has its origins in the USA. There the need for large buildings to be erected quickly and reliably, coupled with increasing technical complexity, led to the involvement of an ever higher number of technical people in the design, programming and construction of a building. The management of these people became less of an architectural issue, and more of a management issue. It seems that the 'construction manager', as a specialist, emerged during the 1930s[1]. It was probably the result of a few clients, architects and contractors becoming familiar with each others' working patterns and evolving a method of procurement that was suitable to the task at hand.

In the UK evidence that the US construction industry could perform better, and increasing dissatisfaction with the output of British industry, prompted people to examine the management techniques used in the USA. Unfortunately, it was assumed that the approach adopted by the Americans (i.e. 'construction management') could not simply be transferred across the Atlantic. It seems that management contracting was the first attempt in the UK at duplicating the American practice. As such it was a compromise between the two methods of traditional general contracting and construction management. As management contracting grew in popularity and became more generally acceptable, so the basic problems of the UK construction industry emerged once again and showed the method to be unsuitable to the majority of British building projects. It was clear that the 'traditional' forms of procurement were unsuitable for the increased technical complexity of modern construction projects, but it was also clear that the construction professions in the UK found it very difficult to give complete acceptance to the management contract. This became evident in two ways. First, management contracting became more a marketing tool for ambitious contractors than a real alternative management strategy. Second, clients modified many clauses in the contract in order to shift contractual risks back on to the contractor. The combination of these two factors resulted in the situation where many so-called 'management contracts' were no different from the traditional method of procurement. As would be expected under these circumstances, the same old problems emerged and management contracting rapidly fell into disrepute.

The basic problem with management-based procurement systems lies with the contractual links, information links and authority. The British construction professions have their roots in systems of authority which date back to the middle of the last century. Because these professional traditions are so well established, it is difficult to form a team of people who have not worked together in the past and then to expect them readily to modify their traditional roles. It seems therefore that novel forms of procurement work best when the members of the team have worked together before. When the situation is unfamiliar or risky, the contributors to the team feel more vulnerable than usual. It is under these circumstances that people tend to entrench themselves contractually, to try to ensure protection from litigation. Unfortunately, it is under these precise circumstances of unfamiliarity and complexity that the newer forms of procurement are most needed. It is ironic that the increased need for flexibility and dynamism results in rigid hierarchies of outdated management structures.[2]

The perceived failure of management contracting to provide the desired results has, in recent years, opened the way for attempts to introduce a purer form of construction management into the UK. The diagram in Fig. 21.1 shows how the contractual links of such a procurement system are formed. However, it is important to appreciate that this kind of diagram shows only the *contractual* links; it cannot hope to convey the implications of construction management for a project's organizational structure.

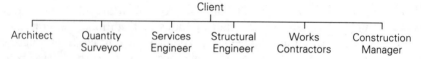

Fig. 21.1 Contractual relationships in construction management.

21.2 USE OF CONSTRUCTION MANAGEMENT CONTRACTS

The construction management method of procurement is most suitable for use where some or all of the following circumstances are present:

1. The client is familiar with construction, and knows some or all of the professional team.
2. The risks associated with the project are dominated by timeliness and cost (e.g. the client may be a private sector client requiring a commercial building).
3. The project is technically complex, involving diverse technologies and sub-systems.
4. The client needs to retain the right to make minor variations to requirements as the project proceeds.
5. The nature of the project is such that it makes sense to separate professional responsibility for the design of the project from professional responsibility for the management of the project.
6. The client requires an early start on site.
7. The cost to the client needs to be competitive, but the control of cost in terms of securing 'value for money' is more important than simply securing the least possible cost.

These criteria are somewhat similar to those favouring the use of management contracts. As with management contracting, some or all of these circumstances may combine to make construction management the best option. However, as with any form of procurement, the primary deciding factor about suitability must be the personnel who are going to be involved. There is an overriding need to ensure that they understand what is to be required of them and how they are supposed to fit into the team. If this is misunderstood, then chances are than everything else will be as well. There are many similarities between management contracting and construction management; the differences between them are in truth more to do with the application of management principles than with detailed contractual provisions.

The circumstances in which it is desirable to use construction management are expanded below.

21.2.1 The client's experience

In order for construction management to work properly, the client must take an active role in the management of the process. There must be regular and effective feedback from the project team to the client. The appointment of a client's project manager may help this process, but that of itself does not transmute the procurement process into a 'project management' model. The need for familiarity applies not only to the *product* of the construction industry, but also to the idiosyncrasies of the process of construction. In order to fully appreciate this, it is desirable if not essential that the client has some experience of having worked with the construction manager, and some of the other consultants, on previous occasions.

21.2.2 The importance of time and cost

Risk is very difficult to identify in construction projects. None the less, in order to be able to configure an appropriate management strategy for a project, the client must make some explicit decisions about the nature of the risks associated with the project. For construction management to be most effective, it is essential that the entire team, including the client, understand that they are commissioning a process that is intended to be speedy by comparison with other procurement processes, and that the need for speed may compromise decisions about least cost.

21.2.3 Technical complexity

Construction management seems to have been used mainly on 'shell and core' projects. These are buildings which are not fitted out by the developer until they are let, which reduces the level of technical complexity and also eliminates many site co-ordination problems. It may therefore seem very odd to quote technical complexity as a reason for using construction management! The point is that complex building projects need to be managed organically, rather than hierarchically, and this requires a procurement system that allows for dynamic and flexible working relationships. By this it is implied that the management structure will be adaptable throughout the life of the project, and that the significance of each contributor's input will vary from one stage to another.

21.2.4 The need to make minor variations

The need to be able to make variations is not paramount, but minor changes must be accommodated. If frequent changes are envisaged, then the administration of them could snarl up the communicative and supervisory processes and make the project more like a traditional form of procurement. If no changes are envisaged, then other procurement systems such as design and build may be appropriate.

21.2.5   The separation of design and management

Not all projects are suited to construction management. In some cases, design is such an intrinsic part of the project that it cannot be separated from management. In such a situation, design *is* management. However, there are many commercial buildings where design is not the overriding feature of the job. In such cases, the designer's role is reduced to manipulating the relationships between spaces in the early stages, and thereafter manipulating the façade. If all other activities related to design have been delegated to consultants, then the problem of co-ordination ceases to be a design problem and becomes a pure management problem. This is the situation most suited to construction management.

21.2.6   The importance of an early start

Many clients are driven by the need to optimize their use of finance. In order to make the whole process work in a competitive business environment, early start on site can become critical to the success of the project. And in order to get started on site at the earliest opportunity, questions relating to the fundamental design issues must be settled and resolved at an early stage. Here the comments in the preceding section are also pertinent. If the project must generate income at the earliest opportunity, the client cannot afford the luxury of having a comprehensive design statement translated into a sophisticated architectural concept. The client's need is simply to house economic operations in a shell that is marketable.

21.2.7   The importance of 'value for money'

Although economic competition is advisable in many cases, it does not mean that least cost is the primary objective. In order to compete successfully in the market, business premises must be attractive, integrated with their surroundings and flexible. In addition, their provision must be timely. Therefore, 'value for money' becomes more important than least cost. There must be some mechanism where alternatives to competitive tendering may be considered, and incorporated. Construction management has the capacity to allow for contracts either to be put out to bid or negotiated.

21.3 CONTENTS OF CONSTRUCTION MANAGEMENT CONTRACTS

21.3.1 General

Since there is no standard contract for construction management, the contractual characteristics tend to vary from one project to another. However the central feature of a construction management project is that the client contracts directly with the trade contractors who are doing the work, and the co-ordinator of the construction work has no contractual responsibility for their performance. If the 'construction manager' *does* have contractual liability for the performance of the trade contractors, then the arrangement is not really construction management at all, and will probably be found on analysis to be some form of management contracting.

The separate trade contracts are each let directly by the client, in much the same way that the client has a direct contract with each of the consultants. In this way, the construction manager becomes a management consultant in the same way that the architect becomes the design consultant. While the construction manager would be expected to manage the overall process, it is not beyond the bounds of possibility that the architect might manage the process during the design stage, using the construction manager as a consultant for advice on fabrication, assembly and co-ordination. When the time comes to work up the initial proposals into detailed 'bid packages', it is sensible for the roles to be reversed; the construction manager runs the process and the architect becomes a consultant.

Depending upon the nature of the project, overall responsibility may shift during its different stages, or it may start and finish with the construction manager. This implied flexibility (relating the actual management structure to the needs of the particular job) is essential for successful management of the project. Indeed, it would probably not make sense to have a 'standard form' contract for construction management since, by standardizing the contractual terms, this flexibility might be lost. More important, once a process like this becomes established, issues that need to be weighed carefully in the balance at the outset of the project cease to be issues. Attention ceases to be focused on the strategic questions and roles become taken for granted. This makes the whole system prone to the problems that it has been designed to overcome. Therefore, it would be wise to avoid the introduction of a standard form, unless it was one which forced the parties to make decisions about the apportionment of risks, and the management of particular risks, according to the circumstances of the project in question.

The appointment of a construction manager necessarily removes much supervisory and management responsibility from the architect, particularly in the production information and construction stages of the process. This requires that design and management become separate issues, and the responsibility of different people. If the two functions are not separated, then the procurement process may well resemble design and build rather than construction management.

The separation of design from management requires the construction manager to be a specialist in management. This calls for skills quite different from those of a general contractor, and probably different from those of a management contractor. The wise client should steer clear of firms who claim to be specialists in all these things. In any event, the client should always be wary of contractors using the appellation as a marketing tool, rather than as an accurate description of the services which they offer.

21.3.2 Typical contractual provisions

The following examples of contractual provisions are based upon construction management contracts that have recently been used in London.

Although drawings/specifications/schedules of rates and contract particulars are furnished by the client, the construction programme must come from the construction manager. The construction manager has the responsibility for co-ordinating the different work packages and must therefore be named in the contract between the client and the trade contractor as the person responsible for co-ordination and timing. This responsibility arises in so far as the construction manager is the agent or representative of the client.

All instructions must come through the construction manager. Indeed, it is not unusual to find trade contracts stating that *all* instructions of the construction manager have to be followed. This is by contrast with JCT contracts, which only compel the contractor to conform with those instructions that are expressly authorized by the contract.

The construction manager may require information from the contractor, in order to achieve co-ordination. The corollary of this is that the construction manager must issue all reasonably necessary information to the contractor. This includes datums and levels for setting out. Certificates are issued by the construction manager after being counter-signed by the architect.

Since many of the trade contracts will be for specialist work, there needs to be some provision as to the trade contractor's liability for design. The conditions need to be sufficiently flexible to allow for the variety of situations that may arise, ranging from no design at all at one extreme to a significant design input at the other.

There are many contemporaneous trade contracts, so that no single trade contractor can be given exclusive or uninterrupted possession of the site. The interaction between the various trade contractors is critical. A contractor who is fixing work to earlier work which has been done by others, has the responsibility for checking that the earlier work is sound. Any earlier work which might affect the success of a particular contractor's work, even though under the overall supervision of the construction manager, should usually be within the skill and experience of the contractor. This obligation to check other work, then, would match the common law position which requires a contractor to be satisfied about himself of achievability before commencing work. The clause is needed to make it a responsibility of the contractor to *warn* the construction manager of potential problems *before* starting work.

Materials, goods and workmanship provisions, and opening up for testing and inspection, etc., are very similar to the usual type of clauses found in JCT contracts and need very little revision for the purposes of construction management trade contracts. Materials cannot be removed from the site without permission of the construction manager.

The contractor will usually be required to keep permanent supervision on site. The construction manager and the architect need access to the works and to other specific places where work is being carried out for the purposes of the contract.

Variations (definition and procedure) and expenditure of provisional sums are issues which can be dealt with in a similar manner to JCT contracts. However, it seems fairly normal in construction management trade contracts for the contractor's estimate of the cost consequences of variations to form a starting-point for negotiations with the construction manager. The amount of payment, and its timing, are then subject to whatever can be agreed between the contractor and the construction manager. If they cannot agree, the bill rates should be used in the usual way as a basis for the valuation of the variation.

The contract sum can only be changed by application of express conditions of the contract, and in no other way.

Interestingly, the bills of quantity do *not* form part of the contract. As far as the contracts are concerned, there are no quantities. Any descriptions of quantities are presumably provided for the basis of planning and control, but do not bind the parties to anything.

Provisions as to completion, defects liability period, assignment and sub-letting are all fairly normal. However, there is sometimes a blanket assignment clause which allows the client to assign the benefit of the contract at any time to a particular firm named in the conditions. This would presumably be the funding body.

Responsibility for insurance is spread between the parties. The contractor must indemnify the client against third-party liability claims, whether for injury or damage, and must maintain an insurance policy to cover this. The client is obliged to maintain an insurance policy for loss or damage to the works, but this excludes damage to plant and machinery, etc. which are the contractor's responsibility.

The contractor is obliged to commence work within 14 days of being instructed, and must maintain progress according to the programme. If the contractor's failure to maintain progress results in delays to other contractors, then this is deemed to have been within the contractor's contemplation at the time of signing the contract. The contractor would therefore be liable to compensate the client in full for what the client has to pay the other contractors.

One provision of certain construction management trade contracts, which has recently caused a great deal of controversy in the industry, is the power given to the construction manager, in the event of certain breaches by the trade contractor, to estimate any loss or damage suffered by the client. The clause in question sought to ensure that the client could summarily claim or withhold this money from the trade contractor until such loss or damage was ascertained on a more final basis. Two recent cases on this power related to a particular clause which contained the words, 'if the contractor is in breach of any of his obligations. . .'. This was held to mean that the breach must be established before the clause could be brought into operation. As a result, a construction manager who simply estimated the loss and made a deduction was acting beyond his powers. The Court of Appeal ruled that when this form of words is used, the breach must be incontrovertibly established before any set-off can be applied to payments to the contractor.[3] It remains to be seen whether this particular clause will be redrafted so as to achieve its intended effect, or whether clients will accept the current position.

Extensions of time can be granted for certain events (though not for bad weather) and are estimated by the construction manager in consultation with the architect. Similarly, loss and expense claims, including those which arise from disruption caused by other trade contractors, are ascertained by the construction manager.

Determination can be by either party under certain specific circumstances. Further detailed clauses contain provisions for payment, interim certificates, set-off, retention, final certificate, construction industry tax deduction scheme, antiquities, and so on. None of these provisions contains any surprises.

Finally, it is interesting to observe that, despite claims from many quarters that the JCT provisions are outdated, complex or inadequate, many of the construction management contracts currently in use contain detailed provisions which are similar if not identical to the equivalent JCT clauses.

21.4 ALLOCATION OF RISK IN CONSTRUCTION MANAGEMENT

The risks in construction management contracts are substantially the same as those in management contracts, due to the similarity of the occasions upon which they should be used. However, subtle differences are found in the way in which these risks are commonly apportioned.

21.4.1 Time

The obligations as to time are entirely related to the construction manager's programme. This means that a client who wants speedy progress should appoint a construction manager who has proven experience of being able to complete projects quickly. Too ambitious a programme will result in inflated tenders from the trade contractors, and too conservative a programme will result in a slow project. The skill of the construction manager lies in judging the speed of construction.

Construction management has been shown to produce some of the fastest building known in this country. However, this must be weighed against the type of project being undertaken. Shell and core building is very fast anyway, and produces a building which still requires the occupier to fit it out.

The risk of delay lies, in theory, entirely with a defaulting trade contractor. However, the extent to which that contractor can actually be penalized depends on its financial resources. A small trade contractor could incur claims for delay which amount to far more than its annual turnover, and could rapidly become insolvent. This is why trade contractors may be required to have sureties and guarantors. Without these, the risks to the client could be enormous.

21.4.2 Money

The direct contract between the client and the trade contractor, without the intervention of such administrative mechanisms as are found in general contracting, means that payment of certificates should be prompt. This should improve performance and minimize costs of finance to the trade contractor. These costs would be passed on to the client anyway, so it is in the client's interest to help the contractor to keep them down.

Since each contract is with the client, there is a high degree of confidence in each of the contract sums. The contract sum in each case cannot be altered except by express provisions of the contract. The choice that the client has between tendering and negotiating should encourage the use of the correct technique according to the particular circumstances of each trade contract. Provided the client restricts the use of variations, the financial commitment of the client should be predictable.

The fact that quantities are not contractual avoids the traditional hold which a contractor can have over a client as information becomes more definite. The risk of actual quantities being different from those anticipated should now lie with the contractor; this is as it should be, because such issues are well within the skill and experience of a trade contractor.

21.4.3   Default

The inclusion of design responsibility in trade contracts increases the possibility of default. This design liability is essentially no different from that undertaken by sub-contractors in traditional procurement models. Since there is no intermediary contractor between the client and the contractor, there is no need for collateral warranties, except those intended to benefit third parties such as a funding institution.

21.4.4   Completion

The circumstances under which either party can determine the contract are fairly straightforward and familiar. There is no blanket provision for the employer to be able to determine the contract at will, as there is in management contracting. This means that, as usual, each contractor is not only obliged to complete the works, but has a right so to do.

The need for the client to be able arbitrarily to terminate the project is not compromised. Since the work is divided into packages, this risk is substantially reduced. No one contractor has the right to continue working for the whole of the project, or if they have, then perhaps the packages have been divided up incorrectly! Although the client is obliged to conclude each active work package, there is no obligation to finish the entire project. The client's risk is thus substantially reduced, without a corresponding increase in the risk to individual contractors.

21.4.5   Quality

The extent to which the client is protected from having to accept inferior work depends on the adequacy of the architect's description and specification of the work to be carried out. The contractor is obliged to ensure that all work conforms to the descriptions in the contract documents, and that the relevant testing and inspection have been carried out.

It would be difficult to think of any more thorough way of effectively making the contract assure the client of the quality of workmanship and materials.

REFERENCES

1. Gutman, R. *Architectural Practice*. Princeton Architectural Press, New York, 1988.
2. Bresnen, M. *Organizing Construction: Project Organization and Matrix Management*. Routledge, London, 1990.
3. *Rosehaugh Stanhope (Broadgate Phase 6) plc* v. *Redpath Dorman Long Ltd* (1990) 50 B.L.R. 69; *Beaufort House Development Ltd* v. *Zimmcor (International) Inc.* (1990) 50 B.L.R. 91.

PART EIGHT ────────────────

Contract Disputes

─────────────────────────────

22

Damages for breach of contract

The primary remedy for any breach of contract is an award of damages. This remedy is always available, unlike the remedy of repudiation (Chapter 23), which is only available in cases of serious breach. In addition to the normal mechanisms for claiming damages for breach, some contracts include provisions for what are called **liquidated** or **liquidated and ascertained damages**.

22.1 DAMAGES

These are assessed with the intention of making the innocent party's position (so far as money can do this) equivalent to what it would have been if the contract had been properly performed. In this respect, the innocent party is entitled to be compensated for all losses suffered which are not 'too remote' from the defendant's breach. To decide which losses fall within this rule, English law has adopted a complex test.[1] First, an item of damage will be recoverable if it could have been regarded as likely to arise in the usual course of things following the breach of contract. In other words, damage which is reasonably foreseeable is not too remote. Second (and alternatively), it may be recoverable if such damage could have been within the contemplation of the parties, at the time that they made their contract. This means that what is reasonably foreseeable depends upon the knowledge possessed by the contracting parties, at the time that they made their bargain.

This is not the place for a detailed discussion of damages for breach of contract, but a brief account of the more important points will be useful. It is important to distinguish **damages for breach of contract** from 'liquidated damages', which are of special importance in construction cases. Liquidated damages are dealt with in the second part of this chapter.

22.1.1 Breach by the contractor

If a contractor's work is defective or incomplete, this usually constitutes a breach of contract. An argument sometimes arises as to whether the employer's damages should consist of the cost of putting right the deficiencies, or the amount by which the value of the property is diminished. While **diminution in value** is appropriate where repair would be uneconomic and/or unreasonable, the normal measure of damages will be based on **cost of repair**. Further, this should be assessed not at the date of breach, but rather at the date when repairs ought reasonably to have been put in hand.[2]

This ruling can be of great significance in times of high inflation, as is shown by *Dodd Properties* v. *Canterbury CC*.[3] This case did not involve a building contract, but a building which the defendants had negligently damaged. The plaintiffs claimed that they were entitled to damages for the cost of repairing their premises. By the time that the case was tried, the plaintiffs had deferred the reinstatement work for 10 years. They had been waiting partly because of their financial circumstances, and partly in order to be certain that the defendants, who were denying liability, would actually be held liable. It was held by the Court of Appeal that, since the plaintiffs' decision to defer was a reasonable one, the damages should reflect the £30 000 which the repairs would now cost, and not merely the £11 000 which they would have cost 10 years earlier.

In recent years, the courts have shown increasing sympathy for the physical discomfort and emotional frustration suffered by people being forced to live in unsuitable accommodation. This is reflected, in cases concerning defective *dwellings*, by awarding such victims a fairly modest additonal sum of damages by way of compensation. Such awards have become almost standard practice, but the Court of Appeal in *Hutchinson* v. *Harris*[4] made it clear that the practice should not be allowed to extend to cases concerning *business premises*. No doubt every employer feels 'vexation' when a breach of contract occurs, but on its own this is not sufficient for an entitlement to damages.

The case last mentioned is also a good illustration of another important principle governing damages, namely that plaintiffs are under an obligation to take all reasonable steps to keep their loss to a minimum.[5] An award of damages will not include anything which is found to result from the plaintiff's 'failure to mitigate'. As a result, in *Hutchinson* v. *Harris*, where an architect was guilty of negligence in supervising a conversion project, the client's claim for the loss of rental income failed. The court found that the employer could easily have done what was required to render the premises lettable and then let them. Since this had not been attempted, the architect could not be held responsible for this loss.

Where a contractor's breach consists of failure to complete the work altogether, an additional factor comes into play. In such c̲... has been held that the damages awarded to the employer should be based on what it costs to have the work completed by another contractor, less the unpaid balance of the contract price.[6]

22.1.2 Breach by the employer

As a general principle, where the employer is guilty of a breach of a building contract, the contractor is entitled to damages under two headings. The first is damages for any actual loss which has been suffered; and the second is damages for any profit of which the contractor has been deprived. Examples of this principle are almost unlimited, but a good idea of the kind of losses which are commonly suffered can be gained from Chapter 12, dealing with contractors' claims for loss and expense under express contractual provisions. It has long been settled that such claims are assessed in exactly the same way as damages for breach of contract.

Where the employer's breach is sufficient to justify the contractor in terminating the contract (a matter which is dealt with in Chapter 23), the contractor is entitled to damages reflecting everything which would have been received under the contract, or the proportion of it which remains outstanding at the date of termination, less what it would have cost to complete the work. It has been clearly established that the damages should include the profit element on work which remains to be done.[7]

It is generally accepted that a contractor who has partly completed the work when the contract is wrongfully repudiated by the employer has an alternative. Instead of seeking damages for breach of contract, the contractor may claim a reasonable sum for the work done. This course of action would naturally be of great benefit to the contractor in cases where the contract would have been disadvantageous (because of under-pricing, for example). However, the limits of this option should be noted. Where a plaintiff attempts to sue for wasted expense because of repudiation, the plaintiff is not to be put into a *better* position than if the contract had been performed.[8] In other words, if the plaintiff has made a bad bargain, damages may not be used to improve the bargain. Whether this approach might also be applied to contractors' claims for a *quantum meruit* remains to be seen.

22.2 LIQUIDATED DAMAGES

As we have mentioned earlier, there is a special category of damages known as 'liquidated damages'. This term applies to a predetermined sum which becomes payable by a party to a contract if certain specified breaches occur. This type of entitlement is in place of the normal right to claim damages measured by the amount of loss.

22.2.1 Nature and purpose of liquidated damages

In order for there to be a successful claim for 'liquidated damages', there must be a clause in the contract making it an express provision. Most building contracts contain such a clause. In particular, most building contracts provide that a contractor who is guilty of delay beyond the contractual completion date (as extended where appropriate) shall pay or allow a certain amount of liquidated damages for every day or week of delay. Such clauses are found in JCT 80 (clause 24, 'Damages for Non-completion'); IFC 84 clauses 2.6 and 2.7; and ICE 6 clause 47.

Liquidated damages provisions are, in principle, perfectly acceptable. Indeed, they are to be encouraged as they enable the parties to know where they stand. They also save time and money on arbitration or litigation. However, the law recognizes that they are capable of operating rather harshly in cases where the amount to be paid or forfeited is greatly in excess of the loss caused by the breach of contract. Because of this, the courts treat such clauses with a fair degree of suspicion. For example, it is insisted that any contractual preconditions of their use be strictly adhered to and, in most cases, any ambiguities are interpreted against the employer. Indeed, the law goes even further than this, by ruling that, if what appears to be a provision for 'liquidated damages' is in reality a 'penalty clause' (i.e. an attempt to terrorize the contractor into completing on time), then it is unconscionable and wholly unenforceable. In such circumstances, the employer is left to claim **unliquidated damages** in respect of whatever loss or damage can be proved.

The distinction in law between liquidated damages and a penalty is thus of crucial importance. Unfortunately, it is a difference of fact and degree rather than a difference of kind, and is thus difficult to express with any great precision. However, some assistance on the matter has been forthcoming from the courts. The most notable guidelines, which have been long accepted as the best available, were given by Lord Dunedin in 1915:[9]

(i) The terms used in the contract are not conclusive, though they may be persuasive.

(ii) Unlike a penalty, liquidated damages represent a genuine attempt at a pre-estimate of likely damage.

(iii) In deciding into which category a particular contract term falls, account must be taken of circumstances at the time of making the contract, not at the time of breach.

(iv) The following 'tests' may be helpful, or even conclusive:

(a) if the sum stipulated is 'extravagant and unconscionable' compared with the greatest amount of loss which could be caused, it is a penalty;

(b) if the breach consists simply of non-payment of money, and the sum stipulated is a greater sum, it is a penalty;

(c) if a single sum is payable for a range of breaches of varying severity, there is a presumption (but no more) that it is a penalty;

(d) the fact that an accurate pre-estimation of the likely damage is almost impossible to achieve does not prevent a stipulation from being classed as liquidated damages. In fact, it is in precisely these cases – public buildings, housing association projects and other non-profit-making ventures – when a liquidated damages clause is most useful.

As Lord Dunedin's first guideline makes clear, whether or not something constitutes a penalty is a matter to be decided by the courts, not by the parties to the contract. For this reason, statements like 'all sums payable by the contractor to the employer. . .shall be paid as liquidated damages for delay and not as a penalty' (ICE 6 clause 47(3)) will not have their intended effect at law. Similarly, express terms which state that the amount for liquidated damages is a genuine pre-estimate of the employer's likely loss (ICE 6 clause 47(1)(a)) cannot take precedence over the guidelines.

Although the vast majority of the cases in this area have concerned stipulations for the payment of a defined sum of money, it is clear that other contractual stipulations may also fall foul of the 'penalty' rules. An example of this can be seen in a civil engineering case, *Ranger* v. *G.W. Railway*.[10] The contract provided that failure by the contractor to proceed regularly with the works would enable the employer to forfeit all money due and all tools and materials. Also, if these were not enough to cover the cost of completion, the contractor would be liable for the shortfall. It was held by the House of Lords that this provision was a penalty since the value of the money and goods forfeited might far outweigh the cost to the employer of completing the work.

A similar decision was reached in *Public Works Commissioner* v. *Hills*,[11] where a railway construction contract provided that, in case of delay, the contractor should forfeit all retention money under that contract and two other contracts. Here it was pointed out that retention money naturally increases as time goes on, and thus bears no relation to the employer's likely loss from delay – as a result, the forfeiture provision was to be treated as a penalty.

A third example of this principle is the case of *Gilbert-Ash* v. *Modern Engineering*,[12] in which a sub-contract provided that, if the sub-contractor failed to comply with any provisions, all payment from the main contractor could be suspended or withheld. Once again, the provision was held to be a penalty, this time because a trivial breach could lead to the retention of a wholly disproportionate sum of money.

The attitude of the courts towards liquidated damages clauses is based upon the assumption that, unless controlled, they operate unfairly against the contractor by over-compensating the employer. However, it must not be overlooked that there is another side to this argument. A valid liquidated damages provision in a contract may serve to *limit* the claims of an employer who has suffered greater loss than the amount provided for. Ironically, in such circumstances it may be to the employer's advantage to argue that the clause is a penalty since, as we shall see, this would then enable an action for the actual loss! In practice, however, it is doubtful that the stipulated loss is so much greater than the employer's likely loss as to be a penalty, and yet less than the loss which is actually suffered.

It can happen that a 'liquidated damages' clause fixes a sum which is likely to be *less* than the employer's actual loss. Where this can be seen from the outset, the clause in question is effectively a kind of exemption clause and must be treated as such. In particular, it would bring into action the very complex rules which govern exemption clauses, including (in theory) the provisions of the *Unfair Contract Terms Act 1977*. However, the way in which that Act is drafted means that it will only apply where either the employer is a 'consumer' or the contract is made on the contractor's 'written standard terms of business'. In relation to JCT contracts, which are drafted following negotiations by all sides of the construction industry, the second of these conditions is unlikely to be fulfilled. As to the first, not many 'consumers' initiate building projects of sufficient size to justify the use of JCT 80!

22.2.2   Operation and effect of liquidated damages clauses

In cases of delayed completion, the employer will wish to claim liquidated damages in accordance with the contract. To do this, the employer must show that:

1. The clause is not a penalty.
2. There is a definite date fixed by the contract from which the damages can run. As we have already seen, this date may be the completion date originally fixed, or any other date which has been substituted under the provisions of an extension clause. In the latter case, the procedures for extending time must have been properly applied.
3. Any specified contractual procedures (e.g. a contract administrator's certificate or the giving of written notice) have been complied with.
4. The employer has not waived his or her rights.

Where all these conditions are satisfied, the first and most obvious effect is that the employer will be entitled to claim or deduct the stipulated sum, irrespective of actual loss or, indeed, whether any loss has been suffered at all. Thus in *BFI Group* v. *DCB Integration Systems*,[13] a contractor completed a warehouse on time under JCT MW 80, with the exception of the roller shutter doors. The contractor allowed the employer in to fit out the warehouse, and by the time this had been done the doors had been delivered and fitted. It was none the less held that the employer was entitled to claim the full amount of liquidated damages provided in the contract.

A liquidated damages clause is said to be 'operative' in the sense that either it applies or it *would* apply but for a valid extension of time or an employer's waiver of rights. Where this is the case, it represents the sole ground of claim; it is not open to the employer to disregard it and claim unliquidated damages at common law. In *Surrey Heath BC* v. *Lovell Construction*,[14] for example, where it was alleged that the fire which delayed completion was itself due to the contractors' negligence, the employer nevertheless granted an extension of time and then claimed damages for breach of contract to cover the loss of rental income from the premises. This claim, it was held, must fail; the losses were covered exclusively by the liquidated damages clause, which was inapplicable here because of the extension granted. An even more striking example is *Temloc* v. *Errill*,[15] in which the employer had inserted '£nil' in the Appendix as the rate for liquidated damages. This was held to preclude any claim at all for delay, although it should be noted that the position would have been different if the whole liquidated damages clause had been struck out, or even if the Appendix had been left blank!

An important practical consequence of the principle just illustrated occurs where there is a fluctuations clause in the contract, and costs increase at a time when the contractor is guilty of delay. Unless the contract provides otherwise[16] the contractor, despite being late, will be able to pass on these increased costs to the employer; the latter's remedy is limited to a claim for liquidated damages.[17]

·As stated above, an 'operative' liquidated damages clause provides the employer's sole remedy for delay. By contrast, a clause which has become 'inoperative' for various reasons will leave the employer with a perfectly valid breach of contract claim for unliquidated damages. The assessment of this claim will compensate the employer for whatever losses can be proved. It is for this reason that it may be in the employer's interest, in cases where losses actually exceed the stipulated sum, to argue that the clause is in truth a 'penalty', since this allows a claims for damages at large. It also appears that the employer whose own acts (such as a delay for which no extension of time can be granted) have rendered a liquidated damages clause ineffective, can resort to a common law claim.[18] However, it is doubtful whether the employer would be allowed in such circumstances to claim more than would have been received as liquidated damages. If this *were* allowed, the employer would appear to benefit from his or her own breach of contract, and this is something which the law does not usually allow to happen.

22.2.3 Liquidated damages clauses in the main standard forms

The operation of the principles described above may be demonstrated by reference to the clauses found in the main standard form contracts. For example, clause 24 of JCT 80 provides that before liquidated damages can be claimed or deducted the contract administrator must issue a certificate of non-completion (certifying that the contractor has failed to complete on time) and the employer must give the contractor written notice of intention to deduct liquidated damages. This double requirement of contract administrator's certificate, plus employer's written notice, can lead to complications where extensions of time are granted. In *Bell* v. *CBF Residential Care*[19] it was held that, on each occasion that the completion date was validly extended, the contract administrator must issue a fresh certificate of non-completion and the employer must give fresh written notice. However, the position has now been altered by a 1990 amendment to JCT 80 – it is still necessary for the contract administrator, on each occasion that a new completion date is fixed, to issue a fresh certificate of failure to complete, but the employer's original notice of intention to deduct liquidated damages remains in force until it is specifically revoked.

The position under ICE 6 clause 47 is that liquidated damages become payable (or deductible) when the contractor has failed to complete the works within the prescribed time or any validly granted extension. Clause 47 does not specifically require the engineer to certify non-completion, but this will in effect happen anyway since clause 44(4) requires the engineer to make a decision on any possible extension of time not later than 14 days after the due date for completion.

One further point which is specifically dealt with is what is to happen if an extension of time granted retrospectively means that liquidated damages should not have been paid or deducted. Both forms of contract provide that, in such circumstances, the employer must repay the money, but only ICE 6 states that interests must be paid on this sum. In fact, a Northern Ireland court has interpreted the wording used in JCT 80 as requiring the employer to pay interest,[20] but this decision is widely regarded as incorrect.

REFERENCES

1. *Victoria Laundry (Windsor) Ltd* v. *Newman Industries Ltd* [1949] 2 K.B. 528.
2. *East Ham BC* v. *Bernard Sunley & Sons Ltd* [1966] A.C. 406.
3. *Dodd Properties (Kent) Ltd* v. *Canterbury CC* [1980] 1 All E.R. 928.
4. *Hutchinson* v. *Harris* (1978) 10 B.L.R. 19.
5. *British Westinghouse Electric Co. Ltd* v. *Underground Electric Railways* [1912] A.C. 673.
6. *Mertens* v. *Home Freeholds Co. Ltd* [1921] 2 K.B. 526.
7. *Wraight Ltd.* v. *P.H. & T. (Holdings) Ltd* (1968) 13 B.L.R. 26.
8. *C. & P. Haulage* v. *Middleton* [1983] 3 All E.R. 94.
9. *Dunlop Pneumatic Tyre Co. Ltd* v. *New Garage & Motor Co. Ltd* [1915] A.C. 79.
10. *Ranger* v. *G.W. Railway* (1854) 5 H.L.C. 72.
11. *Public Works Commissioner* v. *Hills* [1906] A.C. 368.
12. *Gilbert-Ash (Northern) Ltd* v. *Modern Engineering (Bristol) Ltd* [1974] A.C. 689.
13. *BFI Group of Companies Ltd* v. *DCB Integration Systems Ltd* [1987] C.I.L.L. 348.
14. *Surrey Heath BC* v. *Lovell Construction Ltd* (1988) 42 B.L.R. 25.
15. *Temloc Ltd* v. *Errill Properties Ltd* (1987) 39 B.L.R. 30.
16. As is done by both JCT 80 and ICE 6.
17. *Peak Construction (Liverpool) Ltd* v. *McKinney Foundations Ltd* (1970) 1 B.L.R. 111.
18. *Rapid Building Group Ltd* v. *Ealing Family Housing Association Ltd* (1985) 29. B.L.R. 5.
19. *A. Bell & Son (Paddington) Ltd* v. *CBF Residential Care & Housing Association* (1989) 46 B.L.R. 102.
20. *Department of the Environment for Northern Ireland* v. *Farrans Construction Ltd* (1981) 19 B.L.R. 1.

23

Suspension, repudiation and determination

As we have seen in Chapter 22, the legal remedy of damages can be awarded for any breach of contract, whether major or trivial. This chapter deals with other remedies which are available for more serious breaches of contract. In particular, we are concerned with breaches of contract which lead to the work being stopped, either temporarily or permanently. This can come about in three ways, **suspension, determination** and **repudiation** each of which will be dealt with in turn.

23.1 SUSPENSION OF WORK

The general principle is that the contractor has no legal right to suspend work, and the employer has no legal right to order its suspension. Once the contract work has commenced, it is the contractor's obligation to carry it through in a regular fashion, and the employer's duty to do nothing which will hinder the contractor in this task. As a result, an unjustified suspension by either party will amount to a breach of contract for which damages may be claimed. Further, the circumstances of the suspension may be such as to show that the guilty party no longer intends to be bound by the contract. This may constitute a **repudiatory breach** (dealt with below), in which case the other party may terminate the contract altogether.

The general principle outlined above can, of course, be modified by express terms in the contract. Indeed, as seen in Chapter 14, many standard form contracts do give the employer power to order the suspension of all or part of the work. However, none of the main standard forms of building contract entitles the contractor to take such a step, although (ironically) there may be the more drastic remedy of bringing the contract to an end altogether.

It follows that while the suspension of work (or the threat of it) is in *practical* terms a potent weapon for a contractor who is in dispute with the employer, its *legal* basis is highly dubious. Although there is little legal authority on the point, it is probable that a contractor who stops work temporarily to exert pressure on the employer will be in breach of the obligation to proceed regularly and diligently with the work (as, for example, under JCT 80 clause 23.1). This was certainly the view of the New Zealand Court of Appeal in *Canterbury Pipe Lines Ltd* v. *Christchurch Drainage Board*.[1] It seems likely that an English court would adopt the same approach, at least where the contractor is complaining of non-certification by the contract administrator. However, the interpretation might well be different in the case of non-payment of certified sums by the employer.

Of course, the fact that a contractor's suspension of work may be a breach of contract does not necessarily mean that it is a *repudiatory* breach. As we shall see below, such a breach entitles the employer to throw the contractor off the site and employ a replacement. In *Hill* v. *Camden*[2] a virtual suspension of the contract work (by withdrawal of labour and most plant from the site, while retaining a presence through supervisory staff) was held by the Court of Appeal *not* to constitute repudiation. Indeed, it has even been held that a sub-contractor's threat to *suspend* work unless a claim for disruption was met showed, by its temporary nature, that there was no intention of *abandoning* the contract altogether.[3]

Although, as already mentioned, the standard forms of building contracts do not recognize suspension as a remedy, the JCT forms of *sub-contract* make provision for this where the main contractor fails to pay what is due. The JCT sub-contract, NSC/4 at clause 21.8, deals with the situation where a nominated sub-contractor has not been paid within 35 days of an interim certificate by either the contractor or the employer. In such circumstances, the nominated sub-contractor is entitled to give 14 days' written notice and then to suspend work. This is in fact the sub-contractor's *only* remedy short of arbitration or litigation since NSC/4 does not entitle sub-contractors to determine their employment on the ground of non-payment. Such a suspension of work will entitle the sub-contractor to an appropriate extension of time and to reimbursement for any direct loss and/or expense.

As far as domestic sub-contractors are concerned, DOM/1 clause 21.6 permits suspension of work 7 days after giving the main contractor notice of default. Again, the sub-contractor will be entitled to an extension of time and to compensation for direct loss and/or expense, and in this situation retains the ultimate power of determination for continued non-payment. However, the practical problems faced in invoking this provision should not be overlooked. To establish underpayment may require the domestic sub-contractor to disprove the main contractor's counter-claims for delay or defective work, matters which (unlike in nominated sub-contracts) are not independently assessed and certified by the contract administrator.

23.2   REPUDIATION AT COMMON LAW

Repudiation of a contract refers to the situation where the misconduct of one of the parties is so serious that the law gives the other party the option to bring the contract to an end. This section explores the issue of repudiation, contrasting it with determination, and examines the ways in which repudiation commonly happens in construction contracts.

23.2.1   Repudiation and determination distinguished

It is important at the outset to understand the distinction between the two concepts of **repudiation** and **determination**, and the legal consequences of that distinction. The common law right to 'repudiate' a contract can arise in either of two ways. First, one party may make it clear that it has no intention of performing its side of the bargain. Second, that party may be guilty of such a serious breach of contract that it must be treated as having that intention. In both cases, the innocent party has a choice: either to 'affirm' the contract and holding the other party to its obligations (while claiming damages as appropriate for the breach) or to 'accept the repudiation' and bring the contract to an end. If repudiation is opted for, then *both* parties are released from any further contractual obligation to perform. However, the terms of the contract remain relevant to such matters as establishing liability (e.g. where there is an exemption clause), assessing damages (including liquidated damages) and resolving disputes (e.g. where there is an arbitration clause).

By contrast, many building contracts make provision for 'determination of the contractor's employment' in specified circumstances. Not all of these circumstances amount to repudiatory breaches of contract; indeed, some of them are not breaches at all. Such 'determination' clauses normally lay down procedures (giving notice, etc.) which must be followed if the determination is to be effective. They also deal with the consequences, financial and otherwise, of determination.

Some events would justify repudiation of the contract at common law, as well as triggering a determination clause in the contract. What must be appreciated is that the innocent party has a completely free choice as to which remedy will be pursued. However, the innocent party must elect for one remedy or the other, and cannot combine the best elements of the two remedies in some complex way. Thus, for example, a party who seeks the favourable remedies provided by a contractual determination clause must follow the specified procedures. Failure so to do may result in having to rely on common law rights instead, but this can only be done if the contractor's breach is a repudiatory one.[4] Likewise, where a clause of the contract provides for determination in circumstances where the common law does not, the innocent party can *only* take whatever remedy the contract offers. This situation is exemplified by a case[5] in which a local authority contract provided that, in the event of unauthorized sub-contracting, the authority could either determine the contract or claim £100 liquidated damages. When the plaintiffs breached this provision, the defendant authority determined the contract, employed another contractor to complete the work and then sued the plaintiffs for their extra expense (a total of some £21 000). However, it was held that since the plaintiffs' breach would not have justified termination of the contract at common law, the defendants were limited to those remedies specifically given by the contract. These did not include unliquidated damages and so the plaintiffs' claim failed.

23.2.2   Nature and effect of repudiation

As mentioned above, repudiatory conduct by a contracting party does not of itself bring that contract to an end. This will come about only when the innocent party chooses to 'accept the repudiation' and notifies the guilty party to that effect. Such notification, once made, is irrevocable. Indeed, notification by the innocent party of intention to 'affirm' the contract is also irrevocable. Since intentions may be implied from conduct as well as expressed in words, it is important for the innocent party to make clear decisions and to act promptly upon them. In the Canadian case of *Pigott Construction* v. *W.J. Crowe Ltd*,[6] for instance, plastering sub-contractors were told in September that they would soon be required. However, due to delays arising because the main contractor failed (in breach of the main contract) to provide temporary heating, they were not called upon until the following April. It was held that, even if this delay could have been treated as repudiatory, the sub-contractors' failure to complain about it (despite inspecting the site in March) deprived them of the right to determine the sub-contract. As a result, the sub-contractors were not in a position to demand a renegotiation of their prices.

An even stronger case is *Felton* v. *Wharrie*[7] where, under a 42-day demolition contract with a liquidated damages provision, the contractor delayed beyond the completion date and, on being asked when he expected to finish, replied that he could not say. Thirteen days later, when the employer without warning entered the site and refused to allow the contractor to continue with the work, it was held that his purported 'acceptance' of the contractor's repudiatory breach came too late.

One particular problem which the law has not yet satisfactorily resolved is whether an innocent party who 'affirms' a contract can insist on carrying out that contract in the face of the other party's clear (though wrongful) wish to repudiate it. Such insistence has been upheld by a bare majority of the House of Lords in *White & Carter* v. *McGregor*.[8] However, it was accepted by at least one of the majority judges that this would not be so unless the person concerned had a 'legitimate interest' in performing the contract rather than claiming damages. In a later case, *Hounslow* v. *Twickenham*,[9] a contractor claimed to be entitled to continue with a JCT 63 contract which the employer had purported to repudiate. Megarry, J. was firmly of the opinion that the *White & Carter* principle did not apply where performance of the contract required the co-operation of the other party, especially where it consisted of work done on the other party's property. If this view is correct, it means that the *White & Carter* principle will seldom apply in the context of a building contract.

The *Hounslow* case raised another issue of enormous practical importance, and unfortunately dealt with it in a way which has attracted considerable criticism. It was there held that where an employer purports either to 'accept the contractor's repudiation' or to operate a contractual provision for determination but the contractor disputes the validity of the employer's act, the employer will not be entitled to an interim injunction compelling the contractor to leave the site. If this is correct, it means that the contractor can effectively prevent the employer from getting in another contractor to complete the work, even if it is later found that the employer's determination was perfectly valid. Such a conclusion creates an intolerable situation in practical terms, and it is significant that the decision has been rejected by an Official Referee in England[10] and by the High Court in New Zealand.[11]

23.2.3   Conduct amounting to repudiatory breach

General

It sometimes happens that one contracting party ('A') is in breach of contract and the other party ('B') treats this as a repudiatory breach, but it is later held that the breach in question was not sufficiently serious to have this effect. The question which then arises is whether this mistake means that B, who clearly intended no longer to be bound by the contract, is now guilty of a repudiatory breach! There are good reasons for suggesting that this *should* be the result since it enables the parties to know where they stand. However, the courts have shown some reluctance to punish a party for an honest but mistaken belief as to its rights and remedies, and it has thus been held by a majority of the House of Lords that to invoke a contractual remedy in error, unless it is totally abusive or in bad faith, does not in itself constitute repudiation of the contract.[12]

Employer's breach

Various acts by the employer can result in a repudiatory breach. These are listed and explained below:

- *Failure to give possession of the site*. While minor interference by the employer with the contractor's possession of the site is not a repudiatory breach,[13] an outright refusal to give possession in the first place will be so. Similarly, wrongful ejection of the contractor from the site is such a breach.[14] As to delay in giving possession, the crucial question (and it is one of degree) is whether the employer's conduct indicates an intention no longer to be bound by the contract. For example, where an employer delayed giving possession of the site for 2 months despite repeated requests from the contractor, and also announced that part of the contract work was to be omitted and given to another contractor, it was held that these two breaches, taken together, amounted to a repudiation of the contract.[15]

- *Non-payment of sums due*. As a general principle of contract law, failure to pay on time what is due will not be treated as a sufficient breach to justify the other party in terminating the contract.[16] More strongly, failure to pay on time what is owed on *another* contract will not be a repudiatory breach.[17] This, indeed, is why it is so common to find express rights of determination for non-payments. However, while late payment (or short payment) is not in itself repudiatory, a continued refusal to pay may become so.

  The practical problems which may arise in this area are exemplified by the case of *Bradley* v. *Jefco*,[18] in which a £113 000 sub-contract for electrical work was made orally, with no terms as to time or methods of payment (although it was accepted that interim payments were intended by the parties). After a succession of 5 payments which were both late and short, the plaintiff sub-contractors withdrew from the site, whereupon the defendant contractors threatened that after 7 days they would treat this as a repudiation and employ a substitute at the plaintiffs' expense. The plaintiffs then submitted a claim for £31 000, to which the defendants offered a mere £5000.

  On these facts it was held that the plaintiffs were not entitled to terminate the contract for the original failures to pay, and that they would thus have been guilty themselves of a repudiatory breach, had not the defendants waived this by giving them 7 days to return to work. However, the defendants' subsequent derisory offer was sufficient to shatter the plaintiffs' confidence in ever getting paid, and it thus justified them in bringing the contract to an end at that stage.

- *Withholding of certificates.* If the contract administrator refuses to certify at the appropriate time, or negligently under-certifies, this may well constitute a breach of contract on the employer's part. It certainly will do so if the contract administrator's conduct is due to positive interference by the employer. Such events will undoubtedly enable the contractor to claim damages, or possibly to recover what is due without the necessity of a certificate.[19] Whether they will justify termination of the contract will once again depend on whether the breach is sufficiently serious to be regarded as repudiatory.
- *Hindrance of the contractor.* A breach by the employer of the duties of non-hindrance and positive co-operation may be so serious as to indicate an intention not to be bound. This was held to be the case where an employer wrongfully ordered the contractor not to complete the work.[20] It was also held to be so where the employer failed to provide the necessary drawings as required by the contract.[21]

Contractor's breach

Various events may give rise to an accusation that a contractor has repudiated the contract. These fall under the following groups:

- *Abandonment or suspension of the work.* Perhaps the most obvious example of 'repudiatory breach' by a contractor is total abandonment of the work in circumstances where this is unjustified.[22] Whether less extreme action by the contractor will have this effect is, as usual, a question of fact and degree. For instance, contractors who were complaining of late payment retaliated by withdrawing their labour and most of their plant from the site and thus slowed down progress considerably. However, they retained a presence on site through their supervisory staff, and they did not discourage their sub-contractors from working. It was held by the Court of Appeal that these tactics did not amount to repudiation by the contractors.[23]
- *Defective work.* As a general principle which applies to lump sum contracts, defects in the work do not entitle the employer to refuse payment altogether. The only remedy is to claim damages for the cost of rectification.[24] However, very serious defects may justify the conclusion that there has not been 'substantial performance' by the

contractor. Where this can be established, the employer need pay nothing. For example, the installation of a central heating system at an inclusive price of £560 was defectively carried out. The system was only 90% efficient (70% in some rooms) and gave off fumes in the living-room. The Court of Appeal held that the plaintiff was entitled to nothing for this work; the defendant was not limited to setting off the £174 which it would cost to put right the defects.[25]

It is even possible that an accumulation of lesser defects may amount to a repudiatory breach of contract, even though none of them would be sufficient on their own. It was held in *Sutcliffe* v. *Chippendale & Edmondson*[26] that contractors' 'manifest inability to comply with the completion date requirements, the nature and number of complaints from sub-contractors and their own admission that... the quality of work was deteriorating and the number of defects was multiplying' entitled the employer to order them off the site. The employer had justifiably concluded that the contractors had neither the ability, competence or the will to complete the work in accordance with the contract.

- *Delay*. For delay by a contractor to justify the employer in bringing the contract to an end at common law, it must be shown either that the delay is so great as to demonstrate the contractor's intention not to be bound by the contract or that time is 'of the essence'. This latter point will be satisfied if the contract expressly makes time of the essence, or if this can be implied (which will seldom be the case in a building contract); furthermore, once delay has occurred, the innocent party may make time of the essence (where it is not already so) by giving reasonable notice.
- *Miscellaneous*. As a final reminder that the question whether a breach of contract is sufficiently serious to be treated as a repudiation is one of fact and degree, we may take two examples. In a South African case, failure by a contractor to obtain a required performance bond was held repudiatory.[27] However, an opposite conclusion was reached in respect of a contractor who sub-contracted in contravention of an express term in the contract.[28]

23.3 DETERMINATION UNDER JCT 80 AND RELATED SUB-CONTRACTS

As explained above, building contracts commonly provide for the contract to be brought to an end in various circumstances, some but not all of which concern a breach of contract by one of the parties. We now consider the 'determination' clauses of JCT 80 and its related sub-contracts NSC/4 and DOM/1.

23.3.1 Determination by the employer under clause 27

Grounds for determination

Clause 27.1 entitles the employer to determine the contractor's employment for certain defaults, namely:

1. Suspension of work without reasonable cause.
2. Failure to proceed regularly and diligently.
3. Failure to comply with a contract administrator's instruction to remove defective work, so that the works are materially affected.
4. Unauthorized assignment or sub-contracting.

Clause 27.3 (which now applies to private as well as to local authority versions) entitles the employer to determine the contractor's employment if the latter (directly or via employees) is guilty of corrupt practices relating to the obtaining or execution of contracts. The difference between this and the previous group is that here there are no notification procedures to be complied with.

Clause 27.2 makes provision for automatic determination of the contractor's employment on certain events which, in effect, means 'contractor's insolvency'.

Procedures

Where the contractor is guilty of any of the defaults specified in clause 27.1, the contract administrator is to issue a written notice specifying the default. If the default is then continued for 14 days, or is repeated at any time, the employer may within 10 days of the continuance or repetition determine the contractor's employment by issuing a notice to this effect. It is expressly provided that the notice of determination is not to be given 'unreasonably or vexatiously'. This would presumably prevent the employer from using a technical breach of contract which is causing no loss (e.g. unauthorized sub-contracting of some unimportant part of the work) to escape from a disadvantageous contract.

Both the notices are supposed to be sent to the contractor by registered post or recorded delivery. It has been held by courts in the Commonwealth[29] that conditions governing the method of sending notices must be strictly complied with, if the notices are to be valid. However, it seems that the English courts take a more liberal approach and will uphold a notice which actually arrives, irrespective of the method used.[30] Furthermore, a notice which fails to satisfy the contractual requirements may still be a valid notice of repudiation at common law (provided, of course, that the contractor is guilty of a sufficient breach to justify the employer in taking this step).

A good example of the last point is provided by a case in which main contractors sent a letter to labour-only sub-contractors, requiring them to comply with a condition which dealt with the length of the working day. Eleven months later and without further warning, the main contractors sent a telex purporting to terminate the sub-contract for breach of this condition. It was held that this telex did not comply with the contractual provisions for termination after due warning, since a reasonable person would have seen no connection between the two notices. However, it was a valid termination of the contract at common law.[31]

Consequences of determination

Clause 27.4 sets out the rights and duties of the parties following a determination of the contractor's employment under clause 27. The position, briefly, is as follows:

1. The employer may employ others to complete the works, and may for this purpose make use of the contractor's temporary buildings, plant, tools, equipment and materials.
2. The employer may (except where the determination occurs because of the contractor's insolvency) insist on taking an assignment from the contractor of all sub-contracts. The employer may then pay sub-contractors directly and recover any sums so paid from the contractor.
3. All of the contractor's equipment, etc. must be removed from the site, but only when the contract administrator has given the instruction so to do.
4. The contractor is not entitled to any further payment until the works are completed (by another contractor). The entitlement is then the difference (if any) between what would have been earned by completing the contract and what the breach has cost the employer (the expenses incurred in completion, plus any direct loss and/or damage). If the employer's losses exceed what would have been due to the contractor, the latter is liable for the difference.

23.3.2   Determination by the contractor under clause 28

Grounds for determination

Clause 28.1 entitles the contractor to determine his or her employment on various grounds which may be loosely described as 'defaults' of either the employer or the contract administrator; these are:

1. Failure by the employer to meet the contractor's demand for payment

within 7 days, following the employer's failure to pay a sum certified by the contract administrator within 14 days.

2. Interference by the employer with the issue of any certificate.
3. Suspension of the whole, or substantially the whole, of the works for a continuous period stated in the Appendix (one month is recommended in the footnote) by one or more of 5 specified events. Within this list reference to employers and contractors include those for whom each is responsible. These are:

(a) contract administrator's instructions dealing with discrepancies in the contract documents, variations or postponement of work, unless these are caused by negligence or default of the contractor (*not* including nominated sub-contractors);

(b) late issue by the contract administrator of instructions, drawings, etc. for which the contractor applied in writing;

(c) delay by the employer in executing work or supplying materials;

(d) inspection or testing of work under clause 8.3, including making good, where the work is shown to be in accordance with the contract;

(e) failure by the employer to give such access over its own land adjoining the site as is specified in the contract bills or drawings, or otherwise agreed by the contract administrator and the contractor.

Clause 28.1.4 of the Private editions of JCT 80 provides for determination on certain events which, in effect, mean 'employer's insolvency'.

Procedures

On all the above grounds (including the employer's insolvency), contractors may determine their employment by sending a written notice by registered post or recorded delivery, either to the employer or the contract administrator. Unlike cases of determination by the employer, there is no requirement of a 'warning shot'. However, clause 28 does contain the same prohibition on giving notice 'unreasonably or vexatiously'. In this connection, it is worth noting that all the 'suspension of work' grounds are also matters in respect of which the contractor would be entitled to an extension of time and to compensation for direct loss and/or expense. The availability of these alternative methods of safeguarding the contractor's interests might well make it seem unreasonable to determine in any but the most serious of cases.

Consequences of determination

Clause 28.2 compels the contractor to remove all equipment and materials from the site and to make it possible for sub-contractors to do likewise. This must be done with all reasonable dispatch, but with all necessary safety precautions. In the meantime, the provisions of clause 20 regarding liability for certain kinds of injury or damage remain in operation.

As to payment, the contractor is entitled to:

1. The value of all work completed at the date of determination.
2. The value of all work begun but not completed at that date.
3. The cost of materials ordered by the contractor (which then become the employer's property).
4. The contractor's costs of removal from the site.
5. Any direct loss and/or expense arising out of other matters for which the contractor has a claim.
6. Any direct loss and/or expense caused to the contractor by the determination.

23.3.3   Determination on neutral grounds

There are circumstances beyond the control of both parties which can give rise to determination of the contract. Surprisingly, perhaps, JCT 80 has not collected all of these into a single clause.

Clause 28A

Under clause 28 of the original version of JCT 80, determination by the contractor was enabled where the contract work was suspended by certain causes which could be regarded as 'neutral' (i.e. the fault of neither the employer nor the contractor). This rather unfair situation has now been amended by the creation of clause 28A, which in certain circumstances entitles either party to determine the contractor's employment by written notice which is not to be given unreasonably or vexatiously. The relevant circumstances are where the whole, or substantially the whole, of the contract works is suspended for a continuous period stated in the Appendix by *force majeure* or civil commotion (one month is recommended in the footnote) or by loss or damage to the works caused by a 'Specified Peril' (3 months). In relation to the last ground, clause 28A.2 cannot be relied upon if the event has arisen out of the contractor's own negligence or default. This includes negligence or default of those for whom the contractor is responsible (including nominated sub-contractors).

The consequences of determination under clause 28A are identical to those under clause 28, with the exception that the contractor is not entitled to reimbursement for any direct loss and/or expense caused by the determination.

Clause 22C

Where the contract consists of work on an existing structure and the insurance provisions of clause 22C are stated in the Appendix to apply, an additional ground of determination exists which overlaps rather awkwardly with clause 28A. It is provided by clause 22C.4 that if loss or damage to any part of the work is caused by a specified peril (whether or not due to negligence on the part of the contractor), then either the employer or the contractor may within 28 days serve written notice to determine the contractor's employment. The effectiveness of such a notice depends upon the very vague criterion of whether determination would be 'just and equitable', and the other party is given 7 days to take this question to arbitration.

   If the contractor's employment is indeed determined under this clause, the financial consequences are identical to those under clause 28A. If it is not (because neither party serves notice, or because a notice is successfully challenged at arbitration), the contractor is entitled to be paid for necessary works of restoration and repair as if for a variation.

Clause 32

One further possibility for determination of the contract lies in clause 32, which enables either the contractor or the employer to determine the contract in the event of an 'outbreak of hostilities'. This is defined in such a way as to involve the general mobilization of the armed forces. To determine under this clause, notice has to be served within the prescribed time limits.

   Without such a clause, the question of continuing with the contract would have to be examined in the light of the doctrine of frustration of contract.

23.3.4 Determination under sub-contracts

In general terms, the determination clauses of both NSC/4 and DOM/1 follow, 'one step down', those of JCT 80, as regards both the grounds for determination and the consequences. However, there are some significant differences, both between main contract and sub-contract determination and also between domestic and nominated sub-contracts. The most important of these points are as follows.

Grounds for determination

Clause 29 of both NSC/4 and DOM/1 provides for determination of the sub-contractor's employment by the main contractor. The grounds are virtually identical to those on which the employer may determine the main contract (JCT 80 clause 27), although DOM/1 differs in having no provision for 'corruption' and in making determination on the sub-contractor's insolvency discretionary rather than automatic.

By clause 30 of both forms the sub-contractor is entitled to determine if the contractor, without reasonable cause, either wholly suspends the works or fails to proceed with the works so as to materially affect sub-contract progress. In addition, DOM/1 provides for determination in cases of non-payment. (The contractor's obligation under clause 21 of DOM/1 is to make interim payments on a monthly basis, within 17 days of each falling due.) Although this appears to give a domestic sub-contractor a valuable extra remedy (a nominated sub-contractor's protection lies in suspension and the invoking of any 'direct payment' provision), the practical problems should not be overlooked. What is due to a domestic sub-contractor at any given time is not something which is independently assessed by the contract administrator or quantity surveyor and, as a result, it may be extremely difficult to prove underpayment and thus justify determination.

Clause 31 of both sub-contract forms provides for automatic determination of the sub-contractor's employment if the main contractor's employment is itself determined under JCT 80 clauses 27, 28 or 28A.

Procedures and consequences

While the provisions of JCT 80 are again followed to a great extent, two procedural points are worth mentioning:

1. Determination by both domestic and nominated sub-contractors requires two notices, a 'warning shot' followed by the actual notice of determination. For no very obvious reason, the minimum period between these is 14 days under NSC/4 but 10 days under DOM/1.
2. A nominated sub-contractor's employment is only to be determined by the main contractor in close consultation with the contract administrator, who effectively has a veto on this.

As to the financial and other consequences of determination in sub-contract cases, once again the JCT 80 pattern is largely adhered to, but it should be noted that DOM/1 quite remarkably makes no provision for the sub-contractor to claim for direct loss and/or expense arising out of the determination, even where this has come about through the default of the main contractor or the employer. By contrast, NSC/4 does protect the sub-contractor in this respect. It allows recovery of loss from the contractor on determination under clause 30 (or under clause 31 based on the contractor's default). On determination under clause 31 based on the employer's default, the sub-contractor is entitled to a fair and reasonable proportion of what is paid to the main contractor for work done and losses incurred.

REFERENCES

1. *Canterbury Pipe Lines Ltd* v. *Christchurch Drainage Board* (1979) 16 B.L.R. 76.
2. *J.M. Hill & Sons Ltd* v. *Camden LBC* (1980) 18 B.L.R. 31.
3. *F. Treliving & Co. Ltd* v. *Simplex Time Recorder Co. (UK) Ltd* (1981, unreported).
4. *Architectural Installation Services Ltd* v. *James Gibbons Windows Ltd* (1989) 46 B.L.R. 91.
5. *Thomas Feather & Co. (Bradford) Ltd* v. *Keighley Corporation* (1953) 53 L.G.R. 30.
6. *Pigott Construction* v. *W.J. Crowe Ltd* (1961) 27 D.L.R. (2d) 258.
7. *Felton* v. *Wharrie* (1906) H.B.C., 4th edn, Vol. 2, 398.
8. *White & Carter (Councils) Ltd* v. *McGregor* [1962] A.C. 413.
9. *Hounslow LBC* v. *Twickenham Garden Developments Ltd* [1971] Ch. 233.
10. *Tara Civil Engineering Ltd* v. *Moorfield Developments Ltd* (1989) 46 B.L.R. 72.
11. *Mayfield Holdings Ltd* v. *Moana Reef Ltd* [1973] 1 N.Z.L.R. 309.
12. *Woodar Investment Development Ltd* v. *Wimpey Construction UK Ltd* [1980] 1 All E.R. 571.
13. *Earth & General Contracts Ltd* v. *Manchester Corporation* (1958) 108 L.J. 665.
14. *Roberts* v. *Bury Commissioners* (1870) L.R. 4 C.P. 755.
15. *Carr* v. *J.A. Berriman Pty Ltd* (1953) 27 A.L.J. 273.
16. *Mersey Steel & Iron Co.* v. *Naylor, Benzon & Co.* (1884) 9 App. Cas. 434.
17. *Small & Sons Ltd* v. *Middlesex Real Estates Ltd* [1921] W.N. 245.
18. *D.R. Bradley (Cable Jointing) Ltd* v. *Jefco Mechanical Services Ltd* (1988) 6-C.L.D.-07-19.
19. *Perini Corporation* v. *Commonwealth of Australia* (1969) 12 B.L.R. 82.
20. *Cort* v. *Ambergate, Nottingham, Boston & Eastern Junction Railway Co.* (1851) 17 O.B. 127.
21. *Kingdom* v. *Cox* (1848) 5 C.B. 522.
22. *Marshall* v. *Mackintosh* (1898) 78 L.T. 750.
23. *J.M. Hill & Sons Ltd* v. *Camden LBC* (1980) 18 B.L.R. 31.
24. *Hoenig* v. *Isaacs* [1952] 2 All E.R. 176.
25. *Bolton* v. *Mahadeva* [1972] 2 All E.R. 1322.
26. *Sutcliffe* v. *Chippendale & Edomondson* (1971) 18 B.L.R. 149.
27. *Swartz & Son (Pty) Ltd* v. *Wolmaranstadt Town Council* 1960 (2) S.A. 1.
28. *Thomas Feather & Co. (Bradford) Ltd* v. *Keighley Corporation* (1953) 53 L.G.R. 30.
29. *Eriksson* v. *Whalley* [1971] 1 N.S.W.L.R. 397 (Australia); *Central Provident Fund Board* v. *Ho Bock Kee* (1981) 17 B.L.R. 21 (Singapore).

30. *Goodwin* v. *Fawcett* (1965) 175 E.G. 27; *J.M. Hill & Sons Ltd* v. *Camden LBC* (1980) 18 B.L.R. 31.
31. *Architectural Installation Services Ltd* v. *James Gibbons Windows Ltd* (1989) 49 B.L.R. 91.

24

Non-litigious dispute resolution

Contractual disputes in construction arise because of a series of factors which combine in various ways to produce arguments, disagreements and, ultimately, disputes. Some of these factors are basic to all disputes between humans such as the motivating factors of individuals, human behaviour, organizational behaviour, culture, etc. What makes construction contract disputes different is the nature of the dispute. This, again, depends upon a variety of things such as the terms of the contract, the technological issues of the site and the building, the character of the project personnel, the amount of time and money available, the realism (or otherwise) of people's expectations, project environmental factors, the legal basis of the argument, the magnitude of the issue, and so on. The third group of variables in this area concerns the choice of methods for resolving disputes once they have arisen. What are the options available in the contract, and what other options are there? These are the topics confronted in this chapter.

24.1 BACKGROUND TO DISPUTES

24.1.1 General factors

In trying to understand why disputes occur on building contracts, the key clearly lies with the fact that *people* are interacting in some way. Although many disputes are based upon arguments about technical or legal points, disagreement continues because the *people* involved in the argument can become intransigent. Pride or ignorance may sometimes be more important in influencing the outcome of a disagreement than the nature of the dispute. Researchers into human behaviour have outlined a variety of things which affect the way in which we interact with other people.[1] Chief among these are such ideas as the motivating factors of individuals, human behaviour, organizational behaviour, culture, etc. An understanding of these issues highlights the fact that disputes arise not just because people are entering into building contracts, but rather because a wide variety of people are interacting on a project.

Motivating factors of individuals

It is often assumed that those who work on building projects all have a common objective, but it has been shown, and indeed it is fairly self-evident upon reflection, that most people bring with them very different sets of objectives. These personal objectives can be very difficult indeed to predict, partly because people are from a wide range of backgrounds. The fact that people are from different organizations will also affect their interest in a project. However, this does not mean that all the people from any one organization will have similar objectives. Objectives are influenced by people's upbringing, their education, their family and friends, and even radio and television! To make matters even more complex, objectives change for an individual as time goes by. The complexity of objectives is thus that they can be personal and/or organizational, as well as dynamic. This inherent flux and likelihood of mismatch means that conflict can develop and escalate very quickly.

Pre-conceptions about roles

Another factor which influences the development and escalation of conflict is the fact that most people involved on a building project bring with them a pre-conceived notion about what their role ought to be. An architect will expect to be doing certain things and taking certain decisions. In the same way, an engineer, a quantity surveyor and a builder will all have very definite ideas not only about their own roles, but also about the roles of others. These expectations are often modified by personal objectives and can thus be yet another source of conflict. In addition, the definite and entrenched views which construction professionals have about their expected roles makes it difficult to introduce new systems of building procurement.

Of course, one participant who may well have no preconceptions of this kind is the client. This person is frequently new to the building process and finds it full of surprises! An extremely important function for an architect or project manager is to explain to the client at the earliest opportunity what the conditions of contract actually mean. The client needs to be told in plain English the extent and nature of what is being promised, and by whom it is being promised. If the client understands this, many disputes can be avoided.

Project success or failure

In the light of these issues, it is not at all surprising that conflict on building projects leads to disputes which can very quickly become acrimonious. These disputes, if not dealt with swiftly and equitably, can ruin everybody's chances of 'success', by which we mean the satisfying of one or more of their objectives. In this connection, it is as well to reflect that since objectives are so diverse, it is just as easy for everyone to be satisfied as it is for everybody to be dissatisfied. In other words, each individual's potential for success within a building project is not necessarily at the expense of the others' potential. This is contrary to the seemingly prevalent belief that avarice and conflict are the only routes to success in construction!

The roots of contractual dispute

In order to identify the type of dispute, it is essential to examine the position of the parties in terms of the amount of time and money available, project environmental factors, the magnitude of the issue, and so on. Of particular importance are the duties of the parties to the contract. Contractual disputes tend to arise when one party alleges that the other party has not kept its part of the bargain. Since the performance or non-performance of obligations is at the root of any contractual dispute, it follows that the contracting parties must have a very clear understanding about what it is they are undertaking.

Business relations

A further point which affects the origin of disputes is the preservation of good business relations. There are often circumstances where the parties to the contract are from the same business environment and will probably be contracting with each other again in the future. In these circumstances, they are likely to understand both the rules and each other's needs and requirements. For the sake of future business, they will seek effective and quick resolution of points of disagreement. This is particularly marked in civil engineering, where the client is usually the government or some other public agency. Contractors are very keen to preserve a good relationship with such a client.

On the other hand, there are circumstances where one party is deliberately obstructive and seeks to exploit every possible opportunity to its limit. This can happen where the parties are not likely to work together in the future. In the building industry, as opposed to civil engineering, most work is done in the private sector (about 60–65%), and the number of disputes is much larger as a consequence.

24.1.2 The nature of construction disputes

What are construction contract disputes about? The first factor which defines the nature of a construction dispute is the terms of the contract. Basically a contract is an enforceable promise. And the subject of this enforceable promise is the production of a unique, technical artefact, using temporary management systems.

Enforceable promises

Building contracts, like any other contract, are concerned with making promises, with the expectation that one can be forced to carry them out. A person who has no intention of doing a thing should not sign a contract which says that there is such an intention!

Of course, it can happen that people enter into contracts which they did not completely intend. A shared mistake is no real problem, as the parties can rectify it by mutual consent. However, what sometimes happens is that one party claims, due to oversight or mistake, to have signed a contract which does not accurately reflect his or her intentions. If there is a difference of interpretation, then the type of contract will be important in terms of the way in which it will be interpreted. If it is not a standard form contract, the principle of *contra proferentem* will prevail. This means that any ambiguity in the contract will be construed against the party who seeks to benefit by exclusions or limitations in it. This will usually (although not always) be the party which put it forward.

It is during disagreements about the intentions of contracting parties that such details as notes of telephone conversations, minutes of meetings, correspondence, and the like, may become relevant. These seek to provide evidence of the parties' intentions. However, it will in most cases be too late for the dissenting party to alter the contract. Building contracts, as we have seen, are very comprehensive and specific about what is expected of each party, and it is difficult to claim that the obligations which arise from entering into such a contract were not properly understood at the time it was made.

Technical matters

Disagreements often arise over technical questions. The technology involved in construction is idiosyncratic, difficult to understand and subject to change. Added to this is the change which may be associated with the technology of the client organization. The use of different and/or unfamiliar techniques is often the cause of arguments and disagreements.

For example, the nature of the site is often a source of contention. While the site itself is clearly visible at ground level, it can hold many surprises once excavation starts. It is not enough merely to look at a site in order to ascertain the site conditions. The part where the building is going to sit is actually several metres below the part which is visible. Adequate site investigation is a constant source of problems in the industry. Whose responsibility is it? In order to answer that question, one must look at the clauses in the contract. Are they what is intended? It is depressing to realize how many clients are shocked to discover the extent of their liability for site conditions once problems arise.

Disputes which escalate to arbitration or litigation often hinge on an intricate understanding of some particular technical matter. For example, the failure of the Emley Moor television transmitter;[2] a large tower fell down in a storm, on a moor, in the middle of the night. Nobody actually saw it fall down. How did it fall down? What caused it? Was it the wind, the rain, the frost, creep, metal fatigue, foundation failure or something else? It is a purely technical question to ascertain the cause of such a problem. Once the cause is identified, it is a fairly straightforward matter to allocate blame and with it legal responsibility.

Legal matters

Some disputes are technically simple and turn on what is the law on a specific point. The law is not infinite! There are many day-to-day occurrences which have not been decided upon previously by learned judges. There are many spheres of activity which are not covered by statute. The resolution of a dispute may well hinge upon the ascertainment of the law in a previously undefined area. Also, even where there are statutes or precedents, they may be inappropriate in the particular case. No two cases are identical, so there are often considerable difficulties to overcome in interpreting and applying the law.

One particular legal problem area arises from the doctrine of privity of contract. A basic characteristic of a contract is that it binds only the parties to it; a building contract is between the employer and the contractor, and does not confer rights or impose liabilities upon third parties. The rights and duties of consultants, such as the architect, are dealt with in contracts between them and the employer (conditions of engagement). It is a sad fact that this series of agreements are rarely consistent with each other.

Entitlement and magnitude

The rough division of disputes into **technical** and **legal** is often reflected in two aspects of a claim. The first aspect is that for any claim to succeed legal entitlement to the money must first be proven. After this, the magnitude of the claim must be established. Entitlement arises from the legal interpretation of the contract and associated documents. Magnitude then follows as a factual ascertainment of technical data. In consequence, most disputes contain elements of both types of dispute.

24.1.3   The role of the contract administrator

One of the most distinctive features of construction contracts in the UK is the part played by the contract administrator (whether described as 'Architect', 'Engineer', 'Supervising Officer', 'Project Manager' or whatever). In fact the contract administrator plays not one part but two in a construction project: first, as agent for the employer in such matters as the issue of instructions; and second, as an impartial decision-maker in such matters as certification and the valuation of variations and other claims. The latter role is obviously of considerable relevance to the topics now under discussion – decisions of the contract administrator may avoid or resolve potential disputes, although it must be said that such decisions are often the *cause* of disputes!

The legal principles which govern a contract administrator's certification and decision-making functions are considered in Chapter 14.

24.2   METHODS OF DISPUTE RESOLUTION

It is sometimes, perhaps too often, thought that any dispute which arises out of a construction contract must be resolved by court action or arbitration. This is simply not true! Whether or not there is an arbitration agreement in the contract, it must always be remembered that contracting parties can alter the terms of their contract *at any time, by mutual consent*. This fact is not stressed, or even hinted at, in the clauses of many JCT building contracts. The ICE 6 form, by contrast, introduces a procedure which is designed to exercise the negotiated approaches before resorting to more litigious routes. In any event, whatever the contract says, in a dispute the parties are *not* compelled to resort to the courts for the settling of their differences. They can choose instead to attempt to settle their differences amicably. Of course, if this should happen, it is extremely important to record exactly what has been agreed, and to have it signed by both parties, in case of any future disagreement about what was agreed!

A variety of techniques is available to help the parties come to some form of settlement without resorting to arbitration or litigation. They are known collectively as 'Alternative Dispute Resolution' (ADR) procedures. These procedures are informal, and the terminology which is used to describe them is rather loose and vague. Their chief features are that they are cheap, non-binding and investigatorial rather than accusatorial. Although they are informal, there are currently moves afoot to formalize them. These moves are discussed below in section 24.3.

The terms most commonly found to describe these procedures are 'Conciliation', 'Quasi-conciliation', 'Mediation', 'Private Enquiry', 'Adjudication' and 'Mini-trial'. However, these terms are often used interchangeably, and sometimes inconsistently. Collectively, they may be referred to as **reconciliation**, as Shilston[3] points out. Reconciliation, as a generic term, indicates private, non-adversarial methods of resolving disagreement. It is Shilston's pattern of definitions which form the basis for those given below.

These techniques can be seen as an intermediate step between having an argument or disagreement and referring to the courts. Since reconciliation is voluntary, either party may pull out at any time and refer the matter to the courts instead, if satisfactory progress is not being made. What is more, the parties are not bound to accept the decisions of the person deciding the issue.

24.2.1   Arbitration and litigation

These two methods of dispute resolution (discussed in detail in Chapter 25) are adversarial in nature. Contrary stances have to be taken, and this frequently results in people becoming entrenched in their views. Often in arbitration, and always in litigation, the parties are represented by counsel whose skill and ability lies in the art of arguing and scoring points over each other; they 'play' the adversarial roles with much skill. Unfortunately, this is not conducive to amicable settlement. The expense of litigious actions is so enormous that most cases are settled out of court shortly before they are planned to begin. This is once the parties have done all their preparation and are aware of each other's stance. The scale of costs leaps up once an action starts in court, and there is no certainty for either side of winning their costs. This is why so many cases are settled 'on the steps of the courtroom'.

24.2.2   Conciliation

A 'conciliator' must be absolutely independent of the parties to the contract. Impartiality is essential since the purpose of this process is to precipitate an agreement by persuasion and suggestion. Conciliators do not take sides, take decisions or make judgments. They talk to each party in private, and must be sure not to reveal anything to the other party. Confidentiality is essential in order for discussions to be frank and meaningful. The conciliator may bring the parties together after a while for an open discussion, which he or she chairs and leads.

The conciliator will be seeking to establish common ground, ascertaining the facts which are in dispute. In order to undertake this function effectively, the conciliator needs considerable knowledge of construction disputes. There may be previous judicial precedents which are appropriate to refer to, and the conciliator must be able to advise the parties of these, if necessary.

Where conciliation is adopted, it is ultimately up to the parties themselves to reach an agreement, and to decide upon the precise terms of that agreement.

24.2.3 Quasi-conciliation

Although it is a variation on the procedure described above, quasi-conciliation starts in a very different way. It comes about when one of the parties unilaterally appoints an expert professional to advise on a dispute, perhaps in order to obtain a second opinion. The purpose of the appointment is not simply to maximize the return on a claim, as would be the case where a claims consultant is engaged, but rather to help the party to overcome some technical or contractual difficulty. The investigator may be appointed to discover the facts and to make a recommendation to the party about how to proceed. It is often the case that this quasi-conciliator will need to talk to the other party and find out exactly what is at issue. If the other party also appoints such a professional, then the two of them may get together and compare their findings and their conclusions. In theory at least, they ought to do this impartially.

This type of process is often likely to happen in the public sector, because it is very difficult for a public sector agency simply to appoint such a person without compromising their accountability. However, a contractor can appoint someone unilaterally. In this case, it is not unheard of for the public sector agency to listen to an impartial second opinion.

Once the quasi-conciliator has reached a decision, a report is made to the client which can then be used as a negotiating instrument. In addition, if the dispute continues and goes to court, the report may be used as evidence.

24.2.4 Mediation

This procedure is like an extended version of conciliation. The initial stages will probably follow a very similar process, often referred to as 'shuttle diplomacy', as the mediator consults first with one party and then with the other. However, the end of this process is very different from conciliation, in that if no negotiated settlement results from the process, the mediator will make recommendations to settle based on his or her findings. This process accordingly retains the flexibility of conciliation, while encouraging a slightly more interventionist role for the mediator. As a result, it tends to be less open-ended. It is expected that neither party will pull out and that both will accept the decision of the mediator. It is also expected that this process will give the parties a useful indication of the outcome of an arbitration. This is probably why recourse to arbitration seldom follows mediation.

24.2.5   Private enquiry

This procedure involves the appointment of an independent professional to investigate some aspect of the project. It is commonly used for highly technical disputes, but it is also valuable where the issues to be resolved are sensitive ones. Because the uses to which such enquiries are put are so wide-ranging, there is no fixed procedure for such an enquiry; it has to be created each time to suit the occasion. On the basis of the report produced, the parties are in a much better position to negotiate and reach a settlement.

It is very important that the appointee is given precise terms of reference in order that he or she can identify and carry out the intended task. Where this is done, it is usually found that private enquiries discover technical facts much more quickly than would a judicial enquiry. This is partly at least because arbitrators and judges are prohibited from using their own experience, and must reach a decision purely on the basis of what is put before them. This is by contrast with a private enquiry, where the person conducting the enquiry can make use of personal knowledge and professional expertise in arriving at a conclusion.

One of the greatest benefits of a private enquiry is its speed. It is interesting to note that the private enquiries set up to investigate the Lockerbie air disaster and the King's Cross fire came to their conclusions after a few months had elapsed. This is by stark contrast to litigation. As an example, the case of *IBA* v. *EMI and BICC*[2] arose out of a storm on 19 March 1969 which brought down a television mast. That case finally came to rest in the House of Lords, in 1980, after nearly 12 years of litigation.

24.2.6   Adjudication

The part played by the contract administrator in resolving actual or potential disputes has been mentioned earlier in this chapter, and is dealt with in some detail in Chapter 14. That function requires the contract administrator to act impartially in a quasi-judicial manner, and concern has often been expressed that this may conflict with the person's other role as agent for the employer. It is partly such concerns which have led to the creation of a technique for the resolution of disputes known as 'adjudication'. Under this method, which is advocated by the British Property Federation[4] and adopted in a number of the JCT sub-contracts,[5] the contract provides that disputes over certain matters are to be referred to an independent adjudicator. This person is then expected to make a quick decision on the matter, which the parties agree to treat as temporarily binding, but which is without prejudice to their eventual rights as determined by arbitration or litigation.

The prime objective of this procedure is to enable the construction process to continue, rather than holding it up until rights and obligations can be finally determined. This is particularly beneficial in the case of sub-contracts, where the client is not personally concerned in a dispute between the contractor and the sub-contractor. Swift adjudication of such a dispute means that the client does not suffer by having the project delayed.

The basis of this system, then, is that for the duration of the contract there is always a person available to whom a dispute can be referred. This decision is not legally enforceable in the sense that the decision of a judge or arbitrator is enforceable. However, by signing a contract which includes a provision for adjudication, the parties are indicating that they intend to accept the adjudicator's decision.

In theory, there could be considerable problems associated with the use of adjudication, including the following:

1. The role seems to be quasi-judicial, which might lead the courts to rule that an adjudicator cannot be held liable for decisions reached negligently, except where they are based on the adjudicator's own knowledge or experience[6,7] However, a recent case shows that the adjudicator does not have the same status as an arbitrator since any decision of the adjudicator is not a final award which is definitive of the rights of the parties. Since it is an interim award, it is not definitive, and it cannot be enforced in a summary judgment.[8] This decision seems to threaten the usefulness of the role of an adjudicator. It will be interesting to watch developments in the law in this area.
2. Presumably the system will tend towards an adversarial one because parties who refer to an adjudicator are in disagreement and will have to state their respective cases. This will encourage acrimony.
3. There is also the fear that the project team may neglect to make proper decisions on technical questions such as quality of concrete, for example, leaving such matters instead to the Adjudicator.

For the moment at least, these problems remain theoretical. However, while the BPF system is infrequently used, the same cannot be said of the

JCT sub-contracts which incorporate adjudication provisions. It seems likely therefore that such questions will have to be confronted sooner rather than later.

24.2.7 Mini-trial

This procedure actually requires the disputing parties to present their cases to a Board which consists of themselves! To be more precise, it means that representatives of the employer's and contractor's organizations will conduct something like a 'trial' in front of a panel of senior executives from those organizations. It is important that this group should have the necessary authority to reach and implement decisions, and also that its members should not have been personally involved in the dispute up to this point.

Strictly speaking, this does not really fit the definition of 'Reconciliation', given above, because it is adversarial in nature. The two parties are expected to take opposite stances and to argue their cases in front of the panel. Having heard the evidence, the panel can then negotiate their respective positions until they reach agreement.

24.3 INCORPORATING ADR PROCEDURES

Although, at the present time, most of the techniques discussed above are introduced on a 'one-off' basis when a construction dispute actually arises, there are a number of the current standard form building contracts in which they are incorporated from the outset. As we have mentioned, dispute resolution by adjudication is found in several JCT sub-contracts (and the government's sub-contract GW/S) and also in the ACA Form of Contract which is designed for use under the BPF procurement system. Conciliation has recently been introduced formally into the ICE contract.

The sub-contracts mentioned limit the use of adjudication to disputes between the contractor and the sub-contractor arising out of set-off claims. However, the ACA Form of Contract in fact contains a very comprehensive statement of the powers and duties of the adjudicator, the key to which lies in clause 25.2. This clause gives the adjudicator power to decide upon any issue whatsoever which arises during the course of the work or after its completion or abandonment. Specific mention is made, for example, of the adjudicator's powers to adjust the contract sum, the date for completion, the standard of work (conformance with the contract documents) and the rights of either party to terminate the contract. The clause makes it clear that the adjudicator is acting as an expert, not as an arbitrator. By signing the contract, the parties agree that they will be bound by the adjudicator's decision and will give it full effect immediately, until the 'Taking-Over of the Works'.

The third edition of GC/Works/1[9] includes an adjudication clause (at clause 59). This enables the contractor to refer any dispute which has been outstanding for three months or more to the person named in the abstract of particulars. This person should then nominate an adjudicator who will be a member of the authority, or someone acting for the authority, who has not been previously connected with the project. The contractor, in referring the dispute to adjudication, must enclose a full statement of the problem, as well as copies of any relevant documentation. The project manager and the quantity surveyor have a right to make representations to the adjudicator, who has only 28 days in which to reach a decision. This decision may not be questioned until the project is completed, abandoned or terminated.

These provisions are an intermediate step between having a dispute and going to arbitration, and are clearly intended to cool down a problematic situation. The fact that the contractor must wait three months before being allowed to refer a matter to adjudication means that trivial matters should not be subject to this process. Also, there is plenty of time for the parties to come to an amicable agreement, although this possibility is not suggested in the contract. This adjudication process does not seem to encourage negotiation or consensus. On the contrary, it seems that the contractor can have little involvement once the matter has been referred to adjudication, and is bound by the decision until arbitration proceedings can be commenced.

The ICE 6 contract contains similar provisions, which are entirely new to British main contracts. At clause 66 the procedures for the settlement of disputes are outlined. This clause starts by defining the types of disputes which are covered by these provisions. The definition is wide-ranging and includes most potential sources of dispute. The second part of the clause requires that a dispute be commenced by either party serving a 'Notice of Dispute' on the engineer. This notice may only be served if the person issuing it has first taken all steps or procedures described elsewhere in the contract which may have overcome the dispute, and has allowed sufficient time for reasonable steps to have been taken. This clause, then, is clearly intended to be a last resort.

Whenever a 'Notice of Dispute' is served, the engineer is to decide the issue. It is clearly envisaged that this dispute will be between the employer and the contractor. The engineer's decision is stated to be final and binding upon the contractor and the employer, unless the recommendation of a conciliator has been accepted by both parties, or an arbitrator has revised the engineer's decision and this award has been published. This removes any doubt about the status of an engineer's decision. It is a very definite and serious step on the part of the employer or contractor to challenge a decision of the engineer. If either party does not agree with the engineer's decision, or if the engineer has failed to reach a decision within the time limit (one month), then there are two courses of action available: **conciliation**, or **arbitration**.

Arbitration must be commenced by a 'Notice to Refer'. The procedure to follow in arbitration is discussed in Chapter 25. If no such notice has been given, then either party can by written notice refer the dispute to conciliation. This must be undertaken in accordance with the ICE conciliation procedure, which was published in 1988 and is enclosed with the contract.

The conciliation procedure is very clear and is not intended to be adversarial. The conciliator is bound to begin the process as soon as possible, and also to reach a decision as quickly as possible. The rules invite written submissions from the parties, stating their respective versions of the case, and the conciliator may allow each party to respond to specific points in writing. The conciliator may wish to visit the site or may generally collect any information deemed fit. While the conciliator may meet the parties separately, there is also the option to convene a meeting at which evidence may be sought and submissions invited from the disputers. The rules make it clear that the rules of evidence are not applicable. The decision of the conciliator is to be delivered in writing; and if either party refuses to accept this decision, arbitration can still be commenced within one month.

This last point raises the possibility that these provisions may be used to revive an arbitration claim when the time limit for bringing it has expired. Since clause 66 does not impose any time limits on conciliation, it seems that a party may take this route when it is too late to refer the matter to arbitration. Then, when the conciliator announces a decision, this may be challenged by arbitration within one month! It should be said that, even if this interpretation of clause 66 is correct, it is unlikely that it is what the drafters of ICE 6 intended.

The FIDIC International Standard Form of Civil Engineering Contract (4th edn) contains a provision for the amicable settlement of disputes at clause 67.2.[10] This clause is only operable where notice of intention to proceed to arbitration has already been issued. When this happens, arbitration cannot start unless the parties have attempted to settle the dispute amicably. The parties then have 56 days within which to come to a settlement (unless they otherwise agree), after which time arbitration will commence.

In English law these words do not impose an obligation on the parties to attempt to reach a settlement and could possibly simply prolong the period before which arbitration commences. However, there is of course nothing to stop the parties from attempting to reach agreement without going to arbitration. This clause really only serves as a timely reminder to the parties that they ought to try.

A further development of adjudication is currently being offered as a service for use on any construction project. There are firms now who specialize in offering 'Contract Management Adjudication' services, based on the model used by the BPF in their system of construction procurement. The idea is that the adjudicator becomes a permanent part of the project team, who is there to avoid disputes from occurring in the first place. Such a scheme is said to be complementary to the presence of a strong project manager.[11]

REFERENCES

1. Robertson, I.T. and Cooper, C.L. *Human Behaviour in Organizations*. Macdonald and Evans, Plymouth, 1983.
2. *Independent Broadcasting Authority* v. *EMI Electronics Ltd and BICC Construction Ltd* (1980) 14 B.L.R. 1.
3. Shilston, A.W. Reconciliation in the construction industry. *Arbitration*, February 1988, 45–54.
4. British Property Federation. *Manual of the BPF System for Building Design and Construction*. British Property Federation, London, 1983.
5. NSC/4 and DOM/1 (used with JCT 80); NAM/SC and IN/SC (used with IFC 84); also GW/S (used with GC/Works/1).
6. *Sutcliffe* v. *Thackrah* [1974] A.C. 727.
7. *Arenson* v. *Casson, Beckman Rutley & Co.* [1975] A.C. 405.
8. *A. Cameron Ltd* v. *John Mowlem & Co. plc* (1990) 8-CLD-07-01.
9. Department of the Environment. *Form GC/Works/1 – Edition 3: General Conditions of Contract for Building & Civil Engineering*. HMSO, London, 1989.
10. Hollands, D.E. FIDIC's Provision for Amicable Settlement of Disputes. *International Construction Law Review*, 1, 1989, 33–43.
11. Hellard, R.B. *Managing Construction Conflict*. Longman, Harlow, 1988.

25

Arbitration and litigation

If a dispute cannot be resolved by negotiation and agreement, the only course of action which remains open to an aggrieved party is to take the dispute to some formal legal process. This may mean litigation in court or, in the context of construction disputes, it may well mean arbitration. These options and mechanisms are discussed in this chapter.

25.1 THE NATURE OF ARBITRATION

25.1.1 Arbitration and litigation

As a general principle, any dispute which arises between the parties to a contract may be settled by an action in court. As to *which* court is appropriate, this will depend upon a number of factors including the size of the dispute, its nature and, in some cases, its location. The size of the dispute is relevant because claims up to a certain financial limit tend to go to a county court. Its nature is important because that will affect which division of the High Court is selected. In addition, the location may influence the choice of court since it may be tried locally in the relevant county court or by a circuit judge hearing High Court business.

In practice, building and civil engineering cases of any appreciable size are tried by what are known as 'Official Referees'; these are a small number of circuit judges, based in a separate court in London, who form in effect a sub-division of the Queen's Bench Division of the High Court. Since some 80% of 'Official Referees' business' is construction based, they constitute a specialist court for the construction industry.

As an alternative to taking legal action, it is possible for those in dispute to agree that their differences shall be settled by some other independent person, body or tribunal. For example, it may be felt that a dispute which essentially turns on detailed technical evidence would be better dealt with by a specialist in the particular field than by a judge. Again, parties may believe that a procedure which is less formal than a trial in court will produce a decision more quickly and at less cost. If these and other reasons are sufficiently pressing, the parties are likely to choose arbitration rather than litigation.

It is important to note that whereas there is normally an automatic right to take a dispute to court, the right to go to arbitration is by its nature more restricted. Arbitration can only arise where certain conditions are met; in particular, there must be:

1. A genuine dispute or difference between the parties, of a kind which is 'justiciable at law'. This means that the arbitrator's award must be capable of enforcement as if it were a judgment of a court. It also means that a claim on which the plaintiff would be entitled to summary judgment under Order 14 (see below) can be dealt with in court notwithstanding the presence of an arbitration clause – this is because there is no 'genuine dispute'.
2. A binding contractual agreement to submit that dispute to arbitration by a third party chosen either by the parties or in accordance with their instructions. The arbitrator need not be named in the agreement; the parties may leave it to a professional body to nominate a suitable person.
3. A reference to arbitration in accordance with whatever procedure is laid down in the agreement. Thus, for example, ICE 6 clause 66 prohibits either party from seeking arbitration until their dispute has first been considered by the Engineer. JCT 80 contains no equivalent restriction, but many disputes arising under that contract cannot be taken to arbitration until after practical completion of the works.

Provided that these are all present, arbitration may arise either where the parties agree to take to arbitration a dispute which has already arisen or where the original contract contains an undertaking that any future dispute will be dealt with in this way. The latter method is far more common in construction disputes.

One further point which is worth making is that while a valid arbitration agreement may be made orally, such an agreement will not be subject to the Arbitration Acts of 1950 and 1979. These Acts lay down detailed rules about the way in which arbitrations are to be conducted. They include details of how they are controlled by the courts in terms of hearing appeals, removing arbitrators for misconduct, and so on. They apply *only* where the arbitration agreement in question is in writing. Of course, this requirement will automatically be satisfied in relation to a standard form building contract which contains its own arbitration clause.

25.1.2 Arbitration and other procedures

While the *purposes* of arbitration and litigation may often coincide or overlap, there is no likelihood of confusion over which method of dispute resolution is in operation in any given case. One need only ask about how the proceedings commenced because each can only be started in one way. Litigation is set in motion by one party issuing a writ on the other. Arbitration is set in motion by a party requesting the other party to concur in the appointment of an arbitrator.

However, it may on occasion be rather less easy to tell whether what is taking place is an 'arbitration' in the full sense or some lesser means of valuation, certification or adjudication. The parties to a lease containing a rent review clause, for example, may indeed submit the question of what the new rent should be to an 'arbitrator' in the full sense; equally, however, they may refer the matter to an independent 'expert' for a decision based upon knowledge of the market and of valuation techniques.

It is unfortunate that the borderline between arbitration and these lesser procedures should be blurred since at least two important legal consequences flow from the distinction. In the first place, it appears that the normal right to appeal against an arbitrator's award does not apply to a mere valuation. Even a 'speaking valuation' is, at least in the absence of fraud, legally binding on the parties.[1] Second, and partly as a result of this inability to appeal against the decision of an 'expert', it seems that the expert is open to an action for negligence.[2] Arbitrators, by contrast, are immune from such an action.[3] However, it should be stated that the position is not entirely clear-cut. It may be that the arbitrator's immunity also covers a 'quasi-arbitrator' – i.e. an 'expert' who is expected to adopt a 'judicial' approach to reaching a decision on something which will bind the parties.

In the construction context, it seems that an architect is not normally to be regarded as an arbitrator (or quasi-arbitrator) when exercising certification functions under the contract.[4] The same is probably true of an engineer,[5] although it is at least possible that an engineer's decision under ICE 6 clause 66 might be different.[6] As a result, architects and engineers may be liable to their clients in contract for negligent over-certification leading to loss. However, it seems that the law of tort will not permit a similar claim *by a contractor* in the event of negligent under-certification or refusal to certify.[7] This whole topic is discussed in Chapter 14.

The position of an 'Adjudicator' under such sub-contracts as DOM/1 clause 24 and IN/SC clause 25 looks even more uncertain. The clauses under which such persons are appointed seem to bear all the hallmarks of valid arbitration agreements. However, the Court of Appeal has held that they are *not* arbitrators, as the contracts make provision for their decisions to be reviewed at subsequent arbitration.[8] What remains to be seen is whether their function is none the less sufficiently 'quasi-judicial' to prevent them from being liable in negligence for their decisions.

25.2 DIFFERENCES BETWEEN ARBITRATION AND LITIGATION

There is a substantial area of overlap between *arbitration* and *litigation*, in which either may be used. Later in this chapter we shall consider various factors which might influence the parties in deciding which to choose. For the moment, however, we are concerned rather with those features which are unique to one or the other and which may therefore prevent a choice from arising.

25.2.1 Jurisdiction

The jurisdiction of the courts to adjudicate upon disputes between contracting parties is virtually unlimited (although the contract may provide that it cannot be exercised until after the parties have been to arbitration). By contrast, an arbitrator is empowered to decide only those disputes which are specifically referred to, and which fall within the scope of the arbitration agreement under which the appointment is made. It may be therefore that, for certain kinds of dispute, litigation is the only available solution.

Most standard form building contracts contain arbitration clauses drafted in wide terms. For example, JCT 80 includes 'the construction of this contract, or any matter or thing of whatsoever nature arising hereunder or in connection herewith'. ICE 6 refers to 'a dispute of any kind whatsoever...in connection with or arising out of the contract'. It has been decided by the House of Lords that such wording is sufficient to cover a dispute as to whether the contract has been repudiated or frustrated.[9] It cannot, however, empower the arbitrator to decide whether or not the contract was ever validly created. The jurisdiction of arbitrators to decide anything at all depends upon this point, and they will not normally be permitted to decide on their own jurisdiction. Where a problem of this nature arises, the best procedure is for an application to be made to the court for a declaration as to whether or not the arbitrator has the necessary jurisdiction.

It appears that the phrase 'arising under' is narrower than either 'arising out of' or 'arising in connection with' a contract, and that it does not include claims in tort for misrepresentation or attempts to establish a collateral contract.[10] Where the wider form of words is used, the arbitrator has power to rectify the contract on the ground of mistake or misrepresentation.[11] Such power is now given expressly under JCT 80 clause 41.4.

25.2.2 Powers

In former centuries arbitrators were expected to decide disputes not according to legal principles, but on the basis of what they regarded as just and equitable. While this remains the position in many countries, it is emphatically not so in England, even if the parties agree that the arbitrator should have such power.[12] Arbitrators faced with contracts which are difficult to interpret must find the answer within the contract wording, rather than in their own knowledge of what goes on in the construction industry.[13]

This insistence that arbitrators' decisions must be based on legal principles means also that they can only award those remedies for which the contract in question makes provision. Thus, for example, a contractor cannot be ordered to do remedial work as an alternative to paying liquidated damages.[14]

In one very important respect, it seems that an arbitrator's powers may actually be *wider* than those of a court dealing with the same dispute. An arbitration clause may empower the arbitrator to 'open up, review and revise any certificate, opinion, decision, requirement or notice'. JCT 80 contains such a clause. It has been said by the Court of Appeal that this gives to the arbitrator powers which a court would not normally have.[15] The only situations in which a court will have these powers are where either the certificate in question was legally invalid (e.g. because of fraud by the contract administrator), where the arbitration machinery has broken down or where the parties specifically agree that the court shall have all the powers which the contract gives to the arbitrator.[16] If this ruling is correct, any dispute which calls into question a contract administrator's certificate or refusal to certify (and most construction disputes do) must in effect be taken to arbitration. Otherwise the contract administrator's decision will be unchallengeable.

The *Crouch* decision has been very heavily criticized on grounds both of law and policy.[17] However, while the judge in one later case refused to follow the decision,[18] other cases have actually extended it. It has been held that the crucial factor is not that the arbitration clause takes away the court's jurisdiction, but rather that it gives to arbitrators a reviewing power which neither they nor a court would otherwise possess. Thus architect's certificates have been held unchallengeable in court under a MW 80 contract, where the arbitration clause gives no reviewing power to the arbitrator[19] and also under contracts which contain no arbitration clause at all.[20] However, these extensions have been doubted by the Court of Appeal.[21]

25.2.3 Remedies

A plaintiff who takes a dispute to court may have two very powerful remedies which are not readily available at arbitration. First, in very clear-cut cases there may be a power to obtain 'summary judgment' under Order 14 of the Rules of the Supreme Court (RSC). Where this is so, it means that the plaintiff wins the case once and for all on the basis of affidavit evidence – i.e. without the expense or delay of a full-scale trial. This can save up to 80% of the costs and up to 2 years' waiting time.

Whether or not the plaintiff seeks summary judgment under Order 14, it may be appropriate to apply for 'interim payment' under RSC Order 29. This enables plaintiffs to claim that they *will* surely be awarded at least that much money when the case is ultimately heard. If the court is satisfied as to this (and it must have regard to any possible counter-claims by the defendant), it may award a reasonable proportion of the damages which the plaintiff is likely to obtain. Of course, if the later proceedings do not confirm the award, then the money must be repaid.

Order 14

The basis on which a court may give summary judgment under Order 14 on all or part of a plaintiff's claim is that the defendant has no defence to that claim or part-claim, or no defence except as to the amount of damages. In the latter case, the plaintiff need not even quantify the claim, and the court may give judgment on liability, leaving the damages to be assessed separately. The plaintiff's application must be accompanied by an affidavit stating his or her belief that there is no defence. However, whether or not there is in fact a sufficient defence is for the court to decide on an objective basis.

Since summary judgment under Order 14 effectively denies to a defendant the opportunity to argue the case in full, it follows that a court must feel convinced that there is no arguable defence before making such an award. Such phrases found in the judgments as 'indisputably due', 'as plain as could be' and 'beyond reasonable doubt' indicate that the onus of proof on the plaintiff is a heavy one. In the construction context, a contract administrator's certificate is usually sufficient evidence that a sum is due, unless the defendant is able to challenge the certificate in some way. If not, then vague allegations of defects or delay, without good supporting evidence, will not prevent the contractor from obtaining summary judgment.

Order 14 is intended to provide a speedy method of disposing of disputes to which in truth there can be only one answer. In consequence, the court should not allow such proceedings to escalate into a full-scale trial. However, if the defendant raises a point of law which can be disposed of after a brief argument, the court can deal with it.[22]

Some construction cases raise particular difficulties over the use of Order 14 proceedings. This happens especially where there is an arbitration clause, and where the defendant seeks to establish a set-off or counter-claim. The basic principles appear to be as follows:

1. The mere presence of an arbitration clause does not take the case outside Order 14. Provided that the court is satisfied that there is no arguable defence to all or part of the plaintiff's claim, it will give summary judgment on the relevant part. It will then stay proceedings under section 4 of the *Arbitration Act 1950*, to enable the remainder of the claim to be decided at arbitration.[23]
2. A genuine right of set-off operates as a defence to all or part of a claim and, to that extent at least, prevents any award of summary judgment.[24]
3. Where the court regards an alleged set-off or other defence as somewhat 'shadowy', it may give the defendant *conditional* leave to defend. Alternatively, the court may give summary judgment but order a stay of execution, possibly on condition that the defendant pays into court or otherwise gives security for the sum in dispute.[25]
4. Where the defendant has a counter-claim which does *not* amount to a set-off, it seems that the plaintiff will be entitled to summary judgment. Further, there is no reason for the judge to suspend the execution of that judgment until the counterclaim is tried.[26]

Order 29

An application for interim payment under Order 29 is based on the plaintiff's assertion that, if the action proceeded to trial, judgment would be obtained against the defendant for a substantial sum of money. If the court is satisfied on this, it may order the defendant to make an interim payment of such amount as it thinks just, not exceeding a reasonable proportion of the ultimate liability.

Although this remedy is quite independent of summary judgment under Order 14, it is common in construction cases to find plaintiffs seeking both as alternatives. Furthermore, there are various similarities between them. For example, it appears that the standard of proof required is the same for both. A judge who refuses to award summary judgment because of a potential set-off or counter-claim, cannot at the same time be sufficiently convinced of the plaintiff's ultimate success to order the defendant to make an interim payment.[27] However, where the court in Order 14 proceedings is only prepared to give the defendant *conditional* leave to defend, there is nothing to prevent it at the same time ordering an interim payment.[28]

Further resemblances to Order 14 may be seen in the fact that Order 29, too, may operate notwithstanding an arbitration clause in the contract,[29] and in the courts' refusal in Order 29 cases to be drawn into difficult and complex questions of law or fact.[30] However, one most important distinction is that a plaintiff may be deprived of an interim payment under Order 29 where the defendant has a counter-claim which falls short of being a set-off.[31]

As to the appropriate *amount* of an interim payment, it has been suggested by the Court of Appeal[32] that:

1. Where the court believes that the plaintiff will recover £X, and may recover much more, then £X is a reasonable award.
2. Where the court believes that the plaintiff will recover £X, but is unlikely to recover much more, then he should receive only a 'reasonable proportion' of £X.

25.2.4 Limitation of actions

The rules of law which require any legal action to be commenced within a certain period apply as much to arbitrations as they do to legal proceedings. If a case goes to court, the question is whether the plaintiff issued the writ within the statutory period; if it goes to arbitration, the question is whether notice requiring arbitration was served on the other party within that time. It is vital to appreciate that the plaintiff does not, by satisfying one of these requirements, also satisfy the other. To avoid the danger of being out of time for one or other of these procedures, the plaintiff should both issue a writ and serve notice of arbitration.

Quite apart from the *Limitation Act 1990*, building contracts frequently contain their own provisions as to both the earliest and latest time in which disputes can be taken to arbitration. For example, JCT 80 clause 41.3 provides that, with certain exceptions, no arbitration can be commenced before the works reach practical completion or the contract is terminated or abandoned, unless the parties specifically agree. More important, perhaps, JCT 80 clause 30.9 makes the 'Final Certificate' conclusive evidence of a number of matters unless arbitration to challenge it is commenced within a mere 14 days of its issue.

Such time bars will not operate in cases of 'deliberate concealment' of a breach of contract.[33] Furthermore, the courts have jurisdiction under section 27 of the *Arbitration Act 1950* to extend time for the commencement of proceedings on general grounds of 'hardship'. However, such an extension was refused in a case where the contractors' only excuse for a 20-week delay in commencing arbitration was ignorance of the contractual terms.[34]

Problems have arisen under the form of wording used in ICE contracts. ICE 6 clause 66(6) provides that, if an engineer's decision on a dispute is to be challenged by arbitration, this must be done within 3 months. Similarly, if the engineer has failed for one month to give a decision which has been requested by the contractor (3 months if a 'Certificate of Substantial Completion' has been issued), the matter must again be taken to arbitration within 3 months. If this is not done, the decision (or lack of it) becomes unchallengeable.

Unfortunately, while the ICE conditions specifically apply only to those 'disputes' which arise when one of the parties serves a 'Notice of Dispute' on the engineer, they do not prescribe any particular *form* for such a notice, nor indeed for an engineer's decision. As a result, it is sometimes difficult to know whether an engineer's response to a contractor's demands constitutes a 'decision' or not; indeed, the wording of the 5th edition was even less clear on this matter. Thus in *ECC Quarries* v. *Merriman*,[35] for example, a contractor wrote to the engineer on 19 February, asking for a decision on a claim for extra work. Nothing was then done until 31 July when, following a 'without prejudice' meeting, the engineer wrote in terms which effectively rejected the claim, but without describing this as a decision or adjudication. It was held that the contractor should have commenced arbitration either by 19 August (if the engineer's letter of 31 July was not a 'decision') or by 31 October (if it was). Since the contractor had failed to do either, the right to arbitration was barred.

25.3   CHOICE OF PROCEDURE

25.3.1   Reasons for choosing arbitration or litigation

Assuming that a contracting party is not forced by one of the factors described above into either arbitration or litigation, the crucial question is which of these procedures should be chosen as a means of resolving the dispute. As to this, no definite answer can be given, but there are various matters which may be taken into account in any particular case, of which the following are among the most important.

Advantages of arbitration

The advantages most commonly claimed for arbitration are that it is cheap, quick, suitable for matters of technical complexity, convenient and commercially expedient. These points are discussed below:

- *Cost.* It is often said that arbitration is cheaper than litigation. Unfortunately, while this *can* be true in simple cases where a short informal procedure (e.g. without legal representation) is used, it tends not to be so in complex construction disputes. Indeed, in such cases where the procedures adopted are similar to those of a court, arbitration is likely to be the more expensive option. This is because the parties must pay for the arbitrator, the venue, and such other items as a transcript of the proceedings.

- *Speed.* Again, while arbitration in simple cases is likely to be much quicker than litigation, this is dependent upon the parties' willingness to adopt a suitable procedure. If what is required is effectively a trial, than litigation is likely to be quicker since judges are more ruthless than arbitrators in enforcing the prescribed time limits for the various procedural stages, and in refusing to give extensions of time. This is not to say that arbitrators lack the necessary powers, rather that they do not always have the confidence to apply them.

- *Technical complexity.* It may be that where the legal issues in a case are relatively straightforward, but the factual questions are complicated (e.g. as to detailed matters of design loading), it is better to have the dispute heard by an arbitrator possessing relevant technical qualifications. However, where 'complexity' means only 'construction industry practice', this is well understood by the Official Referees since these judges spend most of their time hearing such cases.

- *Convenience.* Arbitration can be arranged to suit the parties (and the arbitrator) and, for example, it may be possible to hold hearings in the evening or at a weekend. Once again, however, this is less of a viable option in a complex case where lawyers and experts are involved.

- *Commercial factors.* Other matters which might influence a party in favour of arbitration include its rather less confrontational nature. This may be important where the parties' contractual relationship is continuing. It is also somewhat easier to keep the proceedings private.

Advantages of litigation

The perceived advantages of litigation include the ability to join third parties in the action, the availability of legal aid, the ability to deal with legal complexities and a more decisive approach by the decision-maker. These are expanded below:

- *Third parties.* The right to take a dispute to arbitration is conferred not by law, but by the terms of a contract. In consequence, only the parties to that contract are bound. This means that where (as is commonly the case in construction disputes) more than two parties are involved, they can only be brought into the same arbitration proceedings if either they all agree or provision is made for this in *all* the relevant contracts. JCT 80, together with NSC/4 and NSC/2, attempts to achieve this, but the drafting is difficult and it is not certain whether or not it succeeds.

- *Legal aid.* A party who qualifies for legal aid will almost certainly prefer litigation to arbitration since legal aid is not available for the latter.
- *Legal complexity.* Where a dispute is essentially over a point of law (which includes the meaning to be given to a term of the contract), it is probably better to have it decided by a judge rather than by an arbitrator without legal qualifications. Indeed, where a dispute can be narrowed down to being *only* on a point of law, it may be resolved by an Official Referee on a 'construction summons', which is a quick and simple procedure not involving a full-scale court case.
- *Hard cases.* Whether it is justified or not, there is a belief among lawyers specializing in construction cases that arbitrators are instinctively reluctant to rule wholly in favour of one party or the other, but prefer, to some degree at least, to 'split the difference'. As a result, it is felt that a contractor who makes a wholly spurious claim against the employer is likely to come away from arbitration with at least something, whereas a judge would have less hesitation in denying the claim altogether. Consequently, a party who genuinely believes that its position is 100% justified may, if free to choose, be sensible to litigate rather than to arbitrate.

25.3.2 Staying proceedings

In some standard form contracts, such as those relating to insurance, it is common to find a clause which makes an arbitrator's award a condition precedent to the right to bring an action in court. These are called *Scott* v. *Avery*[36] clauses, after the case in which their effectiveness was first recognized. Such clauses are rarely found in modern construction contracts. However, where a contract contains an arbitration clause, there is a procedure whereby one party may seek to prevent the other from outflanking that clause by suing in court. Under section 4 of the *Arbitration Act 1950*, defendants in such circumstances may apply to have a legal action against them 'stayed', so that arbitration can take place. Provided that the defendant satisfies three conditions (discussed below), the proceedings will be stayed unless the plaintiff can show good reason why the matter should not go to arbitration.

Where an arbitration agreement is 'non-domestic' (i.e. it is one which provides for arbitration outside the UK, or to which one of the parties is a foreigner or foreign resident), section 4 does not apply. It is replaced by section 1 of the *Arbitration Act 1975*, which is for the most part in similar terms. However, this provision gives the court no discretion – if the three conditions are satisfied, proceedings *must* be stayed.

The statutory requirements

For a defendant who issues a section 4 summons to succeed in having legal action stayed, the first of the three conditions which must be established is that there is a 'dispute' which falls within the terms of the arbitration agreement in question. This will rule out cases where what is in dispute is the very existence of either the contract itself or the arbitration clause, for as we have already noted it is not for an arbitrator to determine the existence or extent of his or her own jurisdiction.[8] It will also rule out cases in which the plaintiff's claim is 'indisputable' – here the court can give summary judgment under RSC Order 14, notwithstanding the presence of an arbitration clause.[21] However, this does not apply where there is no part of the claim which can be regarded as 'indisputable'; thus where a defendant in a 'non-domestic' case admitted liability but none the less challenged the amount of every part of the plaintiff's claim, the Court of Appeal held by a majority that Order 14 could not apply and that the defendants were entitled to have the action stayed, even though this was purely a delaying tactic.[37]

Second, a section 4 summons must be issued by the defendant 'before delivering any pleadings or taking any other step in the proceedings'. This can be a trap for the defendant because it is by no means clear precisely what will constitute a 'step in the proceedings'. Even quite trivial matters may fall within this definition, with the result that the defendant may inadvertently lose the right to arbitration by taking some minor step.[38] However, the courts have on occasion suggested that defendants should only be barred when their actions impliedly show an intention to elect litigation rather than arbitration.[39]

Third, the success of a section 4 summons is dependent upon proof that the defendant was and is 'ready and willing to do all things necessary to the proper conduct of the arbitration'. Clearly, a defendant who refuses to agree to the appointment of an arbitrator in accordance with the arbitration agreement cannot satisfy this requirement. What is *not* clear, however, is whether a defendant can claim to be 'ready and willing', despite an avowed intention to deny liability at arbitration on the ground that the plaintiff is out of time. There are indications that this is possible.[40]

The court's discretion

Once the defendant satisfies the conditions described above, the onus then switches to the plaintiff to convince the court that there is a good reason why the matter should not be referred to arbitration. There is a great deal of case law on this point, as a result of which the following may be identified as the kind of cases in which a stay of proceedings may be refused (i.e. where the dispute will be tried in court):

1. Where more than two parties are involved and it is not possible to deal with all the disputes in a combined arbitration.[41]
2. Where the dispute turns largely on a question of law,[42] although a modern court will probably take a less strong view on this.
3. Where the dispute raises a question of fraud or professional negligence.[43]
4. Where there are substantiated fears that the named arbitrator may not be impartial.[40]
5. Where one party will qualify for legal aid in litigation and may be unable to afford the cost of arbitration, at least where this poverty is itself caused by the other party's conduct.[43]
6. (Possibly) where arbitration cannot be opened until after completion, at least where it appears that the party seeking to stay proceedings is merely attempting to delay matters.[45]
7. One situation in which it appears that a stay will *not* be refused (i.e. the case *will* go to arbitration) is where it involves reviewing any certificate issued by the contract administrator. As we have already seen, this is something which may well lie within the jurisdiction of the arbitrator but not of the court,[14] so that to grant a stay of proceedings would mean that the matter could not be opened up at all.

25.4 PROCEDURE AT ARBITRATION AND LITIGATION

It is not possible here to give a detailed account of the legal procedures which are involved in taking a case to court or to arbitration. However, it may be of some use to give a brief sketch of how litigation is conducted under the Rules of the Supreme Court, followed by a description of the main differences which are to be found in arbitration.

25.4.1 Litigation

Litigation consists of certain *preliminary proceedings*, followed by the actual *trial*.

Preliminary proceedings

As a general rule, the plaintiff's action commences by the issue of a writ, which is then served on the defendant. If the case is to be defended, the defendant must give notice to this effect. The defendant may then, where appropriate, serve a 'third-party notice' on anyone else from whom a claim is to be made in the same proceedings. Such a claim might be based on the basis of a breach of duty which the third party owes to the defendant. It might alternatively be a claim under the *Civil Liability (Contribution) Act 1978* for a contribution towards the liability which both the defendant and the third party have *towards the plaintiff*. Procedures of this kind play an important part in construction cases, where 'defective building' litigation often involves not only the employer and the main contractor, but also the architect, structural engineer and/or sub-contractors.

Once the parties are identified, the plaintiff should immediately make an 'application for directions'. This leads to a hearing at which the Official Referee, in conjunction with the parties, will deal with such matters as the form and time-scale of the pleadings, make orders for discovery of documents and expert evidence, and set a date for the trial.

The next stage in the proceedings is the exchange of 'pleadings'. These are formal documents in which the parties attempt to identify and, where possible, narrow down the area of dispute between them. Pleadings are important because a party who has not 'pleaded' a particular point is not permitted to rely on that point when the case comes to trial, although modern judges are more willing than their predecessors to allow pleadings to be amended.

The pleadings begin with a 'Statement of Claim', in which the plaintiff sets out the remedy which is being sought and the facts on which the claim is based. The defendant then issues a 'Statement of Defence' which includes, where appropriate, any counter-claim. The plaintiff may 'reply' to this (at the same time putting forward a defence to any counter-claim which has been made). In theory, each of these documents, and any further ones which are needed, should be served within 14 days of the previous one, and the pleadings are deemed to be 'closed' 14 days after the last document is served. In practice, however, extensions of time are readily granted by the judge.

A particular form of pleadings which was pioneered by the Official Referees is the 'Scott Schedule', whereby a mass of detail (e.g. as to defects in a building, or items of work to be paid for) is numbered and tabulated in columns. This is done in such a way that the parties can make comments on and place a figure against each item, following which the judge in turn can insert comments.

Other preliminary matters which are worth noting include the following:

1. A request for 'further and better particulars'. This means that a party asks for more details of his opponent's case.
2. A 'notice to admit facts'. If the other party refuses to admit that the fact in question is true, and that fact is later proved in court to be true, the other party is liable for pay all the costs involved in proving it.
3. An order for 'discovery of documents'. As to this, it is clear law that a party must disclose all relevant documents, even those which are to its disadvantage, which are or have been in that party's custody or power. If they cannot actually produce them (e.g. because they have been destroyed), they must be listed and described.

The rules on 'discovery of documents' are subject to an important exception, in that certain classes of document are 'privileged' (i.e. exempt). Of these, two are of particular relevance in construction cases. First, an expert report, for example, on the cause of defects in a building, which is commissioned by one of the parties need not be disclosed to the other side if (but only if) it was prepared solely or primarily for the purposes of litigation.[46] Second, 'without prejudice' correspondence which attempts to settle a dispute is immune from discovery; indeed, it has recently been held by the House of Lords that the 'privilege' accorded to such correspondence may extend to other proceedings as well. In *Rush & Tompkins* v. *GLC*[47] an employer settled the claims of a main contractor for a total sum which included an agreed amount in respect of the claims of a sub-contractor. It was held that documents relating to that case, in which the main contractor expressed views as to the size of the sub-contractor's claims, did not have to be disclosed in later proceedings by the sub-contractor against the main contractor.

Another procedural device developed by the Official Referees in construction cases is the practice whereby the reports of the parties' expert witnesses are exchanged some months before the trial, in the hope of revealing areas of substantial agreement. Indeed, the success of this practice has led to the introduction of two more. Official Referees now on occasion direct that expert witnesses should meet for discussions prior to the trial (out of reach of the parties' lawyers!) and also that the proofs of evidence to be given by *witnesses of fact* should likewise be exchanged in advance.

A final feature of preliminary proceedings concerns an important tactic which may be employed by the defence. This is the *payment into court* of a sum of money, which may or may not be accompanied by an admission of liability. A plaintiff who decides to accept this sum takes it in full satisfaction of all claims against the defendant, but will still be entitled to recover costs up to the date of the payment-in. If, on the other hand, the plaintiff rejects this offer and is not subsequently awarded a higher sum by the court, the plaintiff will bear total responsibility for all the costs incurred after the date of the payment-in! Since the costs in a major construction dispute can easily reach six figures, it follows that enormous sums can turn on the award of a relatively small amount of damages. Such considerations could naturally affect the judge in reaching a decision. The rules of court accordingly provide that the judge must not even be informed that a payment-in has been made, far less the amount involved.

Trial

In the great majority of cases, the parties are represented in court by barristers. The plaintiff's counsel opens the case by outlining the issues and identifying the relevant documents. In an attempt to reduce the time spent in reading out lengthy documents, Official Referees frequently require counsel to provide written summaries of their opening speeches and the documents on which they rely. Counsel then calls witnesses, questioning each one before handing them over to be 'cross-examined' by counsel for the other party or parties. When this is completed, the plaintiff's case is said to be closed, and the defendant's counsel in turn presents the defence case and calls witnesses. Finally, both counsel make their closing speeches, which include their arguments on the relevant principles of law.

It remains for the judge to announce a decision, which is normally done some time after the trial. This decides the issue of liability and, where appropriate, that of the measure of damages to be awarded. The judge also deals with any question of interest on money awarded, the general principle being that the plaintiff should be compensated for being kept out of pocket, and awards costs (usually against the losing party).

25.4.2 Arbitration

General points

The procedure to be adopted at arbitration is a matter to be decided upon by the parties and the arbitrator, rather than by the courts, and there is absolutely no need for it to follow closely the lines of an action in court. Thus, for example, the strict rules of evidence may be ignored, and the arbitration agreement may validly provide that the parties are not entitled to be legally represented. However, the courts are quick to treat as 'misconduct' anything which detracts from the basically adversarial nature of the proceedings and which turns the arbitration instead into a personal voyage of investigation by the arbitrator.

Although the parties are thus quite free to adopt informal procedures, the Arbitration Acts appear to operate on the assumption that they will not do so. These Acts accordingly contain various provisions designed to give arbitrators powers to control the proceedings which are similar to those of a High Court judge. The basic position, subject to anything in the arbitration agreement to the contrary, is that the parties are obliged to 'do all other things which during the proceedings on the reference the arbitrator...may require' (section 12(1)). If the arbitrator hesitates to rely on this to order such things as discovery of documents or the giving of security for costs, section 12(6) makes it clear that a court can so order on an application from the arbitrator. Furthermore, it is provided by section 5 of the *Arbitration Act 1979* that, if a party fails to comply wth any order made by an arbitrator in the course of the reference, the court may empower the arbitrator to continue the proceedings *ex parte* (in the absence of the defaulting party).

Apart from these purely procedural matters, the resemblance of arbitration to litigation is further strengthened by statutory provisions empowering an arbitrator to make interim awards, add interest to whatever sum is found to be due and give directions as to the payment of costs. And while provision for 'payment into court' is lacking, the common arbitration practice of making a 'sealed offer' amounts to much the same thing.

JCT Arbitration Rules

These rules, which were published by the Joint Contracts Tribunal, in July 1988, are designed to be used with all the JCT forms of contract and sub-contract. The relevant arbitration clauses have all been amended so as to provide that, if a dispute arises and is to be submitted to arbitration, it is these rules which will govern the conduct of the proceedings.

The rules provide a choice of three procedures, each of which may be suitable for different types of dispute. At one extreme is the 'Full procedure with hearing' (rule 6), which would be expected to follow fairly closely the litigation model. This is regarded as appropriate for large and complex cases, where disputes over the facts are such that witnesses ought to give evidence orally and be subjected to cross-examination. By contrast, the 'Procedure without hearing' (rule 5) is one in which the arbitrator reaches a decision on the basis of written statements, documents such as specifications, letters, site minutes and experts' reports and (if necessary) a site inspection. This procedure is recommended for such matters as valuation of work, investigation into the cause of defects and interpretation of the contract.

Rule 7, 'Short procedure with hearing', is specifically designed for situations in which the parties require a quick binding award, so that the contract work can continue with the minimum of delay. Examples would be where there is a dispute as to whether certain work is in accordance with the contract, whether practical completion has been achieved or whether consent (e.g. to sub-letting) is being unreasonably withheld. In such cases, the arbitrator may in fact inspect the site and give a decision on the spot, confirming it in writing within 21 days. This procedure clearly anticipates oral submissions by or on behalf of the parties. However, there are no pleadings, no evidence other than relevant documents (plus of course the inspection itself) and no order as to costs (i.e. the parties each pay their own).

As to which of the three procedures is to be adopted in any given case, the intention is that this is to be decided by the parties themselves within 21 days of the arbitrator's acceptance of the appointment. The 'Short procedure with hearing' can only be used if the parties specifically agree to it; if they do not, and they are also unable to agree on which of the others is appropriate, then the arbitrator decides (and the presumption is in favour of a documents-only submission).

Thereafter, the time limits for each stage of the proceedings are tightly drawn, and the parties may not agree to extend them without the arbitrator's consent. If they are adhered to, the 'Short procedure' should be completed within 4 weeks and the 'Procedure without hearing' within 16 weeks. Even the 'Full procedure' is meant to lead to a hearing within 14 weeks, although this will only happen in the rather unlikely event that all the prescribed dates are met!

Apart from outlining the basic procedural framework and prescribing time limits, the JCT rules contain a number of provisions dealing with the arbitrator's powers. In particular, rule 12 confers on the arbitrator personally those procedural powers which would otherwise require the backing of the court under section 12(6) of the *Arbitration Act 1950*. Further, the arbitrator is specifically authorized to seek personally any legal or technical advice he or she requires, to make site inspections and, unless either party requests otherwise, to give an award without stating reasons.

ICE Arbitration Procedure

The Institution of Civil Engineers, like the Joint Contracts Tribunal, has prescribed rules for arbitrations arising out of any of its own contracts; the current edition was published in 1983. These rules are much more detailed than their JCT counterparts, and are intended to form a comprehensive procedure from the occurrence of the dispute to the issue of the arbitrator's award. Notwithstanding the detail, however, the emphasis throughout is on flexibility; the arbitrator may be given a wide range of powers, but discretion in deciding which (if any) to exercise and over such questions as costs is equally wide.

It is impossible in a short space to give a useful account of the content of the ICE rules, but one or two areas in which they surpass those of the JCT are of particular interest. The ICE rules provide an arbitrator with useful powers to give summary judgment or to order interim payment which are very similar to those of a judge under RSC Orders 14 and 29. Further, there are certain special procedures: a 'Short procedure' similar to that of the JCT; a 'Special procedure for experts', in which the arbitrator and the experts decide technical questions without the 'help' of lawyers; and a procedure to facilitate speedy arbitration during the currency of the works.

25.4.3   Dismissal for want of prosecution

The law on limitations means that a party's rights may become statute-barred if proceedings are not commenced in time. Quite apart from this, a court has an inherent jurisdiction to 'dismiss for want of prosecution' an action which *has* been commenced in time but which the plaintiff is guilty of excessive delay in continuing. This is of considerable importance in the construction context, where the complexity of cases often makes it difficult for parties to comply with the time-scales for the various procedural stages which are set out in the Rules of the Supreme Court.

The principles on which a court will take this drastic step were reviewed by the House of Lords in *Birkett* v. *James*.[48] Briefly, they are as follows:

1. An action will be dismissed where the plaintiff's delay is 'intentional and contumelious' (e.g. where there is failure to obey a specific order of the court).
2. An action will be dismissed where there has been 'inordinate and inexcusable delay' by the plaintiff or its lawyers *and* this creates a substantial risk that a fair trial will no longer be possible or will cause serious prejudice to the defendant.
3. An action will not normally be dismissed where the limitation period has not yet expired (since the plaintiff could simply issue another writ).
4. An action is more likely to be dismissed where the writ itself was issued at the last minute, although here it must be shown that any 'prejudice to the defendant' has been materially increased by *post-writ* delays.

Until recently, this was an important point of difference between litigation and arbitration, for it had been ruled by the House of Lords that an arbitrator did not have an equivalent power to dismiss a claim for want of prosecution. However, such power has now been given to arbitrators by statute.[49]

25.4.4   Judicial control of arbitration

The *Arbitration Act 1950* contains a number of provisions under which the courts exercise a measure of control over arbitrations. In appropriate circumstances, the powers of the court include:

- Removing an arbitrator and appointing a replacement.
- Remitting an award to the arbitrator with guidance as to how a decision should be reached.
- Setting aside an award altogether.

Briefly, these powers apply as follows:

- An arbitrator who 'fails to use all reasonable dispatch in entering on and proceeding with the reference', may be removed, in which case he or she forfeits all remuneration (section 13(3)).
- Where there are reasonable grounds for believing that an arbitrator is not impartial, he or she may be removed (section 24(1)) and any award which has been made may be set aside (section 23(2)). This may arise where the arbitrator is too closely connected with one of the parties,[50] although the fact that an architect or engineer named as arbitrator is an employee of the client has never been regarded as an *automatic* reason for disqualification.[51] In other cases, arbitrators have been removed for showing bias against a witness on racial grounds, or simply for using such sarcastic and hostile language as to convince one party that their mind is already made up and that a fair hearing is impossible.[52]
- An arbitrator who has 'misconducted himself or the proceedings', may be removed (section 23(1)) and his award may be set aside (section 23(2)) or remitted to him or her (section 22(1)). 'Misconduct' here bears a wider meaning than 'bias', and is most often found where it is the arbitrator's *procedure* which is at fault. In particular, any breach of the rules of 'natural justice' will amount to misconduct if it would lead a reasonable person to think that the arbitrator could not or would not fairly determine the issues on the basis of the evidence and the arguments. Thus, where an arbitration in which the plaintiffs claimed some £130 000 was in fact undefended, the arbitrator extended the proceedings over many days and then, without giving reasons, awarded a mere £12 500. It was held that, if the arbitrator had criticisms to make of the plaintiffs' case sufficient to justify this decision, he

should have voiced them and given the plaintiffs an opportunity of dealing with them. The arbitrator's failure to do this led to his removal and the setting aside of the award.[53]

Other examples of misconduct for this purpose include such things as hearing one party in the absence of the other;[54] refusing to disclose to one party a document received from the other;[55] failing to view the property after telling the parties that this would be done;[56] and refusing to adjourn proceedings to enable one party, who was surprised to find that his opponent was legally represented, to instruct counsel himself.[57]

• The court's power under section 22(1) to remit an award to an arbitrator, instead of setting it aside altogether, is not subject to any specific limitations. Clearly, it is available in those cases of misconduct where there is no reason to doubt that the arbitrator is trying to reach the right conclusion and is only at fault in a technical sense. However, it appears that it can also be useful wherever some defect in the arbitrator's award means that it cannot be enforced as an order of the court. This would apply, for example, to an award which is not sufficiently certain, final and possible.

25.4.5   Appeals

Where a case is tried by a court, it will almost invariably be possible to appeal against the decision. In the case of trials before an Official Referee, there is a right of appeal to the Court of Appeal on a point of either law or fact. However, an appeal on fact is only possible if either the Official Referee or the Court of Appeal gives leave. It seems that, in the interests of finality and certainty, leave should not be granted unless the court believes there is a real prospect of success.[58]

Appeals against an arbitrator's award

Section 1(2) of the *Arbitration Act 1979* provides for a right of appeal to the High Court (normally, in construction cases, an Official Referee) 'on any question of law arising out of an award made on an arbitration agreement'. However, the procedural rules governing this right of appeal are extremely complex, have given rise to a great deal of litigation and, further, have been interpreted by the courts in a highly restrictive way. Briefly, the position is as follows:

• An appeal against an award requires either the consent of all parties to the arbitration or the leave of the court,[59] which is only to be granted where determination of the question of law will substantially affect the parties' rights.

- In order to facilitate such appeals, the court may order an arbitrator to state the reasons for the award. To apply for such an order again requires consent of all parties or an order of the court; further, it must be shown that the arbitrator was told *before* making the award that reasons would be required.
- According to the House of Lords,[60] leave to appeal should be granted or refused in accordance with the following principles:
  (a) There should be no appeal against a decision in respect of a 'one-off' clause or arising out of 'one-off' events unless the court, by merely looking at the award and without hearing legal argument, can see that the arbitrator's decision is *clearly* wrong in law. It is worth noting that the Court of Appeal regarded a modified ICE 5th edition contract as 'one-off' for this purpose![61]
  (b) As regards a decision in respect of a standard form contract, where an authoritative decision would assist the development of the law, an appeal should be allowed if there is a *strong prima facie case* that the decision is wrong.
- From a decision of the court on *preliminary* matters, such as whether or not to grant leave to appeal, or whether or not to require the arbitrator to give reasons, a further appeal lies to the Court of Appeal. This requires leave to be granted by the High Court, and this should only be granted in cases where the appeals guidelines themselves need clarification! There is *no* appeal from a decision to grant or refuse such leave.
- From a decision of the court on an *actual appeal*, an appeal to the Court of Appeal requires leave to be granted by either the High Court or the Court of Appeal. It also requires a certificate by the judge that the question of law is one of general public importance. There is *no* appeal from a refusal (or presumably a grant) of such a certificate.[62]

Preliminary points of law

Section 2 of the *Arbitration Act 1979* enables an application to be made to court, at any time during arbitration proceedings, for a ruling on a particular point of law. Such an application is again subject to complex procedural rules. In particular, it requires the consent either of the arbitrator or of all the parties. What is more, the court must be satisfied that the question of law is of a kind which might found an appeal under section 1 and also that the early determination of that point may produce substantial savings in costs for the parties.

It is not clear whether or not an arbitrator who refuses to give consent can be guilty of misconduct. It *is* clear, however, that the possibility of a further appeal to the Court of Appeal will be treated even more restrictively than appeals under section 1[63] because of the delays which might be caused to an on-going arbitration by this procedure. Leave must be granted by either the High Court or the Court of Appeal and, further, the judge must certify that the question of law involved is one of general public importance.

Exclusion agreements

Under section 3 of the *Arbitration Act 1979*, it is possible for the parties to arbitration to make the arbitrator's decision absolutely final and binding by excluding the possibility of any appeal. Where this is done, it will also exclude an application to the court to determine a preliminary point of law or to order the arbitrator to give reasons for his award. In the case of a 'domestic arbitration agreement' (i.e. one which does not provide for arbitration outside the UK and to which none of the parties is a foreigner, a foreign resident or a company incorporated in or controlled from abroad), such an agreement is valid *only* if entered into *after* the arbitration commences. A 'non-domestic arbitration agreement', by contrast, can validly exclude the court's jurisdiction *in advance*.

REFERENCES

1. *Jones* v. *Sherwood Computer Services plc* (1990) *Independent*, 15 January.
2. *Arenson* v. *Casson, Beckman Rutley & Co.* (1975) A.C. 405.
3. *Supply of Goods and Services (Exclusion of Implied Terms) Order 1985*.
4. *Sutcliffe* v. *Thackrah* (1974) A.C. 727.
5. *Kennedy* v. *Barrow-in-Furness Corp.* (1909) HBC, 4th edn, ii, 411.
6. *Monmouthshire CC* v. *Costellow & Keple Ltd* (1964) 63 L.G.R. 429.
7. *Pacific Associates Inc.* v. *Baxter* [1989] 2 All E.R. 159; *Leon Engineering & Construction Co. Ltd* v. *Ka Duk Investment Co. Ltd* (1989) 47 B.L.R. 139.
8. *A Cameron Ltd* v. *Mowlem & Co. plc* (1990) 8-C.L.D.-07–03.
9. *Heyman* v. *Darwins Ltd* [1942] A.C. 356.
10. *Fillite (Runcorn) Ltd* v. *Aqua-Lift* (1989) 45 B.L.R. 27.
11. *Ashville Investments Ltd* v. *Elmer Contractors Ltd* [1988] 2 All E.R. 577.
12. *Home and Overseas Insurance Co. Ltd* v. *Mentor Insurance Co. (UK) Ltd* [1989] 3 All E.R. 74.
13. *Norwest Holst Civil Engineering Ltd* v. *Proteus Tileman Ltd* (1988) 5-C.L.D.-05–16.
14. *BFI Group of Companies Ltd* v. *DCB Integration Systems Ltd* [1987] C.I.L.L. 348.
15. *Northern Regional Health Authority* v. *Derek Crouch Construction Co. Ltd* [1984] Q.B. 644.
16. *Supreme Court Act 1981*, section 43A (inserted by section 100 of the *Courts and Legal Service Act* 1990).
17. Wallace, I.N.D. *Construction Contracts: Principles and Policies*, Sweet & Maxwell, London, 1986, pp. 228–71.

18. *Partington & Son (Builders) Ltd* v. *Tameside MBC* (1985) 32 B.L.R. 150.
19. *Oram Builders Ltd* v. *Pemberton* (1985) 29 B.L.R. 23.
20. *Reed* v. *Van der Vorm* (1985) 35 B.L.R. 136; *J.F. Finnegan Ltd* v. *Sheffield CC* (1988) 43 B.L.R. 124.
21. *Benstrete Construction Ltd* v. *Hill* (1987) 38 B.L.R. 115.
22. *Chatbrown* v. *Alfred McAlpine (Southern) Ltd* (1986) 35 B.L.R. 44.
23. *Ellis Mechanical Services Ltd* v. *Wates Construction Ltd* (1976) 2 B.L.R. 57.
24. *Hanak* v. *Green* [1958] 2 Q.B. 9.
25. *C.M. Pillings & Co. Ltd* v. *Kent Investments Ltd* (1985) 30 B.L.R. 80.
26. *Tubeworkers Ltd* v. *Tilbury Construction Ltd* (1985) 30 B.L.R. 67; *Rush & Tompkins Ltd* v. *Deaner* (1989) 13 Con. L.R. 106.
27. *Shanning Ltd* v. *George Wimpey Ltd* [1988] 3 All E.R. 475.
28. *British and Commonwealth Holdings plc* v. *Quadrex Holdings Inc* [1989] 3 All E.R. 492.
29. *Imodco Ltd* v. *Wimpey Major Products Ltd & Taylor Woodrow International Ltd* (1987) 40 B.L.R. 1.
30. *Derek Crouch Construction Co. Ltd* v. *Northern RHA* (1983) 24 B.L.R. 60.
31. *Smallman Construction Ltd* v. *Redpath Dorman Long Ltd* (1988) 47 B.L.R. 15.
32. *Newport (Essex) Engineering* v. *Press & Shear Machinery* (1981) 24 B.L.R. 71.
33. *Crestar Ltd* v. *Carr* (1987) 37 B.L.R. 113.
34. *Emson Contractors Ltd* v. *Protea Estates Ltd* (1987) 39 B.L.R. 126.
35. *ECC Quarries Ltd* v. *Merriman Ltd* (1988) 45 B.L.R. 90.
36. *Scott* v. *Avery* (1856) 5 H.L.C. 811.
37. *Associated Bulk Carriers Ltd* v. *Koch Shipping Inc* [1978] 2 All E.R. 254.
38. *Turner & Goudy* v. *McConnell* (1985) 30 B.L.R. 108.
39. *Eagle Star Insurance Co. Ltd* v. *Yuval Insurance Co. Ltd* [1978] 1 Lloyd's Rep. 357; *Skopos Design Group Ltd* v. *Homelife Nursing Ltd* (1988) 5-C.L.D.-03–22.
40. *W. Bruce Ltd* v. *Strong* [1951] 2 K.B. 447.
41. *Taunton-Collins* v. *Crombie* [1964] 2 All E.R. 332.
42. *Bristol Corporation* v. *John Aird Ltd* [1913] A.C. 241.
43. *Turner* v. *Fenton* (1982) 1 All E.R. 8.
44. *Fakes* v. *Taylor Woodrow Construction Ltd* [1973] Q.B. 436.
45. *Gilbert-Ash (Northern) Ltd* v. *Modern Engineering (Bristol) Ltd* [1974] G.C. 689.
46. *Waugh* v. *British Railways Board* [1980] A.C. 521.
47. *Rush & Tompkins Ltd* v. *GLC* [1988] 3 All E.R. 737.
48. *Birkett* v. *James* [1978] A.C. 297.
49. *Arbitration Act 1950*, section 13A (inserted by section 102 of the *Courts and Legal Services Act 1990*).
50. *Verital Shipping Corporation* v. *Anglo-Canadian Cement Ltd* [1966] 1 Lloyd's Rep. 76.
51. *Eckersley* v. *Mersey Docks and Harbour Board* [1894] 2 Q.B. 667.
52. *Turner (East Asia) PTE Ltd* v. *Builders Federal (Hong Kong)* (1988) 42 B.L.R. 122.

53. *Fisher* v. *P.G. Wellfair Ltd* (1981) 19 B.L.R. 52.
54. *Modern Engineering (Bristol) Ltd* v. *C Miskin & Son Ltd* (1981) 1 Lloyd's Rep. 135.
55. *CMA Martin Engineering Ltd* v. *J. Donne Holdings Ltd* (1980) 15 B.L.R. 61.
56. *Micklewright* v. *Mullock* (1974) 232 E.G. 337.
57. *Tatem Steam Navigation Co. Ltd* v. *Anglo-Canadian Shipping Co. Ltd* (1953) Ll L.R. 161.
58. *Hoskisson* v. *Moody Homes Ltd* (1989) C.S.W., 25 May, 69.
59. *Tate & Lyle Industries Ltd* v. *Davy MacKee (London) Ltd* [1989] 2 All E.R. 641.
60. *The Nema* (1982) A.C. 724; *The Antaios* [1985] A.C. 191.
61. *F.G. Whitley & Sons* v. *Clwyd CC* (1983) 22 B.L.R. 48.
62. *National Westminster Bank plc* v. *Arthur Young McClelland Moores & Co.* [1985] 2 All E.R. 817.
63. *Babanaft International Co. SA* v. *Avant Petroleum Inc.* [1982] 3 All E.R. 244.

Index

Numbers in **bold** refer to figures.

Abandonment of work 348
Abatement of price 179
Abstract of particulars 124
ACA form of building agreement 27,
    109, 368
Acceptance
    certain and unambiguous 64
    conduct by 66
    generally 61, 64
    retrospective 67
    unconditional 65
Access over employer's land 149
Access to site 186
Actions, limitations of 47
Additional payment 188
Adjudication 366–8
Adjudicator, definitiveness of decision
    367
Adverse site conditions 203
Adverse weather 143
Affirmation of contract 344, 346
Agreement 61
Allocation of risk *see* Apportionment
    of risk
'All risks' insurance 231
Alternative dispute resolution *see* Non-
    litigious dispute resolution
American practice 318
Antiquities 157
Appeals 392–4
Appendix to contract 124

Apportionment of risk
    generally 19, 226, 267
    methods of payment 28
Appropriate form of contract, selection
    of 121–2
Approximate quantities 172
Arbitration
    advantages over litigation 380–1
    appeals against 392–3
    exclusion agreements 394
    generally 81, 364, 372–94
    ICE procedure 389–90
    JCT rules 388–9
    judicial control of 391
    jurisdiction 375
    litigation, differences between 375
    misconduct 387, 391
    nature of 372
    preliminary points of law 393–4
    procedure 374–5, 387–90
    sealed offer 388
    stay of proceedings 382–4
Arbitrator
    impartiality of 391
    jurisdiction of 383
    powers of 376
    removal of 391
Architect
    conflicting roles of 36
    duty of care 57
    generally *see* Contract administrator
    involvement **6.2**, 96
    liability for design of 112

liability to contractor 57–8
role of 36
Articles of agreement 123
Assignment 202, 242
Assignment, unauthorized 350

Back loading of bill rates 78
Bankruptcy 261
Battle of forms 65
Beneficiary 234
Bid bond see Tender bond
Bidding strategy 11
Bill rates, loading of 78
Bills of quantity 127–9
Bonds
  creation of 236
  duration of 236
  effect of altering contract terms 237
  financial limits of 236
  generally 234–7
  release of surety 236
  tender 77, 235
  types of 234–5
Bondsman 234
BPF system see British Property
  Federation
Breach of contract,
  contractor by 334–5
  damages for
    generally 333–40
    actual loss 335
    cost of repair 334
    diminution in value 334
    emotional frustration 334
    loss of profit 335
    physical discomfort 334
    quantum meruit 335
  employer, by 335
  failure to mitigate losses from 334
  generally 184
  liquidated damages for see
    Liquidated damages
Brief 92
British Property Federation 27, 287,
  368
Budget 92
Buildability 72, 289

Builder, role of see Contractor, role of
Building Procurement, process of 32
Building regulations 116, 153
Building, suitability of 134
Building surveyor, role of 40
'Buildmark' 117
Business relations 360

Cash discount 248
Caveat emptor 53, 84
CCPI 125
Certificate
  conclusiveness of 220
  effect of 166–7
  making good defects, of 140
  recovery without 220–1
  substantial completion, of 140
  withholding of 348
Certification, generally 58, 129, 217–21
Certified sums 180
Chain liability 244
Civil commotion 145, 353
'Claims made' basis 234
Claims
  procedures 188
  quantification of 191–5
  see also under specific grounds
Clerk of works 212, 215
Client's involvement 6.1, 96
Co-ordinating committee for project
  information see CCPI
Co-ordination 93, 155
Collateral agreement 50, 109, 280
Collateral warranty 6, 110, 234
Commencement 135
Communication patterns 104
Competitive bidding, problems with 70
Completion
  date 138
  date for 138
  delay in 139
  generally 137
Complex structure 55, 56
Concept development 92
Conciliation 264
Conditions of contract 123
Conditions of engagement

generally 34
RIBA 37
Confidentiality 202
Construction, defects in 53
Construction, liability for 113
Construction management
  allocation of risk 327–8
  background 318
  bid packages 323
  bills of quantity 325
  certification 324
  changes to requirements 321
  characteristics of 323
  client priorities in 321
  client's experience 321
  co-ordination 324
  commitment to complete 329
  conditions of contract 324
  contractual relationships in **21.1**, 320
  default 328
  early start on site 322
  extensions of time 326
  generally 5, 8–9, 102, 318–28
  instructions 324
  lead consultant in 323
  marketing tool, as a 319, 324
  money 327
  patterns of involvement in **6.8**, 103
  possession of site 324
  quality in 329
  separation of design from
    management 322
  set-off 326
  technical complexity 321
  time 324, 327
  trade contractor's design liability 324
  use of 320
  value for money 322
  variations 325
Construction operations 93
Construction, responsibility for 106
Consultant, skill and care of 15
Consultants, roles of 34
Continuity of creativity 94
Continuity of work 72
Contract administrator
  acting without authority 210

advice to the employer 213
as employer's agent 209–17
authority to appoint a QS 212
certificates 376
delegation of authority 212
extent of powers 210–13
frequency of inspections 215
functions and duties 213–17
generally 4
immunity from liability 222
independent adjudicator, as 217–24
information to the contractor 224–5
inspection and supervision 215
instructions to the contractor 145,
    160, 171, 214, 350
liability to the contractor 222–3
liability for negligent decisions 222
negligence 213
non-certification by 343
obligation to supervise 215
opinions of 221–2
power to vary the works 210
right to reject work 132
role of 209–24, 363
setting out 215
work to the satisfaction of 216
Contract choice 19, 122
Contract documentation 61, 93, 121,
    122
Contract documents
  discrepancies in 130, 186
  interaction between 130
Contract, effect on tort 49
Contract, effect on third parties 51
Contract formation 61
Contract management adjudication 371
Contract price 165
Contract strategy 14, 15, 19
Contract sum
  generally 167–8, 200
  permissible changes to 167
Contract terms
  conflicting 80
  express 79
  generally 78
  implied 79, 82–5
  incorporation by reference 80

Contract work, nature and quality of 121–34
Contractor
cash flow of 223, 257
claims by
costs of preparation 195
damages 183
disruption 183
grounds for 185
see also Loss/expense, time, etc.
common law rights of 184
design liability of 114
determination of employment 344
duties of 153
duty of care 114
duty of compliance of 214
duty to indemnify employer 229
duty to insure 230
duty to warn employer 114
early involvement of 100
expertise of, reliance upon 84
in a professional role 100
inability of, to secure resources 148
insolvency of contractor 159
involvement of **6.5**, 98
liability to architect 58
obligations of
abandonment of work 348
after completion 140
defective work 348
generally 113, 153–60
implied 83
role of 43
Contractor's Designed Portion Supplement 24
Contractual arrangements 69
Contractual chain 244
Contractual disputes
nature of 361
over legal matters 362
over technical matters 361–2
roots of 360
Contractual links 46
Contractual relationships, network of 3
Contractual remedies, enhancement of 47
Cost planning 92

Cost reimbursement 29
Counter-claim 378
Cover bid 78

Damage to property 229
Damages see Breach of contract
Dangerous buildings 45, 54
Decisions 91, 95
Defective buildings 45, 116–17
generally 216, 348
liability for 6
opening up and inspection of 146
responsibility for 106
Defects correction period 140
Defects liability period
contractor's benefit of 141
generally 140, 176
Delay
damages for 139
generally 348
Design and build
aesthetic quality 292
articles of agreement 295
background 285–7
changes to client requirements 298
characteristics of 295–9
client priorities in 292
client's familiarity with 291
commitment to complete 300
compared to general contracting 291
completion in 293
conditions of contract 297
contract sum analysis 288
contractor's obligations under 296
contractor's proposals 287–8
contractual relationships in **19.1**, 289
cost 292
default 300
design responsibility in 286
discrepancies 295, 297
early start on site 295
employer's agent 297
employer's requirements 287–8
features of 287–90
financial risk in 299
generally 6–7, 24, 106, 108, 285–301
guaranteed maximum price 288

nomination of specialists in 293
patterns of responsibility in 294
quality in 292, 300
recitals 295
risk apportionment in 292–3,
    299–301
role of the quantity surveyor 289
roles and responsibilities 288–90
selective tendering for 73
single-point responsibility 289
speed of procurement with 292
statutory obligations 298
sub-contracting 298
technical complexity 293
time 300
use of 290
variations 294
Design
delegation of responsibility 112
finality of 94
liability for 111
negligence in 108
responsibility for 106
team 4
Determination
contractor
    by 351–2
    consequences of 352
    procedures under JCT 80 352
employer
    by 350
    consequences of 351
    procedures under JCT 80 350
grounds for 211, 350, 351–3
neutral grounds for 353
sub-contracts 354–6
under JCT 80 349–56
Direct loss/expense 185–95
Dismissal for want of prosecution
    390
Disputes
avoidance 94
generally 372–3
reasons for 358–60
resolution, methods of 363–8
Documentation see Contract
    documentation

Domestic sub-contractor see
    Sub-contractor, domestic
Drafting of contracts 81–2, 84
Drawings 124–5
Duty of care 52

Early completion 200
Economic loss 48
Eichleay formula 194
Emden's formula 193
Emergency work 154
Employer, insolvency of 352
Employer's obligations
achievability, implied warranty of
    204
co-operation with contractor 184
contract administrator, responsibility
    for 202
duty to co-operate 198
express 200–5
generally 183, 197–205
implied 83, 198–200
misrepresentation 204
necessary nominations 201
non-hindrance 198, 348
payment 165, 200, 343
site conditions 203
standard method of measurement
    205
supply of materials 148
Enforceable promise 361
Engineer, role of 42, **6.3**, 98
Engineering 93
Entire contract 137, 166
Entitlement in claims 362
Estimates, status of 63
Estimating, process of 77
European Community Directive 71
Exceptionally adverse weather 143
Exclusion of people from site 156
Exemption clauses 51
Express terms see Contract terms,
    express
Extension of time
generally 141–51
grounds for 142
procedure for claiming 149–51

External decisions, effects of 95
Extra-contractual work 148

Fabrication drawings 92
Fair valuation 172–5
'Fast-track' contracting 95
Feasibility 18
FIDIC conditions of contract 27, 370
Final certificate 166
Financing charges 189, 194–5
Fire 17, 50
Fitness for purpose 107–9
Fixed price 29
Fluctuations 175–6
Force majeure 143, 158, 353
Formal organization 105
Formula approach for overheads 193
Formula rules for fluctuations 175
Formulations of bids 77
Fossils 157
Freedom of contract 84
Front loading 78
Frustration of contract 85

GC/Works/1 28, 124, 369
General contracting, patterns of
    involvement **6.6**, **6.7**, 101
Global claims 186
Government contracts *see* GC/Works/1
Government powers, exercise of 148
Guarantee 107, 234
Guarantor 234

Head office costs 192
Health and safety 153
Hudson's formula 193
Human behaviour 358

ICE 6 26
ICE minor works contract 26
Immediate cost 192
Implication
    in fact 84
    in law 82
Implied terms *see* Contract terms,
    implied
Inadequate forms of contract 122

Informal organization 105
Information, delay in the supply of
    146, 186
Insolvency
    generally 261
    of contractor 159
    of employer 352
Inspection of work 146
Instructions 129
Insurance
    generally 18, 202, 226–34
    contractor's all risks 229
    damage to works 231–2
    joint names policy 231
    loss 228–9
    loss of liquidated damages 232
    professional indemnity 233
    under JCT 80 229–30
Interest 194
Interim certificate 166, 129
Interim payment 377
International markets 71
Invitation to treat 61

JCT
    generally 20
    JCT 63 21
    JCT 80 21
    JCT with contractor's design (CD
        81) 24, 111, 286
    JCT contractor's designed portion
        supplement 286
    JCT Fixed Fee Form (FF 76) 23
    JCT Intermediate Form (IFC 84) 22
    JCT Management Contract (MC 87)
        25
    JCT measured term contract 25
    JCT (MW 80) 23
Joint Contracts Tribunal *see* JCT
Joint ventures 74

Law of agency 210
Letters of intent 62
Liability
    chain of 6, 8
    contribution to 47
    duration of 109

establishing 105
for defective design 106
insurance 226–8
standard of 107
Limitation of actions 379
Limited fluctuations 176
Liquidated and ascertained debts 179
Liquidated damages
  compared to damages for breach 333
  completion date, importance of 338
  extensions of time, effect of 338
  fluctuations clause, and 339
  forfeit of 201
  generally 335–40
  nature and purpose of 336–8
  operation and effect of clauses 338–9
  penalty, difference between 336
  pre-estimate of likely loss 336
  standard form contracts, in 340
Liquidation 261
Litigation
  advantages over arbitration 381–2
  application for directions 385
  discovery of documents 386
  expert witnesses 386
  generally 364, 372–94
  jurisdiction 375
  payment into court 386–7
  pleadings 385
  preliminary proceedings 385
  procedure 384–7
  statement of claim 385
  trial 387
Local authorities, claims against 53
Lock-out 145
Loss and expense, contractor's claims
  for 183–95
Loss insurance policy 227
Low-risk contracts 7

Magnitude in claims 362
Making good defects 177
Management 155
Management contracting see
  Management contracts
Management contracts
  acceleration 314

allocation of risk 304, 311, 312
background 303
changes to requirements 307
characteristics of 308
commitment to complete 313
competition 307
complexity of projects 306
conditions of contract 310
contract cost plan 308
contractual relationships in **20.1**,
  304
default 314
early completion 306
extensions of time 315
generally 7–8, 25, 303–16
independent architect 305
level of uncertainty 312
money 312
patterns of involvement **6.9**, 102–3
prime cost, definition of 308
professional team, definition of 309
project extension items 315
project, definition of 309
quality in 316
recitals 309
schedules 308
services provided by contractor 309
site facilities 309
size of projects 306
time 314–16
transfer of risk 311
use of 305
works contractors 303
works, definition of 309
Materials
  selection of 110
  suitability of 133
  transfer of ownership in 158
Measured works 128, 173
Mediation 365–6
Method of working 170, 216
Mini-trial 368
Misrepresentation 79, 376
Mistake 67, 375
Motivation 358
Murphy's law 11, 17
Mutual debts 179

National Joint Consultative Committee
  see NJCC
Negligence, tort of
  generally 45, 108–9, 115
  claims for
    enhancing contractual remedies 47
    examples of 52–6
    generally 45, 267
    limit of 48
Negligent acts 48
Negligent advice 53, 48
Neutral events 183
NHBC guarantee 117
NJCC 70
Nominated sub-contractor *see*
  Sub-contractor, nominated
Nominated suppliers *see* Suppliers,
  nominated
Nomination, purpose of 22
Non-litigious dispute resolution
  generally 358–71
  procedures, incorporation of 368
Novation 242

Offer 61
Official referees 372
Omission of work 174, 198
On-demand bond 235
Opening up for inspection 186
Operations notice 158
Order 14 377–8
Order 29 378–9
Outbreak of hostilities 354
Over-valuation 222
Ownership of materials 158–9, 251, 262

Package deal 6, 106
Partial possession 139
Patterns of involvement 95
Payment
  generally 165–81
  refusal to make 347–8
  time of 166
PC sums *see* Prime cost sums
People on site, control of 155
Personal injury 229
Phased start dates 139

Physical damage 49
Planning permission 199
Policy 92
Possession of site
  date for 136
  deferment of 136, 149
  failure to give 347
  generally 135, 199, 201
  voluntary relinquishment 140
Practical completion 137
Pre-conceptions 358
Preambles 128
Preliminaries 128
Preparatory work, payment for 63
Price 11
Price adjustment formulae 175
Prime cost sum 128, 248, 251
Principal debtor 234
Private enquiry 366
Privity of contract 100, 280
Procurement
  non-traditional 74
  strategy 69, 70–5
  systems 4–9, 104
Production cost savings 72
Production information 93
Professional indemnity 109, 227
Professional liability 108
Professional pride 31
Profit 192
Programme 130
Progress 136–7
Project managers 104
Project success 360
Prolongation 192
Provisional sums 128, 187, 248
Proximity of relationship 49, 52
Public liability 227
Public procurement 71
Pure financial loss 115

Qualified bids 16
Quantity Surveyor, role of 39, 217
Quantum meruit 62, 335
Quasi-conciliation 365
Quasi-judicial capacity 222, 367
Quotations 63

Reasonable care and skill 107, 108
Reasonable time, definition of 186
Reasonableness, test of 257
Recitals 123, 168
Reconciliation 364
Regular and diligent progress 136,
    185–6, 188, 343, 350
Relevant events 143
Remedies, choosing between 184
Remoteness, test of 333
Representations 79
Repudiation
    common law, at 344
    conduct amounting to 346–7
    contractor's conduct amounting to
        348–9
    determination, difference between
        344–5
    employer's conduct amount to
        346–8
    nature and effect of 345–6
Repudiatory breach 198, 342
Responsibility 93
Responsibility, delegation of 96
Retention money 129, 138, 140,
    176–8
Retention of title 160, 262
Retroactive terms 67
RIBA plan of work 37
Risk
    acceptance of 17
    analysis of 15
    avoidance of 18
    contractual 11
    dealing with 14
    doing nothing about 19
    economic 11
    generally 10
    identification of 14
    insuring against 18
    management 10
    mis-management of 12
    responding to 15
    transfer of 15
    type of 12
    uniqueness in construction 12
Root of the contract 169

Schedules 126
Scope 92
Scott schedule 385
Sectional completion 139
Separate trades contracting 25
Serial contracting 73
Set-off
    contractor's right 129, 178–81
    rights in sub-contracts 181
Shuttle diplomacy 365
Site inspection 45
Site obligations 201
Site safety 216
Specialists' involvement **6.4**, 98
Specifications 126
Specified perils 144–5, 230, 231,
    354
Stages of work 91
Standard forms
    amendments to 20
    use of 19
Standard method of measurement
    127–9, 173
Standard of materials 133
Standard of work 132–4
Standing offer 69
Star rates 174
Statutory authority, carrying out of
    work by 149
Statutory liability 115
Statutory obligations 153
Statutory requirements 110, 199
Statutory requirements, divergence
    between contract and 154
Statutory undertaking, as
    sub-contractor 156
Stay of proceedings *see* Arbitration
Strict liability 108
Strike 145
Sub-contracting, unauthorized 350
Sub-contractor
    defaults of 266–81
    defective work by 281
    design liability of 114
    determination *see* Determination,
        sub-contracts
    direct payment of 260–2

domestic
    defaults of 267–8
    generally 246–7
generally 5–6, 241–81
liability of main contractor for
    defaults of 267
liability to employer 266–7, 280–1
main contractor's right of set-off 256
main contractor's vicarious liability
    for 267
named 252, 277–9
nominated
    alternative method 249
    basic method 249
    benefits of 247
    chain liability 275
    chain of contracts 270
    collateral agreement 269, 270
    contractor's refusal to accept
    273–5
    defaults of 268–77
    defective work 268
    delay by 270–1
    delay on the part of 147
    design by 108–9
    employer's commitment to 248
    employer's responsibility for 276
    encouragement to repudiate 275
    exclusion of liability 268
    generally 6
    insolvency of 276
    liability for design of 277
    liability to employer 49
    quality of work 268
    renomination of 272
    repudiation by 272
    under ICE 6 252
    under JCT 80 249–50
pay-when-paid 256–8
payment of 255–6, 259–62
position in tort 267
proximity of relationships 281
remedy for non-payment 343
retention money 264
rights
    against employer 259
    against main contractor 255–9

    on termination of main contract
    258
    over materials 262–3
    suspension of contract 343
    tortious liability 281
    types of 245
Sub-systems as projects 94
Subject to contract 65
Subrogation 228
Subsequent owners, actions by 53
Substantial completion 137
Substantial performance 231
Summary judgment 377
Supervising officer 4
Suppliers, nominated
    chain of liability 277
    generally 6, 250–1
    procedure 250
    under JCT 80 277
Supply, chain of contracts in 56
Supply of materials by employer 148
Surety 234
Suspension of work 211, 342–4, 348,
    350, 352
System building 286

Techniques, selection of 110
Temporary multi-organizations 33
Temporary suspension of work 199
Tender bond 77, 235
Tendering
    construction management 74
    contractor's procedure 77
    costs of 75
    myth 77
    negotiated 72, 74
    open 70
    problems in 75
    procedures 68, 69
    purposes of 69
    selective 72
    selective, for design and build 73
    single stage selective 71
    two stage selective 72
    withdrawal of 76
Tenders, types of 69
Testing of materials 216

Time
  'at large' 142
  obligations related to 135–51
  'of the essence' 139, 349
Tort *see* Negligence, tort of
Trade discount 251
Traditional general contracting 4–6,
  1.1
Turnkey projects 6, 286

UK practice 104
Unannounced participants 32
Unconditional bond 235
Under-valuation 223
Unfair contracts 122
Unliquidated damages 336

USA practice 104

Variations
  generally 168–75
  loss/expense for 187
  valuation of 172
  work under different conditions 174
Vesting clause 159
Vicarious performance 242

Weather 16, 143
Wheel of dominance 100
Work, alteration of 170
Work consequent upon variation 172
Workmanship 114, 132, 216
Works commencement data 139